THE
COMPLETE BOOK
OF LOCKS,
KEYS,
BURGLAR AND
SMOKE ALARMS,
AND
OTHER SECURITY
DEVICES

Also by Eugene A. Sloane

THE COMPLETE BOOK OF BICYCLING

THE *NEW* COMPLETE BOOK OF BICYCLING

THE COMPLETE BOOK OF LOCKS, KEYS, BURGLAR AND SMOKE ALARMS, AND OTHER SECURITY DEVICES

Eugene A. Sloane

WILLIAM MORROW AND COMPANY, INC.

NEW YORK   1977

Printed in the United States of America.

1   2   3   4   5   6   7   8   9   10

Library of Congress Cataloging in Publication Data

Sloane, Eugene A
    The complete book of locks, keys, burglar and smoke alarms, and other security devices.

    Bibliography: p.
    Includes index.
    1. Burglar-alarms.   2. Locks and keys.   3. Watch-dogs.   I. Title.
TH9739.S56   643   76-30530
ISBN 0-688-03189-7

BOOK DESIGNER   CARL WEISS
ASSISTANT DESIGNER   ARLENE GOLDBERG

CONTENTS

PART

I

Every twelve seconds across these United States someone's house is burglarized. Every eleven minutes a woman is raped; every twenty-five minutes a person is murdered. Every thirty seconds a violent crime of robbery or assault is committed. Will the next victim be you?

1

EVERY TWELVE SECONDS

Blueprint for Burglary

IT'S FRIDAY afternoon on a cold, blustery day early in December. In front of a comfortable-looking home in an average suburb a car stops. It is 3:30 and no one is in sight. The driver goes to the front door and rings the bell. As he expected at this time of day, with the family car gone, there is no answer to his ring. From a coat pocket he pulls a tool that looks like a bicycle chain with a handle, and wraps the chain part around the doorknob. A quick, unobtrusive wrench and the lock is broken. The door opens easily, he enters and ten minutes later departs the way he arrived.

Thirty minutes later a woman parks her car in front of the house and, laden with packages, approaches the front door. As she fumbles for the key in her purse she notices scratch marks on the doorknob. The key turns easily in the lock, which feels looser than usual. Inside the house she finds . . . a mess.

Contents of drawers have been dumped on the floor, closets ransacked, books pulled from shelves. Missing is $150 in cash, the family silver, a 35mm slide projector and camera, her good jewelry, and her husband's heirloom pocket watch. The TV and stereo sets are still in place. Net haul for the burglar, about $450 after "fencing" the noncash goodies. Not bad for a few minutes' work. The woman resident was lucky, too. Had she arrived home thirty minutes earlier and surprised the burglar, she could have been murdered.

All Too Typical

This brief scenario is an all-too-accurate description of the type of burglary that takes place about every twelve seconds throughout this country. The month, time of day, mode of entry, are all typical of when burglaries peak. That the average semiskilled burglar can easily earn well over $500 a day, is seldom caught, and once behind bars is soon released on bond or if a first (caught) offender, released without bond, is also all too typical of the history of this type of criminal.

Most Homes Are Sitting Ducks

What makes life easy for the burglar, besides the ease with which he is plea-bargained, freed on bond, or paroled right back to his life of crime, is the incredibly poor security of the average home and place of business.

To you a thick door and large shiny pieces of brass or steel for the lock may offer security. To the burglar or home invader, these are a laugh and almost instantly violatable with primitive tools. The average business place, such as a jewelry store, may be a tougher target to crack, but given the incentive, still a fairly easy job for the more skilled burglar. And office buildings and apartment dwellings are just about as easy to break into as the typical suburban or urban residence.

Among the many reasons for the poor security in all of these buildings, two stand out. One is that most of us are not security-minded until it's too late. Then we rush out and buy or have installed a strong lock or a reliable burglar-alarm system. Second, builders and architects unfortunately know very little about security. Or building designers, in an effort to keep costs within budget, skimp wherever possible, which means the physical aspects of security (such as strong locks) are ignored.

Lock manufacturers contribute all too often to the crime wave by making locks with decorative good looks on the outside that are flimsy and weak on the inside. Such locks may look pretty, but they yield easily to a burglar's tools.

You can buy strong locks for your home and business, and effective burglar alarms for every possible security need. That's what this book is all about, to give you an overview of what constitutes good security to protect you and your loved ones and your business from crime.

What This Book Covers

Since you can't move away from crime (the crime rate is growing even faster in the suburbs and country than in the big city), and the crime rate is so high today, it makes sense to spend the few dollars it takes to protect your family and your possessions. If you're in business, your insurance company will insist you do so.

The problem is that there are so many charlatans out there who claim to be locksmiths and burglar-alarm experts, and so much worthless junk for them to install, you need to know at least the basics of what constitutes good security.

In this book you will learn about locks for three grades of security risk; low, medium, and high crime-rate areas, with tips on how to rate your own area. You will learn how to tell a strong lock from a weak one, how locks should be installed, how in fact to install them yourself. Since the best lock is useless if installed on a weak door or door frame, you will learn how to "beef up" these two vulnerable parts of your house. You will learn all about locks for windows and garage doors, how to lock up your possessions such as skis, bikes, TV sets, office equipment, and anything else that can be carried away. I will show you how to keep crooks at yard length by installing perimeter protection devices. Besides the hardware of physical protection I will show you how to buy the best safe to protect your valuables at home or in the store or office. You will learn all about the many types of burglar alarms and which one is best for you. Since hundreds of thousands of people die every year due to the smoke and fumes from fire, you will learn about which type of fire alarm will protect you and your family against this hazard that kills while you sleep. There's much more, too much to enumerate here, in this book that can offer you peace of mind whether you're at home or away, asleep or awake, live in a high- or low-crime-rate area, have very little money to spend on security, or need top security without regard to cost.

First, a Few Statistics You Can Skip

I've been researching and writing this book for three years. As time went on during this period I have become increasingly concerned about the rising rate of crime and what appears to me to be the almost total unconcern of my friends about their own protection. This head-in-the-sand approach certainly changes fast, however, when *they* get ripped off. A typical Sunday afternoon these days begins with a call from a friend that goes something like this: "Say, Gene, I know you've been working on a book about crime prevention, and I sure am impressed with your workshop full of locks and burglar alarms. Last night I came home and the front door lock was broken and a lot of stuff was taken from the house. Could you recommend a good lock?" Or, the phone rings and a worried voice says: "Gene, this is ———. Yesterday afternoon my daughter came home from school and a man followed her into the lobby of our apartment building. She screamed and he ran away, but not until he had threatened to rape her. Could I come over and talk about what I can do to prevent this, and worse?"

The chilling facts are that the FBI Uniform Crime reports, containing crime data from police departments throughout the country, show that crimes of violence have increased over 157 percent during the past decade. The fastest-growing crimes are rape and arson, followed by burglary and murder. What really disturbs me is that even the FBI figures include no more than *half* the crimes actually committed; the other half is not even reported by the victims to police, either because of fear of retaliation by the criminal or because the victim has such a (and I might add justified) lack of faith in the criminal justice system. Thanks to plea bargaining and the bail-bond system, a sizeable percentage of crooks are right back on the street within a few days or a week after being arrested. Do these "returnees" abjure their life of crime? Does the Mafia give heavily to charity? The chances are about equal in both cases; more factually, the answer is that crooks like the easy life, the fast buck, and the relatively low risk involved in their life of crime. And the data demonstrate that with every period of recession and unemployment, the crime rate climbs still faster.

Now let's get on to the facts of security for you, your loved ones, your place of business.

PART

II

THE LOCK FOR YOU

*For every home, a lock to fit the crime risk.
For every business, a lock to fit the need.
Super locks for atom bombs and bonded
liquor. Locks for everything from skis to
TV sets, for fences, windows, garage
doors. All about stronger doors and door
frames, fences and other perimeter protection.
As much as you will ever need to know
about padlocks, and about how to install
your own locks and save a bundle. More
than you may want to know about how
locks work.*

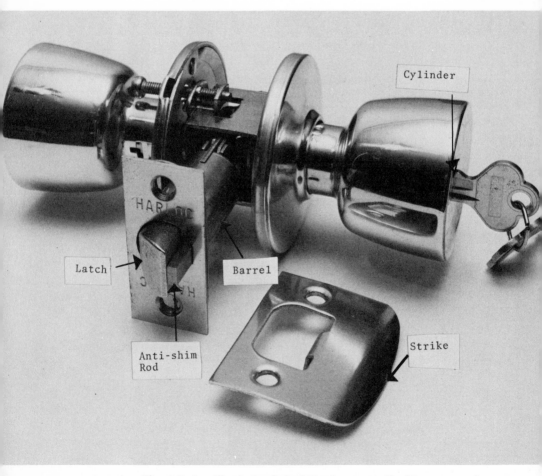

Fig. 1-2 / *Key-in-knob lock is the worst "lock" you can have as primary exterior door protection. This type of lock is easy to defeat; some models can even be broken by a twist from a strong hand.*

2

THE INFAMOUS KEY-IN-KNOB LOCK

Caution: You may have a burglar's friend on your front door!

A KEY-IN-KNOB lock is just that, a lock built into the doorknob. This type of lock says to even the most amateur of burglars: "Hey buddy, come right on in and take what you want out of this house." If you depend on this type of lock to keep criminals out of the house, you are vulnerable indeed. Yet millions of us have only a flimsy key-in-knob lock for protection against a break-in.

This type of lock (Fig. 1-2) is easy to defeat. The lock cylinder, the part the key fits in, is easy to pick open because these cylinders are not high-security and pick-resistant. A simple bicycle chain or pipe wrench can twist the "works" right out of these locks in a second or two (Fig. 2-2). Older models of these locks have a cylinder held in place by only two spring clips. The cylinder is more than easy to pull out by inserting a screw in the keyway and pulling on the screw with pliers (Fig.

3-2). Or, a "slam puller" (Fig. 4-2) which is crook's parlance for an ordinary fifteen-dollar auto-body dent puller, can be screwed into the lock. The heavy cast iron "dumbell" is pushed forward, then pulled rapidly back. When it slams into the rear or handle part, the resulting force can pull many of these lock cylinders out of the lock, after which the door can be opened with a screwdriver. Fig. 5-2 shows a sheet-metal screw inserted in the key-in-knob keyway. Fig. 6-2 shows a spring clip unit.

"Loiding" the Lock

Yet another weakness of these locks is that they can be "shimmed" open by inserting a credit card or metal shim between the door and door frame, pushing the latch back. With the latch retracted, the lock is in the unlocked position and the door can be opened.

Fig. 2-2 / *An actual burglary, in which the key-in-knob lock was twisted and broken.*

COURTESY CHICAGO POLICE DEPARTMENT

(Top)
Fig. 3-2 / *Some older key-in-knob locks are so poorly made the lock cylinder can be pulled out with a pair of pliers. This cylinder is held in place by two spring clips.*

(Center)
Fig. 4-2 / *This auto-body dent puller is also used by burglars to pull the cylinder out of key-in-knob locks.*

(Right)
Fig. 5-2 / *Sheet metal screw forced into keyway of key-in-knob lock, preparatory to "pulling" the cylinder with pliers or the dent puller.*

Fig. 6-2 /   *Incredible as it seems, this key-in-knob cylinder is held in place only by two spring clips. A child could remove it from your door.*

To prevent "loiding" or shimming open this type of lock, manufacturers have added a so-called "anti-shim" (Fig. 12) device, which is a metal rod that holds the latch closed when you lock the door. This would be a good idea if it worked, but it doesn't. If you are cursed with one of these locks, open the door and lock the lock with the key. Now press the latch back with your finger. Note that the latch will move back about one-eighth inch. Since most door frames can be sprung back with a jimmy, a combination of jimmy and "loiding" can open these locks fast. It's important you know too that your door frame is prob-ably as weak a link in your private security as the key-in-knob lock, so before you install another, better lock please read Chapter Nine to make sure your door is worth the trouble and expense. If your exterior doors are hollow-core, no lock can keep a burglar from chopping out the lock or punching a hole through the door very quickly. Or you may need to beef up the door frame.

You don't have to remove the key-in-knob lock. Leave it in place for its latching function to hold the door shut when you close it. Then add a stronger lock just above it, as described in the following chapters.

3

SUPER LOCKS FOR SUPER SECURITY

If you are an attractive target (or a burglar thinks you are) then you need the best locks you can buy. Here is a review of high-security locks for home, stores, business, and industry.

THE SAFEST PATH you can take to assure the safety of your family, possessions, and business enterprise is to think of them as falling into the high risk category. I would take this position no matter where I live. The amount of crime in big cities is horrendous and growing. The crime rate in suburbia and even rural areas is growing even faster than in major cities. Crime and the public fear it fosters are phenomena that hark back to an era when there were no police; it is today a commonplace in this age of violence and not-so-quiet desperation.

How To Assess Your Crime Exposure

If you live or work in one of the areas listed below, you are in a high-crime area. You also need the best locks you can afford.

- Suburbs near large cities
- City neighborhoods near the inner city
- High-income-bracket homes in any location
- Suburbs with over 10 percent minority population
- The inner city
- Stores with valuable, easily salable merchandise such as jewelry, cameras, drugs
- Offices with costly equipment such as typewriters; offices may be in buildings of any size
- Banks, currency exchanges, supermarkets, where large amounts of money accumulate during the day

- Homes and buildings with valuable collections of coins, artwork, or artifacts
- Warehouses with bonded liquor, small machinery, and portable appliances

Make the Security Fit the Crime

In this chapter I will review locks that offer varying degrees of security, starting with the minimum I would recommend for homes in high crime areas. At the other end of the security spectrum, I will describe locks for ultra-high-security risks.

Most of these locks you can install yourself. However, as I have said before and will say again, check the type and condition of the door and door frame before installing any lock. Do read Chapter Nine on doors and frames before installing the locks.

Lever-Tumbler Locks Are Poor Security

Because lever-tumbler locks have in the past been very widely used, I would like to give you the same warning about them I gave about key-in-knob locks. Lever-tumbler locks offer little or no security. These locks (Fig. 1-3) are simple and easy to pick. Skeleton keys for most of them are available in hardware stores.

There are ultra-high-security lever-tumbler locks, but these are an entirely different breed of lock, made by Chubb of England and not widely distributed in this country.

If you find a simple lever-tumbler lock on any exterior door, leave it in place and install one of the locks I mention below over it.

For Reasonable Security at a Price

The least costly lock I can recommend for a high-crime-rate area is an interlocking deadbolt rimlock. This lock (Fig. 2-3) has a "bolt" (the part that moves out from the lock when you turn the key) that fits into matching holes in the "strike." (The strike of any lock is the metal part, fastened into the door frame, into which the bolt fits.) When the bolt is extended into the strike, the lock holds the door closed.

A "rimlock" is one with the lock cylinder (the part the key fits into) flush with the door. The lock mechanism is fastened to the interior of the door, rather than being recessed into a hole in the door. Fig. 3-3 shows an interlocking rimlock that was fastened to the inside of a door. Here, however, the door was weak, and the burglar easily chopped his way around the lock. The lock was left dangling, as you can see. Again, the moral is, don't waste a good lock on a bad door.

You can sometimes put a bad lock on a good door, as in Fig. 4-3. Here the interlocking deadbolt lock strike was broken off by attack with a pry bar placed between the door and the door frame.

Two Cylinders Are Better Than One

The burglar expertly and quickly applied a ten-square-inch piece of self-adhesive paper (such as wallpaper) to the window of an exterior door. With a glass cutter, he cut out the glass around the paper, pulled out the cut piece and noiselessly laid it on the porch floor. Now he could reach in and turn the thumbturn of the lock and open the door from the inside.

Fig. 1-3 / *This type of lever-tumbler lock offers poor security because it is easily picked open.*

Fig. 2-3 / *This strong rimlock with an interlocking deadbolt gives excellent security.*

This little scenario is a very common way burglars break into buildings that have single cylinder locks and a glass or thin wood panel that is easy to cut through. A single cylinder lock is one that has a key-actuated lock cylinder on one side only. On the other side, the inside, the lock is actuated by a thumb-turn.

A double-cylinder lock is one that can be locked with a key from inside as well as from outside the building. You should always install such a lock on any door that has a glass or thin wood panel.

However, I would caution you about

Fig. 3-3 / *A good lock is useless if installed on a weak door. Here an interlocking deadbolt lock held fast while the door was chopped through.*

COURTESY CHICAGO POLICE DEPARTMENT

fire if you have a double-cylinder lock. Since the door requires a key to open it from the inside, you should always keep a key near the door. This way you can get out quickly in an emergency, such as a fire. Put the key on a hook near the floor, out of sight of anyone at the front door outside. This will give you a key near floor level, where the air is clearer in case of smoke.

Tubular vs. Flat Key Cylinders

When tubular key cylinders (Fig. 5-3) first appeared, they were used on vending machine cash boxes. Initially they puzzled thieves, who could not figure out how to defeat them. It wasn't long before special picks were devised by criminals. And soon it was also discovered that the soft brass face of the lock could be sawed through. When the face or keyway is cut, the pins drop out and the lock can be opened (Fig. 5-3).

Tubular key cylinders are used on a variety of locks, including interlocking deadbolts and padlocks. I don't like most of them for the same reason criminals like them.

You can, however, find locks with hardened-steel tubular key cylinders (Fig. 6-3). This is the only type of tubular key cylinder I would use on any lock.

Recommended Interlocking Deadbolt Rimlocks

I have dissected and checked dozens of interlocking deadbolt locks. Of these, I can recommend a few as being strong and well made. Here are my selections:

• *Ideal Security Model DB-9295 (Fig. 7-3).* $25. Has double cylinders. Tests show this lock will withstand

Fig. 4-3 / *Not all interlocking deadbolt locks are strong. This one had a weak cast-metal strike that broke under forcible attack.*
COURTESY CHICAGO POLICE DEPARTMENT

Fig. 5-3 / *Tubular (round) key lock with soft brass face or keyway is easy to defeat with a hacksaw.*

Fig. 6-3 / *This hardened-steel round key lock is tougher, resists cutting with a hacksaw.*

Fig. 7-3 / *An excellent interlocking deadbolt rimlock, made by Ideal. Model DB-9285 bolts to the door. Cylinder on the outside resists pulling attack. Parts are: "A", backplate; "B", bolts to fasten outside cylinder to backplate; "C", bolts that lock both cylinders together through the door; "D", outside cylinder guard; "E", high-security Medeco outside cylinder; "F", keys to Medeco cylinder; "G", interlocking bolt; "H", strike; "I", lock case (mounts on inside of door); "J", inside cylinder keys; "K", inside cylinder and guard.*

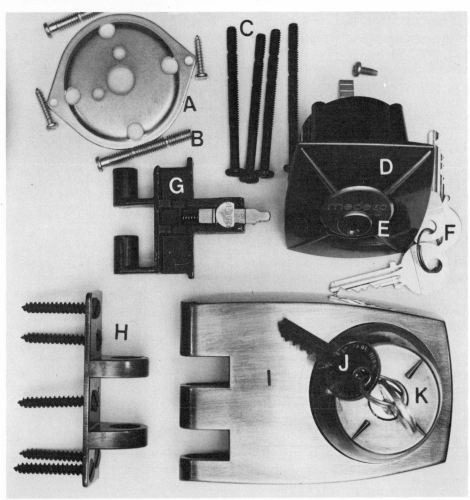

1000 pounds of pull pressure (after which the door broke, not the lock).

- *New England Lock Company, Segal Model NE-688.* $40. Double cylinder, cast bronze case, bronze cylinder.
- *Yale Model 197¼.* $22. Double cylinders. This is a well-made lock. However, like the Segal lock above, it fastens to the door with wood screws, which can be torn loose. Instead I would use machine screws with flat washers under screw hex heads. After installation, round off corners of the bolt hex heads, so they can't be gripped with a wrench and turned. Use lock washers on the inside.

Mortise Locks for Better Security

A mortise lock is one that is recessed into a hole in the door edge. The hole (or mortise) is cut to fit the lock exactly. Because the mortise lock is fitted to a hole in the door (rather than hung on the outside surface of the door like a rimlock) it is much more resistant to forcible attack. Tucked away inside the door as it is, the mortise lock is in a strong position, with wood on three sides, to resist being pried off or out of the door.

Here are the features you should look for in any mortise lock:

- The bolt should be at least one inch long. This length prevents the bolt from being pried out of the lock with a pry bar (jimmy) inserted between the door and the door frame (Fig. 8-3). Another approach is a hooked bolt (Fig. 9-3) used by Adams-Rite, one of the higher-grade mortise lock manufacturers.
- High-grade steel working parts that

resist a pounding attack (Fig. 10-3).

- Bolts made of tough steel, with a hardened, rotating steel pin that is very hard to saw through (Fig. 11-3), or a bolt with a ceramic insert, also hard to saw (Fig. 12-3).
- Cylinder protection that keeps the cylinder from being twisted or rotated. If the cylinder can be twisted or pulled by any tool that can get a grip on it (Fig. 13-3) then it can be pulled right out of the lock case. The lock cylinder should be protected by a hard steel plate with recessed cylinder (Fig. 11-3) or by a beveled (slanted) freely rotating guard. The bevel and hard steel of this guard (Fig. 14-3) turn freely, and it is all but impossible to grip with a tool.

Recommended Mortise Locks

I have dissected a number of mortise deadbolt locks. Of those I inspected, I can recommend the following mortise locks:

- *M.A.G. Ultra 700* and similar locks made by this firm. $40 less cylinders. With two Medeco cylinders, add about $50 (for both, which, like any pair of same-make cylinders, can be keyed alike so one key operates both cylinders). Lock has beveled, free-turning cylinder guards of hardened stainless steel. This lock is easy to install. It can cover defacement to the door made by a pry bar or jimmy burglar tool. The lock has full 1⅛-inch deadbolt (Fig. 15-3), and slides into simple mortise-type cutout (Fig. 16-3). The bolt has freely rotating hardened-steel pin to resist bolt cutters

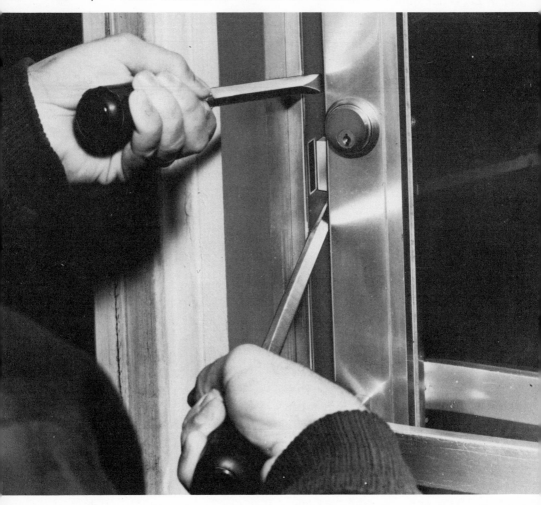

Fig. 8-3 / *The bolt of this lock is too short and so is easily pried out of the lock strike with a pair of pry bars (jimmies). Bolt should be at least one inch long.*

(Fig. 17-3). M.A.G. Engineering and Manufacturing, Inc., 13711 Alma Avenue, Gardena, Calif. 90249.*

• *All Adams-Rite mortise locks* for high-grade residential, commercial, and institutional buildings. The door factory can install these locks at far less cost than a locksmith on the job.

• *All Abloy mortise locks* (Fig. 14-3). Excellent quality, highly pick-resistant locks made in Finland. These locks have a unique eleven-

---

* Company addresses are given for firms that may otherwise be hard to find. Firms such as Yale and Ideal Hardware, whose products are sold by locksmiths or in hardware stores, may not be listed in the Appendices.

disc tumbler cylinder with up to 600 million possible combinations. The chance of another person having a lock with a key that will open yours is extremely remote. The cylinder is also highly drill-resistant. The unusual-looking key can only be duplicated at the factory (Fig. 18-3) for your protection. Abloy's U.S. factory office is at 6212 Oakton St., Morton Grove, Illinois 60053.

- *Yale mortise locks.* In particular, Yale Model YA-314¼. $45. This lock has double cylinders and a stainless steel case.
- *Sargent No. SAR-4825.* $42. Double cylinders.
- *Welch Model WEL 72½.* $40.

All these locks can be installed as primary locks, or as auxiliary locks to the ones already installed.

Bar Locks for Tough Security Problems

Bar locks throw a heavy bar of tough steel across the width of the door. In some cases, they also have a bar or rod of steel the height of the door. They are ugly as sin and very expensive, but offer really top security.

Bar locks are highly recommended on the rear doors of stores, on storeroom doors, and on any door where maximum security is needed.

The two bar locks I can recommend are:

- *Fox Police Bar Lock* (Fig. 19-3). $105. This lock has two high-security cylinders and an armored cylinder plate that guards the outside cylinder. It is installed with bolts through the door, and fastens at two points, as shown. The strike is

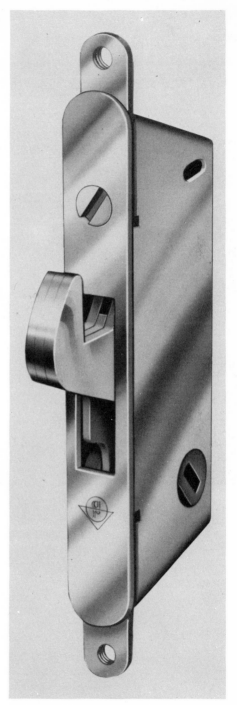

Fig. 9-3 / *A strong bolt is the "hook" design shown here that offers strong resistance to pry-bar attack.*

Fig. 10-3 / *A hammer attack can defeat a weak lock or one with the strike merely a hole cut in the soft aluminum door frame. Strikes in aluminum frames should be reinforced with a steel strike plate.*

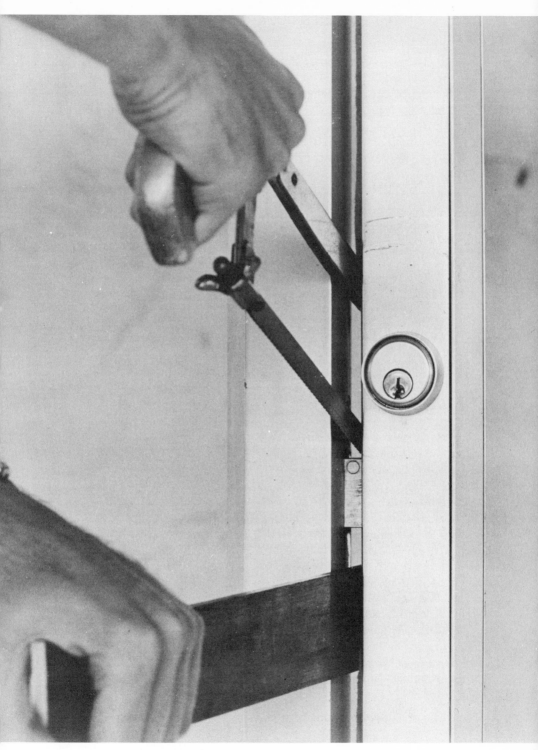

Fig. 11-3 /   *To resist a sawing attack, bolts should have a hardened, freely rotating steel pin insert.*

furnished with extra long 2¼-inch wood screws that penetrate through the finish and into the rough frame. Fox Police Lock Company, 46 West 21st St., New York, New York 10010.

- *Fichet Bar Lock* (Fig. 20-3). $250. In my judgment this is the best bar lock made. From France, this lock has seven locking points, with dead-bolts at top, center, and bottom. It has a ten-disc tumbler Fichet cylinder with over 10 million possible combinations. The cylinder uses a unique key (Fig. 21-3) that can only be factory-duplicated (in the United States). Fichet claims no one has ever picked this cylinder. Fichet, Inc., 408 South Rosemead Boulevard, Pasadena, California 91107.

High-Security Cylinders

No matter who makes the lock, other makes of ultra-high-security cylinders can usually be installed in the mechanism.

A high-security cylinder is one that is highly resistant to picking, drilling, pulling, and twisting, by virtue of the way it is made. These cylinders have hardened-steel pins, unique pin designs, hundreds of thousands or even millions of possible key combinations and generally high-grade construction.

If you already have an otherwise satisfactory rim or mortise lock installed, you can upgrade its security by installing one of the recommended high-security cylinders below:

- *Abloy disc-tumbler cylinders*. About $20.
- *Medeco cylinders*. $28. These cylin-

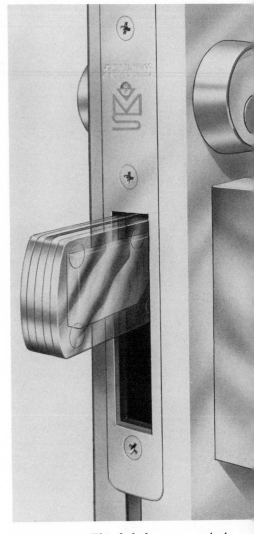

Fig. 12-3 / *This bolt has a ceramic insert that is very difficult to saw through.*

ders have a unique pin-tumbler mechanism. (Fig. 22-3). The pins have a twisting action that makes this cylinder extremely pick-resistant; they are also mushroom-type (see Chapter Eight) to make picking still tougher. Medeco cylinders also have hardened-steel rod inserts

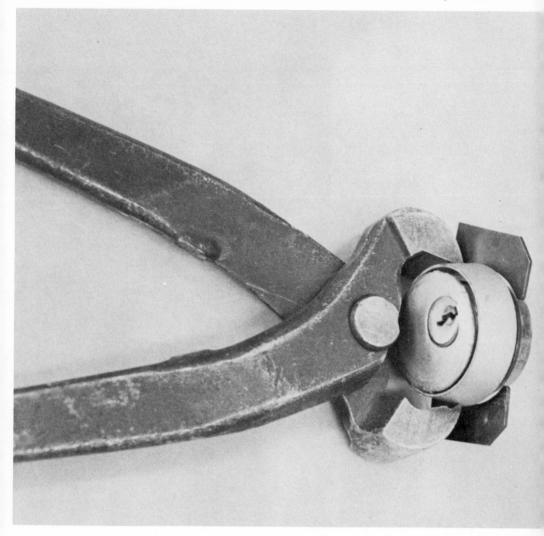

Fig. 13-3 / *A beveled, hardened-steel and freely rotating cylinder guard resists pincer attack that could pull the cylinder right out of the lock.*

to resist drilling, and sharp steel inserts to offer secondary drill resistance. Noninterchangeable key combinations are 23 million. Keys can only be cut on special machines by Medeco-authorized locksmiths. The cylinders are Underwriters' Laboratories-listed. Medeco Secu-

rity Locks, Inc., 220 Apperson Drive, Salem, Virginia 24153.

• *Illinois Duo cylinders.* About $25 (Fig. 23-3). These cylinders have a unique fourteen-disc tumbler action with sixteen thousand possible key changes. Hardened stainless steel guides act as cutting bars to lop off

Fig. 14-3 / *The beveled, hardened, freely rotating cylinder guards (arrows) of this lock make cylinder pulling a difficult if not impossible task.*

Fig. 15-3 / *This mortise lock has a 1⅛-inch bolt with hard-steel pin insert.*

Fig. 16-3 / *M.A.G. mortise lock is easy to install in a simple U-shaped cutout in door.*

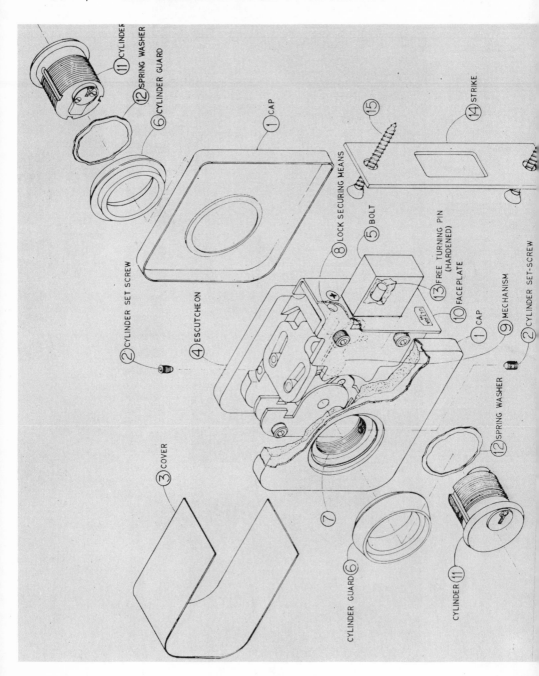

(Opposite)
Fig. 17-3 / *Working parts of M.A.G. high-security mortise lock. Note hardened-steel pin in bolt.*

(Right)
Fig. 18-3 / *Unique key for Abloy lock cannot be duplicated except on a special key cutter at U.S. headquarters of this Finnish lock company.*

(Below)
Fig. 19-3 / *Fox police bar throws a bar of steel across the door, locks in two points.*

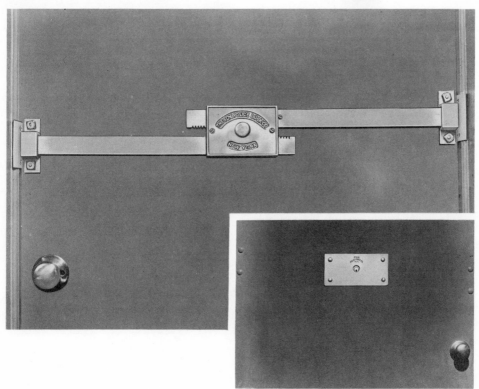

any tool inserted in the keyway in an attempt to turn it by force. The plug is almost impossible to pull because it is securely fastened in the cylinder, which itself is made of hardened stainless steel, as are the lock cam and gears. Keys can be cut only on factory approved key-cutting machines, and by authorized locksmiths. The cylinders are Underwriters' Laboratories-listed. Illinois Lock Company, 301 West Hintz Road, Wheeling, Illinois 60090.

- *Sargent "Maximum Security" cylinders* have up to 24,500 safe key changes, regardless of the number of levels of master keying. Thus there is a 24,500-to-1 chance of an unauthorized person having a key to your Sargent cylinder. The cylinders have twelve pins (tiny brass rods that are key-actuated to lock and unlock the cylinder plug). The pins are in three rows on three intersecting axes. Positions of both pin holes (Fig. 24-3) vary, as do length of the pins. The key (Fig. 25-3) has "dimples" instead of the usual key cuts, and so will last longer.

Best application of these cylinders is as a master-keyed system in a large building, such as a hotel or high-rise office building. Any building that requires multiple levels of master keying can have such a system with the Sargent Maximum Security cylinder with minimum-security compromise because of weaknesses inherent in conventional master-key systems (see discussion on master keying problems below).

When these cylinders are specified for a building, the manufac-

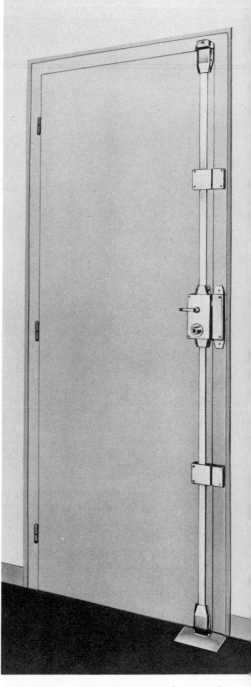

Fig. 20-3 / *This Fichet bar lock is the best on the market. Locking points are at top, center, and bottom.*

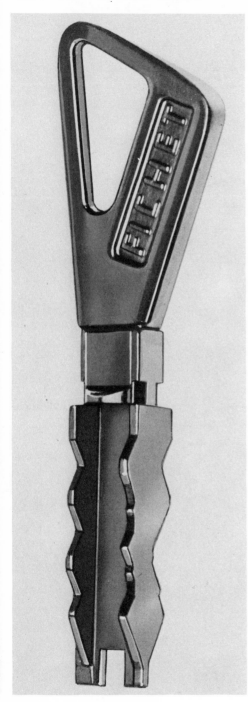

Fig. 21-3 / *Fichet key can only be duplicated at U.S. headquarters of this French firm.*

turer uses a computer to design a special master key code, "scrambled" to assure key security. Thus master keying is possible up to seven levels.

Keys can only be duplicated at the factory. Keys and cylinders are made in a security-tight, off-limit area in the plant. Sargent & Company, 100 Sargent Drive, New Haven, Connecticut 06509.

• *Miwa magnetic cylinders.* From Japan, these cylinders have magnetized pins, the polarity of which lines up with similarly spaced tiny magnets embedded in the key (Fig. 26-3). When the key is inserted in the cylinder, the magnetic force of pins and key magnets (Fig. 27-3) push pins out of the cylinder plug, and the key can be turned to unlock the lock. When the key is withdrawn, the spring-loaded pins fall down into matching holes in the cylinder plug, to lock the plug so it can't be turned. The cylinder is resistant to drilling, and the manufacturer claims it has never been picked open.

Master Keying, a Security Problem

An epidemic of hotel room robberies, concentrated in one hotel, prompted police in one Southwestern city to search all the hotel rooms thoroughly in that badly hit hotel. In one of the rooms police found a small pile of brass shavings on the bed. Taking the room lock apart, it was evident that an expert crook had done likewise, and had cut himself a grand-master key to all the rooms in the hotel, simply by measuring the depth of the pins and duplicating cuts on a key blank that would fit these pins.

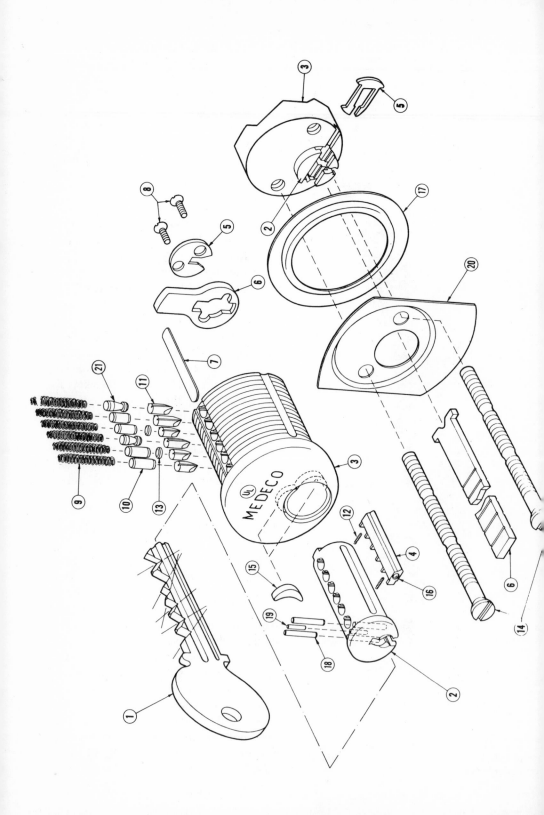

◀
(Opposite)
Fig. 22-3 / *Super-high-security Medeco cylinders can be installed on many existing and new locks. Feature parts are: 1, key with angle-cuts; 15, steel insert to protect pins from drilling; 16, hardened-steel ball; 18 and 19, hard steel security pins; 21, mushroom drive or top pins which make cylinder harder to pick open.*

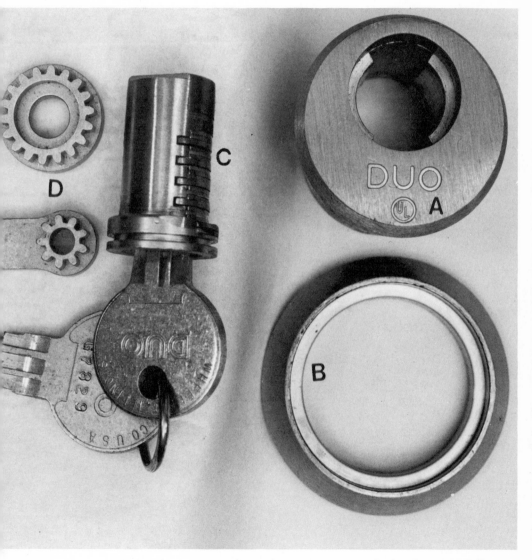

Fig. 23-3 / *Illinois Duo super-high-security cylinder. Parts are: "A", shell (note UL label); "B", cylinder guard; "C" plug; "D", cam and gears.*

MAXIMUM SECURITY
SYSTEM CYLINDER

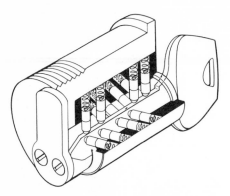

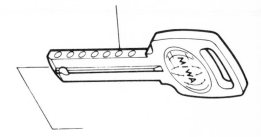

MAGNETIC PINS EMBEDDED

Fig. 24-3 / *Sargent "Maximum Security" cylinder. This unit permits multiple levels of master keying without loss of security.*

Fig. 26-3 / *Miwa (Japan) cylinder key has imbedded magnets of opposite polarity of magnetic drive pins.*

Fig. 25-3 / *Sargent "Maximum Security" key. Note unusual "cuts" which are really dimples of varying depths and spacing.*

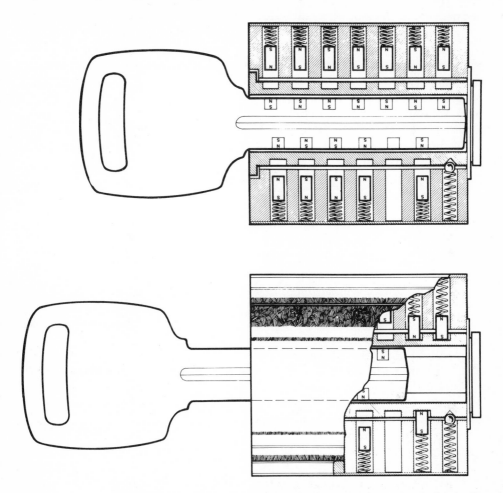

Fig. 27-3 / *Miwa magnetic cylinder uses magnetized drive pins that have opposite polarity inserts in key. As key is withdrawn, bottom, springs above drive pins push these pins down into the plug to lock it.*

In another hotel, a new manager decided to check key security. Taking a guest's room key at random, he was shocked to find it would open room doors other than the one it was supposed to open. What happened was that the hotel was about thirty years old, and the locks and keys were worn. With multiple levels of grand-master keys, it was no wonder that one guest's key fitted other rooms' locks as well.

In yet another instance, the head of a large company with plants throughout the country laid a gold-plated key on the bar in a nightclub and was heard to tell his companion that this one key would open all the important locks in all the firm's plants. The executive had a great-great-great-grand-master key. A smart crook could have asked to see the key (had he also been at the bar) and taken advantage of a momentary lapse of attention on the part of its owner to press the key into the palm of his hand. The indentations of the key cuts would have lasted long enough for any good locksmith (or crooked locksmith) to have made a duplicate key. Such impressions can also be made in foil from a package of chewing gum or cigarettes.

The point here is that for every level of master keying you lose a major percentage of the possible key combinations originally in the lock. And when the lock gets old and the pins and keys become worn, it is possible for an unauthorized key to open the wrong door (the right one for the criminal). The Sargent cylinder-and-key system above is one step toward eliminating these problems. Let me illustrate. Fig. 28-3 shows one set of pins in a conventional pin-tumbler lock; the key is out of the plug and the top pin is down into the plug, past the shear line, so the plug can't turn and the lock is locked. In Fig. 29-3, the key is in the plug and it has raised the bottom pin exactly up to the shear line. Now the plug can turn and unlock the lock. A level of master keying has been added to the cylinder in Fig. 30-3. Now there are three pins, the top pin, the master or split pin, and the bottom pin. Here the key is out and the lock is locked. In Fig. 31-3, the day key (the nonmaster key) is in the lock, the bottom pin is at the shear line and the lock can be opened with the key. In Fig. 32-3 the master key is in the lock, the split or master pin is at the shear line, the plug will turn and the lock can be opened with the key. In Fig. 33-3 the cylinder now has *two* levels of master keying, as you will note from the two split or master pins. Here the key is out and the top pin is down into the plug so it can't turn. You can

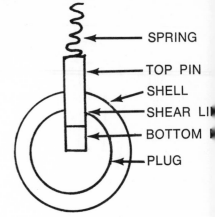

Fig. 28-3 / *In conventional pin-tumbler cylinder, when key is out, spring-loaded drive pin is pushed down into the plug, plug can't turn, lock is locked.*

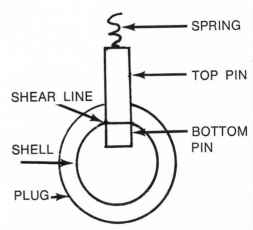

Fig. 29-3 / *When key is in cylinder, cuts of the key match varying lengths of pins, push pins up to "shear line" so plug can turn in cylinder shell and lock can be unlocked.*

see, from all these drawings, that the thin split pins, as shown in Fig. 34-3 of a conventional pin-tumbler cylinder, compromise security. The more splits, the greater the level of master keying and the more likely a strange key will work in that lock and all those like it.

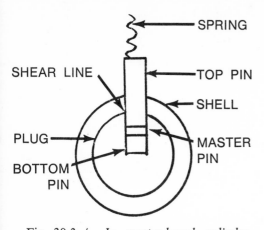

Fig. 30-3 / *In master-keyed cylinder, an extra master pin is added between top and bottom pins. Here key is out of lock, top pin is down into plug.*

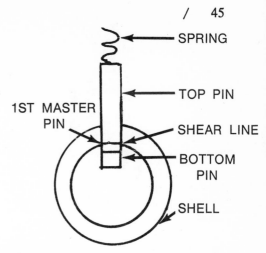

Fig. 32-3 / *Now master key is in plug, master pin is at shear line, plug can turn.*

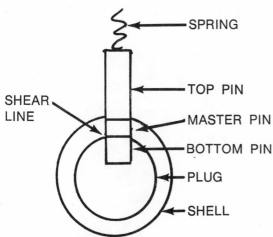

Fig. 31-3 / *Key that fits only one lock is in the cylinder, so bottom pin is at shear line, plug can turn.*

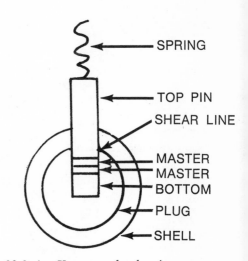

Fig. 33-3 / *Here two levels of master keying are added to cylinder, so there are two master pins, and lock security is reduced.*

And Now for a Word About Underwriters' Laboratories

The UL stamp on the face of a lock cylinder means that the cylinder has withstood a series of timed forcible attacks, within the time limits established by Underwriters' Laboratories. The Lab makes periodic spot checks of randomly selected cylinders to make sure they continue to meet these standards.

These attacks include a ten-minute pick attack such as shown in Fig. 35-3; a five-minute drill attack such as in

CONVENTIONAL CYLINDER

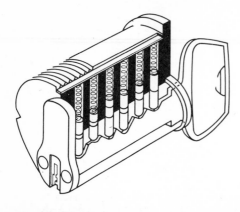

Fig. 34-3 / *Conventional lock cylinder, showing one level of master keying (note small pins between top and bottom pins).*

Fig. 35-3 / *UL label also means lock cylinders resist pick attack, such as shown here.*

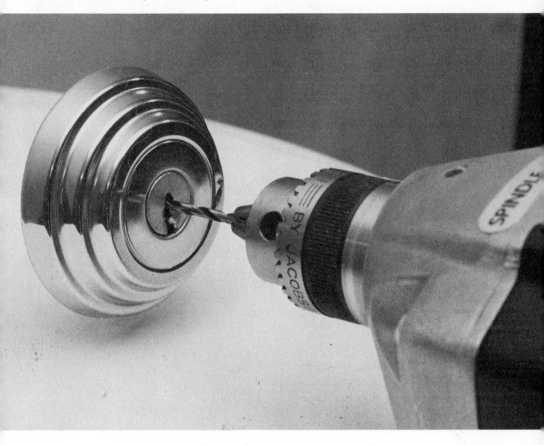

Fig. 36-3 / *UL label means locks are tested to resist five minutes of this type of drill attack. Only high security cylinders can meet this test.*

Fig. 36-3 and insertion of a tool into the lock keyway in an attempt to turn the lock by force. The lock picker attempts to raise the bottom pins, one at a time, up to the shear line, and hold them there by putting turning tension on the plug with the tension wrench shown at left in Fig. 35-3. When all the pins are at the shear line, the plug can be turned with the tension wrench, the lock is picked, and can be opened with the wrench. In the drill attack, the object is to drill out the pins at the shear line so the plug can be rotated with a tool such as a screwdriver, and the lock unlocked. Both lock picking and drilling are a lot more difficult than this simple description. Picking even the simplest pin-tumbler lock can take an experienced locksmith five or ten minutes if he's unlucky, a minute or so if he's lucky and manages to hit all the pins in the correct sequence. So far, more locks are forced open by means other than picking, in this country, although there are pockets of expert lock pickers around the country, notably in New York City and in Miami (do they winter there?).

4

LOCKS FOR
LOW- TO MEDIUM-CRIME-RATE AREAS

When your exposure to crime is minimal, but . . . Here are low budget locks you can afford . . .

IF YOUR LOCAL police or county sheriff's office tells you chances are slim you'll be the victim of a burglary, home invasion, or robbery, you probably don't need the expensive kinds of locks I have recommended in Chapter Three. You do need some sort of protection that will deter a break-in attempt or persuade the criminal to go to an easier target. The locks I will mention and select in this chapter will be recognizably tougher to get through and defeat than the Jell-O key-in-knob lock, even to a beginning burglar.

Tubular Deadbolt Auxiliary Locks

Tubular deadbolt locks can be installed right above your key-in-knob or other door lock. These locks (Fig. 1-4)

require two holes to be bored through the door (see Chapter Eight for installation instructions). The part of the lock holding the bolt goes through a hole bored in the edge of the door, and the lock sections fasten on the outside of both sides of the door and are bolted together through the door. The better locks of this type do a good job of resisting twisting and cylinder-pulling attack.

Since some of these tubular locks are little more than junk, yet look like the better ones, let me give you a few features to look for and guard against:

- *The lock sections on the outside face of the door (and inside) should be bolted together* with strong alloy-steel machine screws (Fig. 2-4). Bolt heads must be concealed on

Fig. 1-4 / *Weiser tubular deadbolt auxiliary lock can be installed above your old lock for greater security.*

both sides of the door to prevent the lock from being removed.

- *The lock bolt should have a freely rotating, hardened-steel rod insert* that rolls under the hacksaw blade and prevents it from being cut. Fig. 3-4 shows a tubular lock deadbolt broken to show the rod insert.
- *The case of the lock should be made of tough steel, not weak die-cast metal as in Fig. 4-4.* Note that one of the bolt pillars has been broken off (A), and with very little force, I can assure you. A far stronger lock shell is shown in Fig. 5-4; "A" shows the steel bolt pillar.
- *The bolt itself should be a full one inch long* for maximum protection, and about $\frac{3}{16}$ to $\frac{1}{4}$ inch of the bolt should be in the lock tube when moved out to the locked posi-

tion. Fig. 6-4 shows three tubular lock bolts. "Bolt "A" is obviously the longer and has more inside the tube. Bolt "B" is, according to the manufacturer, one inch long, but little is left in the lock tube when in the locked position. Bolt "C" broke under hammer attack; the other two survived. Here the rod insert did not offer protection. Fig. 7-4 shows the same bolt as in Fig. 6-4 ("A") at top. Note it is one inch long, and that $\frac{3}{16}$ inch of the full bolt is inside the tube when fully locked.

- *The lock cylinder should be protected* against pulling and twisting attack with a tapered, freely rotating cylinder guard (Figs. 1-4 and 2-4).

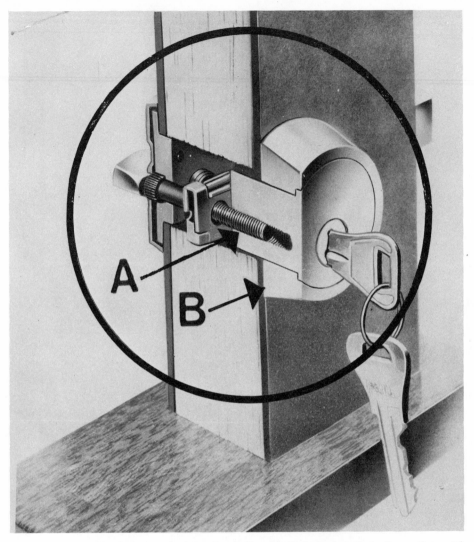

Fig. 2-4 / *Any good tubular deadbolt lock is bolted together with hardened-steel machine screws holding inside and outside cylinders together as shown here in this Weiser Series 4000 lock. "A" shows bolts; "B" shows cylinder guard.*

Recommended Tubular Deadbolt Locks

You can buy these locks with only one cylinder on the outside and thumb-turn on the inside. If your door has a glass window, I suggest double cylinders, one on each side, so a burglar can't just break the glass, reach in and unlock the lock. Prices are given for both double- and single-cylinder locks. Double cylinders can be keyed alike so one

Fig. 3-4 / *The better tubular deadbolts have a freely turning, hardened-steel rod insert that rolls under attack by hacksaw blade. This bolt was broken to show location of the rod, "A".*

key will open both. You will note that I am only recommending a few makes out of the many available. These are all popular brands, so you should be able to find one of them locally.

- *Weiser Series D-4300 double cylinder, $40.*
- *Weiser Series D-4400 single cyl-*

inder, $31. Both Weiser locks (Figs. 1-4 and 2-4) are attached to the door by two ¼-inch heat-treated bolts that pass through a steel plate inside of the cylinder and thread into the back of the outside cylinder; one-inch projection deadbolt with free-turning rod

Fig. 4-4 /   *Interior parts of the tubular deadbolt, where bolts fasten, should be high-grade steel, not easily broken cast metal. Here one of the bolt pillars, "A", was easily broken by bending with a pair of pliers.*

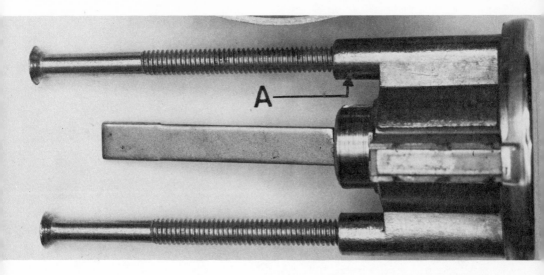

Fig. 5-4 / *By contrast with the lock in Fig. 4-4, this lock has tough steel cylinder shell that withstood attack forces of twisting and bending. Note that post "A" was not broken off when force with pliers was applied.*

insert ¼-inch thick; heavy, free-turning solid brass tapered cylinder guard to prevent gripping or twisting. Weiser Locks, 4100 Ardmore Ave., South Gate, California 90280.

• *Schlage No. SC-B462P, double cylinder,* $35.
• *Schlage No. SC-B460P, single cylinder,* $28. Both models have one-inch deadbolt and cylinder guards. Schlage Lock Company, Box 3324, San Francisco, California 94119.

Automatic Deadlatch Great for Kids

Children, yea, even up to college age, are very forgetful when it comes to locking the door after them. High school kids, as I know all too well, just won't

take the trouble, especially when they come in late at night. The result, an unlocked door all night, and sometimes during the day if they leave after you do. A great way to end this forgetting-to-lock-up problem is to install an auxiliary deadlatching lock that locks automatically when the door is closed. That way at least the door will always be locked, and the lock cannot be opened by sliding a thin shim such as a credit card between the latch and the strike (as in key-in-knob latch locks, see Chapter Two).

The only automatic deadlatch worthy of the name I have found, which will give you security equal to or better than tubular deadbolts, is the Abloy Model 1300 series lock. This Finnish-made lock uses a unique high-security cylinder that is extremely pick- and drill-resistant

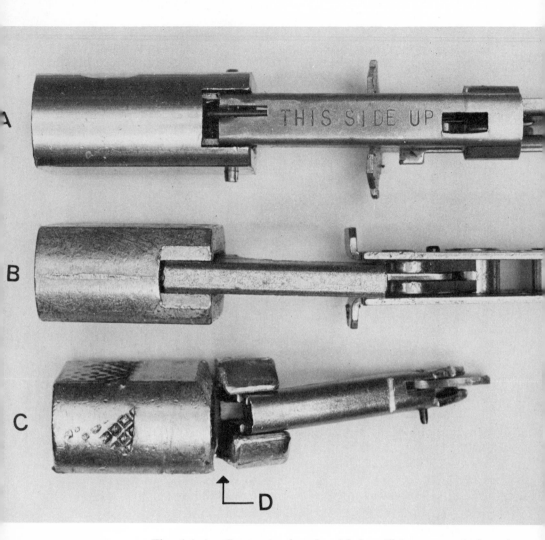

Fig. 6-4 / *Contrasting lengths of bolts. All have a one-inch projection from the lock faceplate when in the locked position. But note the varying overall lengths of the bolts. Bolt "A", from a Weiser lock, has more of the bolt inside the lock mechanism than the other two bolts. Bolt "C" broke at point "D" when twisted in the vise; the other two held up under the same attack.*

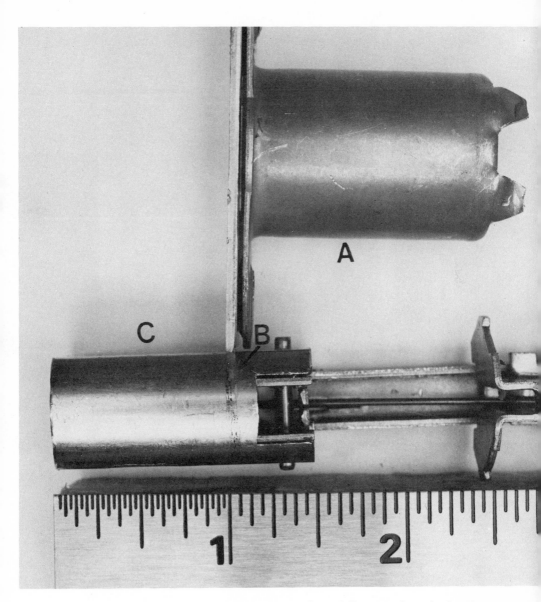

Fig. 7-4 /   *This is what I meant by a full one-inch projection (see also Fig. 6-4) of the bolt outside the lock faceplate. Bolt "C" has one inch outside the lock; about 3/16-inch solid bolt material inside the lock at "B". The bolt tube "A" normally holds the bolt; I took it out just to show you the entire bolt and its extension mechanism.*

Fig. 8-4 / *This Finnish-made automatic deadlatching lock is great when you have kids. It automatically locks the door shut when it closes and has double cylinders and high-security cylinder.*

(see Chapter Three for a description of this cylinder). The lock itself, Fig. 8-4, comes with a double cylinder and can be set to be self-locking. The lock has a unique feature of being self-locking in two positions; one, when the lock is set so an inside thumbturn can open the door from inside but locks it from the outside; two, when the lock is set so it can only be opened from inside or outside with the key.

For example, you may have a door with a window in it, so you want a double-cylinder lock that can be key-locked from inside as well as from outside. You do want to keep the door locked while you're home during the day but not have to worry about whether

INSIDE OF DOOR

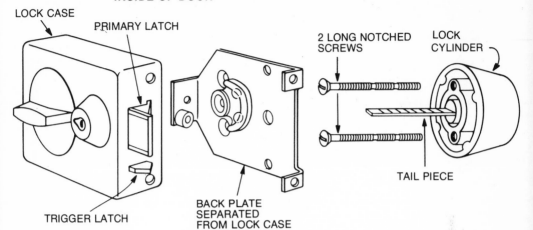

LOCK CASE

PRIMARY LATCH

2 LONG NOTCHED SCREWS

LOCK CYLINDER

TAIL PIECE

TRIGGER LATCH

BACK PLATE SEPARATED FROM LOCK CASE

Fig. 9-4 / *Abloy automatic deadlatch lock has double cylinders, bolts on through door.*

the kids have locked it with their key as they leave or run in and out. The Abloy will give you that option. The lock, when set to lock from both sides automatically, dispenses with the worry about whether the kids have locked up when they arrive late at night. The lock, with the double-cylinder automatic locking features, costs about $35 not installed.

Installation is simple; you should be able to do it yourself. The lock installs on the inside surface of the door, very much like an interlocking deadbolt. Abloy, Inc., 6212 Oakton St., Morton Grove, Illinois 60053. Oh yes, the lock is machine-screw bolted through the door, the cylinder has a freely rotating hard-steel tapered guard on the outside. Full instructions and a template for installation come with the lock. Fig. 9-4 shows how this lock goes together.

5

LOW-COST LOCKS
FOR LOW-SECURITY RISKS

**When you're on a budget and the risk
of crime is not great, reasonable protection against burglars can be yours
at low cost. Here are the locks that
will do the job . . .**

THE HOUSE is as American as apple pie.
The kind Grandma and Grandpa live
in, on a quiet street in a small town.
White clapboard siding. A long verandah
with one of those glider couches and a
couple of rocking chairs. Green shutters,
red brick chimney. The doors are never
locked, nor are the windows. In this
town, crime has never been rampant.

A car with two young men in it pulls
up to the curb in front of the house.
The men get out of the car, walk up
to the front door, ring the bell. No
answer. The house is unoccupied. The
front door is unlocked; both men enter.
Fifteen minutes later they leave, with
bulging pockets.

Stolen from the house are many valuables, including heirloom jewelry and
sterling silverware, a coin collection and
five hundred shares of a negotiable security. The men are not professional
burglars, but rather strangers to the
town in need of funds and with an elastic
conscience—burglars of opportunity and
need.

A simple lock on front and rear doors,
and closed and locked windows, would
have sent these amateur burglars to an
easier target. The town was full of them.

For this type of low crime hazard,
less costly and simpler locks should be
all you need—locks that are a step or
two up in strength and attack-resistance

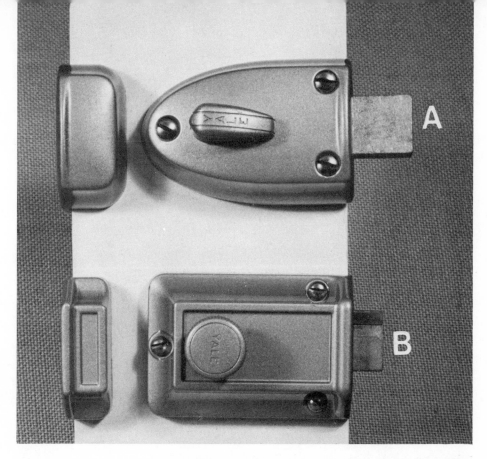

Fig. 1-5 / *Two auxiliary deadbolt rimlocks. The one at the top has a one-inch bolt, which is long enough to prevent it from being pried out of the strike (the part the bolt goes into, mounted on the door frame). Lock "B" at the bottom has a short bolt, easily pried out of the strike with a pry bar inserted between door and door frame.*

from the key-in-the-knob lock and the simple lever-tumbler lock we discussed earlier.

Auxiliary Deadbolt Rimlock

Here is a strong lock that will give you excellent protection. Depending on which make you buy, the lock will cost anywhere from $12 to $22.

First, a few definitions. An auxiliary lock is one you install in addition to the lock now on the door. A deadbolt lock is one with a bolt that must be actuated with a key (or a thumbturn from inside). The deadbolt is easy to install. The lock comes with a template (pattern) that positions all parts accurately in place on the door and door frame.

The only change I would make in installing the lock is to throw away the wood screws that come with the lock and substitute machine screws. The machine screws should go all the way through the door. The hex (six-sided) heads of these screws should be ground to make them difficult to remove.

Here is what you should look for in one of these locks:

- *A full one-inch (or longer) bolt.* Fig. 1-5 shows a lock with such a bolt "A," as compared with one

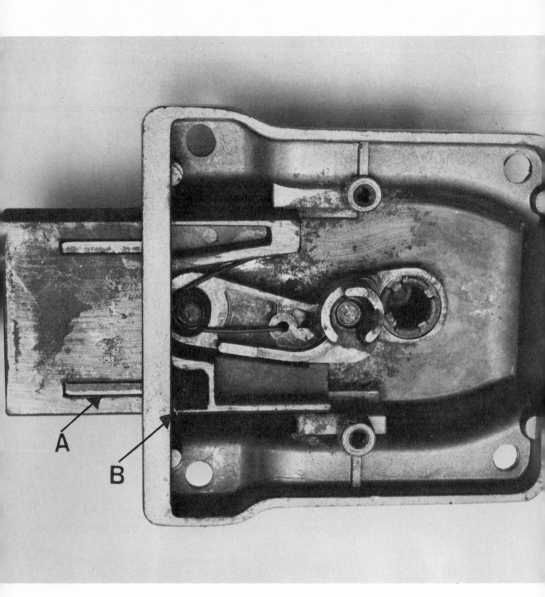

Fig. 2-5 / *With the case cover removed, you can see that this dead-bolt lock is well made. "A" shows hardened-steel inserts in the bolt to resist cutting attack. "B" shows enough of the bolt still inside the lock case, when the bolt is fully extended, to provide strength against forcible attack with hammers or pry bars.*

(Right)
Fig. 3-5 / *The cylinder of this deadbolt rimlock is protected by a beveled guard that comes up flush with the face of the cylinder. The guard allows no place to grip the cylinder and pull it out of the lock.*

having an inadequate bolt length. The shorter bolt can be more easily pried out of its strike with a pry bar.

- *Strong internal working parts.* Fig. 2-5 shows a deadbolt rimlock with the case cover removed. As you look at the bolt you will see two steel insert rods "A" that make the bolt harder to saw through. With the bolt fully extended, in the locked position, you will see at "B" that a lot of the bolt is still inside the case.

I want to point out here that some of these locks have very little of the bolt left in the case when in the locked position. This type of lock is easily defeated by the pry bar that can rip the lock apart. Some of these locks have bolts of soft metal that can be easily cut.

Many of these deadbolt rimlocks are available with one cylinder outside and a simple thumbturn inside. This arrangement is fine if your door is strong and has no window. If not, a burglar could break the window glass or punch a hole through the door and open the lock by reaching inside and using the thumbturn to unlock the door. If you have such a vulnerable door, use a double-cylinder lock that can be key-locked from both sides of the door.

- *A cylinder guard* that leaves no place for a pair of elongated "nippers" that can grip the cylinder and twist and turn it until it comes right out of the lock. If this happens, the lock can be opened with a twist of a screwdriver. Fig. 3-5 shows one such guard.

Recommended Auxiliary Deadbolt Locks

After dissecting a couple of dozen randomly selected makes and models of deadbolt locks, and sawing and hacking, chopping and assaulting them in other ways, I can recommend those listed below as worth the money in attack resistance:

- *Ilco Model 500-54-35.* $12. Single cylinder.
- *Yale Model 112.* $12.87. Single cylinder.
- *Yale Model 112¼.* $18.87. Double cylinder, 1⅛-inch bolt.
- *Ideal Model BX9280 AP.* $22. Single cylinder. Built-in cylinder guard protects cylinder from being pulled out of lock.

6

PEOPLE WHO LIVE IN GLASS HOUSES . . .
SHOULD LOCK THEIR WINDOWS!

Even if you don't live in a glass house you should lock your windows and glass doors. Here's how to do it . . .

NEXT TO DOORS, windows and sliding glass patio doors are the favorite entry point of burglars. And with good reason. Windows of any type—casement, double hung, jalousie—are ridiculously easy to open, given the "locks" that come with them.

For example, the popular thumb-set lock on double-hung windows is held in place only by a few short wood screws. Even if the wood is new, these locks can be ripped out of the woodwork by a pry bar inserted between the sash and the window frame (Fig. 1-6).

Casement windows, with conventional hardware locks, can be opened simply and quietly by slapping a square of adhesive paper over the pane nearest the lock, cutting out the pane, removing it and reaching in and opening the window.

Sliding glass doors are just as easy to open, even with a bar or broom handle stuck between the sliding glass door and the adjoining frame. Most of these glass doors can be lifted up out of their tracks. All it takes is a screwdriver blade inserted in the track from the outside. One lift with the screwdriver, a push inward, and the glass door is removed.

A favorite trick of burglars who invade apartments and condominiums, for example, is to climb from one balcony to another to reach a third- or fourth-floor balcony. It takes a little agility, but it is done, with some regularity, as a friend of mine recently discovered when

Fig. 2-6 / *Deerfield window lock offers bolt and wedge protection against force, and is an excellent window lock.*

she awoke to find a burglar in her bedroom. She had the presence of mind to scream, and the burglar left via her front door. When police arrived, they quickly spotted the telltale indentations in the sliding glass door track, on the outside.

◄

(Opposite)
Fig. 1-6 / *Thumb-set window locks on double-hung windows are held in place by wood screws, can easily be ripped out with a pry bar as shown.*

Recommended Locks for Windows and Glass Doors

The best lock I could find for windows costs around $6 and is made by the Deerfield Lock Company, 945 Wayne Ave., Deerfield, Illinois. This lock (Fig. 2-6) does not depend only on wood screws for strength. The lock uses a combination wedging action and steel bolt that fits into a steel strike for a very strong lock for double-hung windows. This lock comes with very clear installa-

Fig. 3-6 /   *Yale window lock also gives good protection for double-hung wood sash windows.*

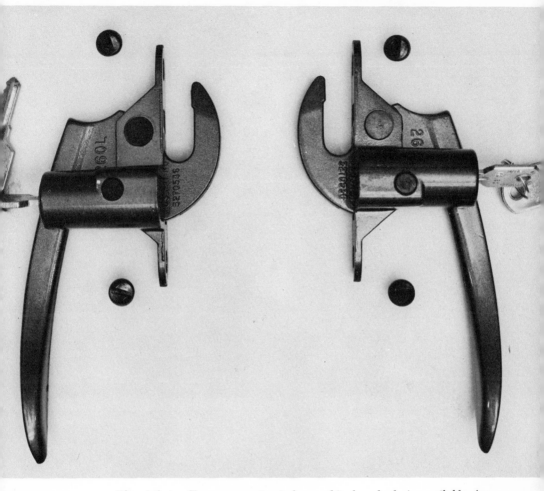

Fig. 4-6 / *For casement windows, this key lock is available for both left- and right-hand opening sash.*

tion instructions and is easy to install. All you need is a power drill and a screwdriver.

Another lock for double-hung windows is the Yale Model YA-L113. It has the same features as the Deerfield lock, except for the wedging action (Fig. 3-6).

For casement windows, Ideal Security Model 260-L (Fig. 4-6) replaces the conventional lock and is available for both left-hand- and right-hand-opening windows (from hardware stores).

If you have a lot of windows to lock, you can order all the window locks keyed alike. This means that one key will open all the locks on all the windows, a definite convenience and safety feature in case you have to get out quickly, as in a fire.

Sliding Glass Door Lock

The only lock that offers both sliding and lifting protection, with all parts on

Fig. 5-6 / Deerfield sliding glass door lock prevents door from being slid open and from being lifted out of tracks from the outside.

the inside, is the Deerfield sliding glass door lock (Fig. 5-6). Like its sister window lock, this unit provides wedging and bolt action, and acts as a sure stop to lifting the glass door out of the tracks. The lock costs about $8.50 and is worth it. If you don't want to spend that much money, you could simply drill a hole into the sliding door frame, and through the tracks. Then you can insert a metal rod through the hole. But do it where it is difficult to push out from the outside.

Which Windows to Lock

I would definitely lock all ground-level and first-floor windows. You can install a second strike when you use the Deerfield window lock, so you can lock the window open for ventilation at a height no burglar could get through.

I would also lock all upper-story windows reachable by climbing anything. Burglars can shinny up drainpipes, climb trees whose branches dip close to upper-story windows, or use adjoining buildings to get to upper-story windows.

If you live in a high crime area, or in a home that is an attractive target to burglars, you should lock *all* windows in the house. Burglars have been known to use fake delivery trucks, or roofer's or painter's trucks and ladders to get to upper-floor windows.

7

HOW TO ADD SECURITY
TO YOUR VULNERABLE GARAGE

Garages are sitting-duck targets for burglars. Most are easy to break into. If you keep valuables in the garage, or could get trapped there by a hiding burglar, you need to know how to make it burglar-proof. Here are the locks to do it . . .

"I AM A BURGLAR. I specialize in garages, mostly in suburban areas, although I 'service' a lot of city garages too. Why garages? Well, first probably because I'm afraid. I don't want to risk getting caught inside a house, or meet you face to face. Garages I can enter quietly at night and know I will never meet you there, or at least the odds are in my favor that I will be left alone. Then too the garage is isolated from the house, even if it is attached. I can work shielded from the street, usually, so I don't have to worry about being spotted by a neighbor.

"Best of all, garages are full of goodies

I can easily turn into cash. Bicycles, power lawn mowers, motorcycles, tools, even a small car or two. Camping equipment. To top off all these attractions, garages are so easy to get into it's like stealing candy from a baby. All I have to do is back my pick-up truck, with its 'lawn-care service' sign on its sides, right up to the garage, and load up. I skip those garages that have nothing valuable I can see from an outside window, and those whose owners have made an obvious attempt to make my entry difficult, noisy, and time consuming."

If I were a burglar, I think that's what

I would say about my specialty. Now let's discuss methods of hardening the garage against burglary.

Overhead Doors

Single garage doors, or sectional ones, have wheels attached to them that run in steel tracks on each side. The best and simplest way to lock these doors, if you can do it from the inside, is to drill a half-inch hole in the track, just above one of the guide wheels. You can then snap a padlock in the track hole. Now, even if a burglar did break in through a window or a doorway, he would only be able to steal what would go out the way he came in. The standard bar locks that come on these doors are easy to defeat; all it takes is a pry bar under the door. A good upward heave on the pry bar and the flimsy door-lock bars will bend enough so the door will open.

Swinging Garage Doors

Hinged garage doors that swing open can be locked in a number of ways. I would use at least two of them.

Most of these doors are locked with a flimsy hasp and a cheap padlock. A "hasp" is a fastening device with a metal loop into which the padlock is fastened. This combination is easily defeated either by cutting the lock shackle with a bolt cutter, or by ripping the entire hasp out of the woodwork with a pry bar. Since the hasp is usually only held by wood screws, prying it out of the woodwork is easy. This type of hasp should be replaced with a hardened-steel hasp and a good padlock. The hasp should be fastened to the door with machine screws: bolts that are highly resistant to

attack by the pry bar. The bolts should go all the way through the door, and have large flat washers on the inside of the door. As for the padlock, please refer to Chapter Ten for a detailed description and specifications and my selection of strong padlocks (and hasps).

The most convenient location for the padlock and hasp is on the outside of the garage doors, where you can open the doors without having to go around to another door, or inside the house, to get into the garage. This lock location is also most convenient for the burglar. I would prefer to see you install the padlock and hasp on the *inside* of the door. If you do, be sure to use flat-head bolts that offer no place to grip them. Or grind the bolt heads round for this same reason.

I would also "pin" the hinges, as explained in Chapter Nine, to prevent the doors from being lifted out. "Pinning" hinges is simply installing a metal pin in the hinge that also protrudes into the door section of the hinge and prevents the door from being lifted out.

The second way I would lock swinging garage doors is with a ¾-inch steel L-shaped bar that fits into a retainer on the door and slides in a track up and down. The locking end of the bar fits into a retainer at the top of the door. A separate bar, at the bottom of the door, fits into a retainer or strike in the floor. Both doors should be fitted with these bars, top and bottom. The retainers or strikes should be bolted to the doors, as should the bolt tracks.

House-to-Garage Doors

One of the weakest security points in any home is the door that goes from the house to an attached garage. Home builders rarely think of this door as needing a good lock, because the garage door can be locked. You should always treat the house-to-garage door as you would any exterior door. The door itself should be solid wood core (not hollow core) and it should have a good lock on it, preferably an interlocking deadbolt (see Chapter Three).

The secondary or entrance door to a detached garage (the door that is the same size as a standard home rear door) should also receive good security treatment. If you keep a lot of valuables in the garage, I would install an interlocking deadbolt on this door, and reinforce it with steel bars (as explained in detail in Chapter Nine).

Garage Windows

There are three treatments I recommend for garage windows. First, since most of the garage can be seen through a window, I would remove temptation from a burglar by whitewashing the window on the inside. The whitewash will let in the light, but keep your valuables inside from being seen from outside.

Second, I would install a Deerfield window lock (see Chapter Six). And finally I would install bars on the *inside* of the window (see Chapter Eleven). Now if a burglar tries to get in by breaking the glass, he will be confronted by steel bars. Because the bars are on the inside, they will be hard to reach either for cutting or prying apart.

Garage Door Openers Can Add Security

A burglar can break into the garage, hide behind your possessions or in a corner, and accost you when you have closed the garage door. For security reasons alone I believe a good automatic, remotely-operable garage door opener is a good investment. From the safety of your locked car you can open the garage doors, scan the garage for an intruder, drive into the garage and after turning off the car motor, close the garage door(s). The better garage door openers can also turn on the garage light as the door opens, and with a time delay, turn off the light within a few minutes. This gives you time to get into the house.

The door opener should also have an inside switch that opens the garage door and turns on the garage light from inside the house. Then, through a wide-angle (180°) door peeper (see Chapter Nine) you can scan the entire garage before you leave the house.

The better door openers have a dual-frequency door control which gives added protection against accidental opening of garage doors by signals from passing radio transmitters, as from police cars and planes overhead.

I prefer the shaft-driven opener to the chain drive, because the shaft drive is much more resistant to forcible attack, as with a pry bar under the garage door.

An excellent garage door opener, with all the features described above, is made by A. E. Moore, Inc., Waupaca, Wisconsin, and sold by Montgomery Ward & Company for around $250.

8

IT'S EASY TO INSTALL
YOUR OWN LOCKS!

You can save upwards of $25 per lock by installing your own. If you can assemble children's toys or build a birdhouse, you can do the simple mechanics of lock installation. Here's how to do it . . .

IN THIS CHAPTER we will discuss how to install interlocking deadbolt rimlocks and the tubular deadbolt locks discussed in Chapters Three and Four and the M.A.G. mortise lock discussed in Chapter Three.

This chapter will be valuable to you even if you don't install your own locks. At least you will know when the lock is properly installed.

A Word About Doors

A great many houses built right after World War II, before cities got around to enacting better building codes, had hollow-core exterior doors. Since the best lock in the world is useless on these doors (Fig. 1-8) you should replace them with a solid-core door. Please refer to Chapter Nine for more details on the doors and the door frames. You can tell a hollow-core door by banging on it; it will sound hollow. Or you can drill a tiny hole in two or three places. If the door is hollow-core, the drill will hit air as soon as it penetrates the thin plywood outer shell of the door. These doors are so flimsy a burglar can kick his way in, or chop out around the lock in seconds.

FROM

Fig. 1-8 / *Hollow-core doors are flimsy, easy to chop through quickly. Exterior hollow-core doors should be replaced with solid wood-core before installing any auxiliary or mortise lock.*

How to Install an Interlocking Deadbolt Rimlock

You will recall we discussed the interlocking deadbolt type of lock in Chapter Three. The instructions below apply specifically to the Ideal DE-9295 lock. Other makes of interlocking deadbolts are installed in much the same way as this one, and all of them come with installation instructions.

This type of lock is installed above an existing lock. The lock itself fastens to the inside of the door. The strike (the part the bolt fits into) is fastened to the door frame. All of these locks come with

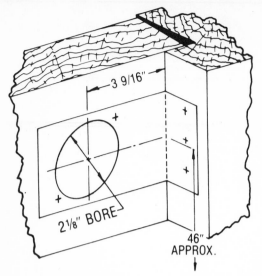

a template (pattern). The template is a full-scale pattern (Fig. 2-8) that shows where to place the lock, and where and what size holes to bore.

Step One: Select a location for the new lock above the old one. A good spot would be about five inches above the old lock. Scotch-tape the template on the door. With a sharp tool (such as an icepick) mark the centerline of the cylinder hole (the big hole) and the two smaller wood-screw holes. Make your marks right through the paper template so they will be pushed in the woodwork.

Step Two: With a 2⅛-inch wood bit, drill the cylinder hole all the way through the door (Fig. 3-8). You will also see two other X's marked on the template outside the 2⅛-inch cylinder hole. You will have marked these into the woodwork in Step One. With a 1/64th bit, drill starting holes for these wood screws; go about halfway through the door.

Step Three: Please refer to Fig. 4-8, showing an "exploded" view of the lock we are installing. In this drawing you will see a round piece of metal, with a flange (collar), called a "retaining plate." This plate has eight holes in it. The outer two, in the lips of the flange, are the

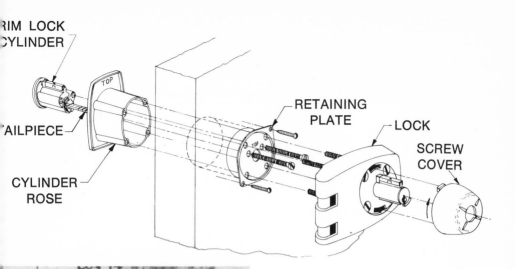

RIM LOCK
CYLINDER

TAILPIECE

CYLINDER
ROSE

TOP

RETAINING
PLATE

LOCK

SCREW
COVER

ones we are concerned with in this step. Note, too, that the word TOP is marked on the plate; this word should be at the top, naturally. Now with the two $\frac{3}{32}$-inch wood screws furnished, screw the retaining plate in place. The plate goes into the cylinder hole you bored in Step Two.

Step Four: Now if you will look at the left side of Fig. 4-8 you will see a piece called a "cylinder rose." It too has the word TOP marked on it, on the inside, and of course the word should be on the top. Shove the cylinder rose, from the front of the door, into the cylinder hole.

Step Five: Look again at Fig. 4-8. You will see two holes in the plate on either side of the word TOP. At the far left of Fig. 4-8 you will see a piece marked "rimlock cylinder." At one end of the cylinder a thin flat brass rod protrudes. This rod is called a "tailpiece." Push the cylinder, tailpiece first, into the cylinder hole, through the cylinder rose (which is not as yet fastened to anything).

With two of the machine screws furnished, bolt the cylinder through the two holes in the retaining plate. These are the two holes on either side of the word TOP, noted above. Note that these are "breakaway" screws. The screws are notched in several places so you can break them off to the right length, which depends on the thickness of your door. The screws should thread as far as possible into the cylinder, and be tightened firmly. Now the cylinder is bolted to the retaining plate, and will resist pulling attack.

Step Six: Now turn your attention to the inside of the door. In Fig. 4-8 you will notice that the lock itself has four holes, evenly spaced around the inside cylinder. Through these holes you now insert the four remaining machine screws, which fit into the four threaded holes in the cylinder rose. Tighten these screws well. Now the cylinder is also firmly bolted to the lock on the inside of the door. The rose serves as a cylinder guard to prevent a burglar from pulling, turning, or twisting the outside cylinder. Before tightening these screws, however, make sure that the front cylinder tailpiece fits into the lock. The tailpiece is notched so it can be broken off to the right length, depending on the thickness of the door. With the key, operate the front cylinder to make sure the lock bolt works smoothly and that the tailpiece is properly located in the lock mechanism.

Step Seven: Now please look at Fig. 5-8, which shows the part of the lock that goes on the inside of the door. This is the cylinder guard. With the lock package you will find a long pin, as shown in Fig. 5-8. In case you were wondering, this pin is used to remove the inside cylinder guard. It fits into a small hole in the guard and releases a catch spring that holds the guard in place. Now, install this guard by fitting it over the inside cylinder and twisting it clockwise

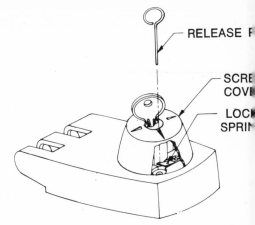

RELEASE P

SCRE
COVE

LOCK
SPRIN

Fig. 5-8 / *Installing inside cylinder guard. Pin is used to remove the guard should cylinder require work.*

until it snaps into place. Check operation of the inside cylinder with the key; make sure the bolt works smoothly.

Step Eight: Now install the strike. In Fig. 2-8 you scribed guide lines through the template to line up holes for the strike. This step is probably the most critical one of all. The fingers of the interlocking bolt must mesh into the holes in the strike (Fig. 6-8). There is very little room for inaccurate alignment of the strike with the bolt. Furthermore, the strike flats or projecting pieces must fit into the main lock body. All of which means the strike must be accurately located for the lock to work smoothly. To work, period. Since the strike is thick brass, you may have to recess it slightly in the door frame so the door will close past it. If you do have to recess it, use a sharp wood chisel and be careful to gouge out no more wood than you need. Use trial and error, testing strike location as you go. When you are ready, screw the strike in place with the wood screws provided. Drill $\frac{1}{64}$-inch guide holes for the screws first.

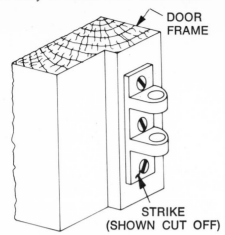

DOOR FRAME

STRIKE
(SHOWN CUT OFF)

Fig. 6-8 / *Template for installing inter-locking deadbolt strike on door frame. Strike must be accurately positioned.*

If, as you drill the guide holes for the strike screws, the drill strikes "air" after the first ¾ inch, you must reinforce the door frame as discussed in Chapter Nine. Striking "air" that soon means you have drilled through a thin, probably soft wood frame, and that there is an inch or so of air space behind it, between the finish frame and the rough frame made of two 2 x 4's. I would also use wood screws long enough to go at least one inch into the rough frame.

How to Install a Tubular Deadbolt Lock

Although I am going to tell you how to install a Weiser Series 4000 tubular deadbolt lock, these instructions apply generally to all tubular deadbolt locks. There will be variations in cylinder hole sizes and assembly instructions, but these will be minor. I know you will be able to cope. Installing a lock is like cooking a meal; if you can read you can follow the recipe, or install the lock. (I know, I have done both.)

OK, let's get to it. You have bought the lock, and it's sitting there still wrapped in the box. Unpack the lock. Read the installation instructions. You will see a printed thin-cardboard piece of paper about 7 inches by 3 inches, with a lot of circles drawn on them, a little like an astrologer's chart. This piece of cardboard is a chart, all right, in that it shows you how to locate holes you will need to drill to install the lock. Holes must be accurately located so the lock will fit the door properly.

We discussed "backset" a few pages back. Backset is the distance from the edge of the door to the centerline of the lock. You should have measured this distance on your old lock and ordered the new lock with the same backset. If not, now is the time to do so, and exchange the lock you now have for one with the right backset. The "astrologer's" chart you saw is actually a template for accurately lining up all the holes you will need to drill. Note that the template does indicate three backsets: 5, 2¾, and 2⅜ inches. On the right of the template (Fig. 7-8) there is a smaller template section for the hole you will need to drill in the edge (the right name is "stile") of the door. This edge or stile template has four centers, one each for four thicknesses of doors; 1⅜-, 1¾-, and 2¼-inch thicknesses. Use the center mark for your thickness of door. If you have a door thinner than 1⅜ inches it had better be steel; otherwise I suggest it is too thin for security. If your door is thicker than 2¼ inches you can mark off your own center. Just measure total thickness, divide this measurement by two and mark that centerpoint on the door stile. With these general observations, let's get down to specific installation steps.

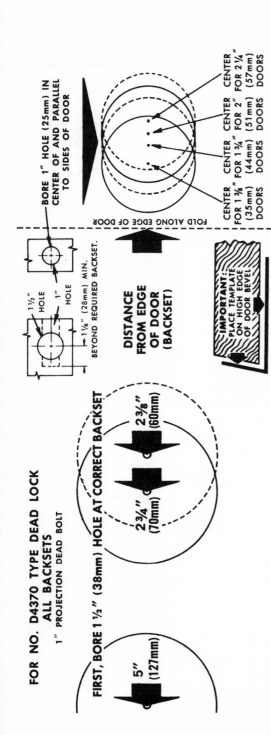

◄
(Opposite)
Fig. 7-8 / *Template for installing tubular deadbolt auxiliary lock. Note that template offers three different locations for "backset" (distance of lock from door edge). Use the backset of existing lock as a guide.*

Step One: Mount the template (Fig. 7-8) on the door about five inches above your old lock, after you have made sure you do not have a hollow-core door and that the door you do have has a lock rail that will accept the new lock. Good doors have a lock rail as in Fig. 8-8. Take care to mount the template so that the dotted-line fold, where you bend the door-edge (stile) part of the template over the edge, is exactly on the high edge of the door bevel (the slanted part of the door edge).

Step Two: With something sharp, such as a nail or icepick (do people still use icepicks?), scribe the centerline point for the cylinder and the lock tube holes. Mark on the door right through the template. Now you can remove the template, and drill these two holes. Drill the cylinder hole with a 1½-inch wood bit. Go slowly and be careful. Stop drilling when you see the very tip of the bit go through the other side of the door. Remove the bit and finish up from the other side. This way you will avoid tearing splinters and hunks out of the door-face veneer, or splitting the solid wood. You should end up with a very clean, very *straight* hole. "Straight" means that the cylinder hole should be drilled perpendicular to the face of the door. If the cylinder hole is drilled cockeyed, if you let the drill bit drift off to one side or the other, the lock mechanism is not going to be lined up so it works easily; if you drill far enough off from true the lock may not work at all. That's why a boring jig,

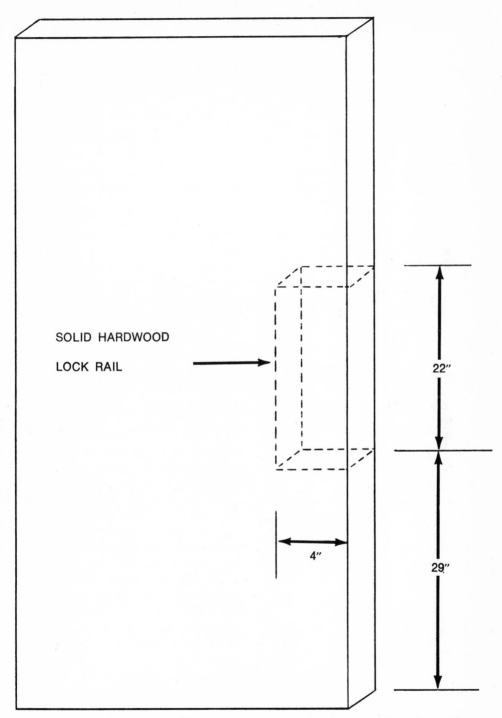

SOLID HARDWOOD

LOCK RAIL

22"

4"

29"

Fig. 8-8 / *Before installing lock, make sure door has adequate hardwood "lock rail" that will accept the lock. Some doors have lock rail only big enough for one lock.*

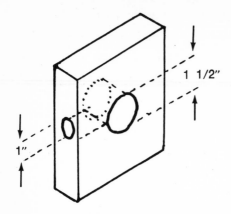

Fig. 9-8 / *Location of cylinder and deadbolt mechanism holes in door for tubular deadbolt auxiliary lock.*

which guides the drill bit, is a good idea, if you can rent the jig for the lock you are installing. You can drill straight, if you are careful; do take your time, though.

Step Three: Now drill the one-inch hole in the door stile for the lock tube, using the centermark appropriate to the thickness of your door. Fig. 9-8 shows gen-

eral location of the tube hole. If you use the template properly (Fig. 7-8) the tube hole will be centered in the door edge (stile) and hit the cylinder hole accurately. The tube hole must of course be drilled straight to prevent binding of working parts. After all drilling, blow out sawdust and wood chips.

Step Four: Install the tube mechanism. This is the part marked "Latch with 1" dead bolt" in Fig. 10-8. If you look at the faceplate of the latch you will see the maker's name (Weiser) stamped on that plate. Then if you look toward the rear of the barrel you will see, just behind the barrel or tube the word UP stamped. Install the bolt mechanism through the hole in the edge of the door with the UP side on top. Screw the faceplate to the door with the two wood screws provided.

Step Five: If you examine the parts of the lock left in the box and Fig. 10-8, you will see four tapered brass rings, two

Fig. 10-8 / *Exploded view of tubular deadbolt lock.*

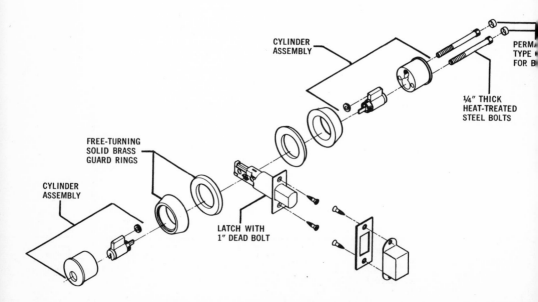

of which fit over each of the two lock cylinders. You should use both rings, with the small ring closest to the door, taper facing outward (Fig. 10-8), for doors 1⅜ inches thick. For doors 1¾ inches or thicker, use the large ring only. Slip one (or both) rings, as above, over the inside cylinder.

Step Six: In Fig. 10-8 you will see a part labeled "Latch with one" dead bolt." If you look carefully, you will see a small rectangular hole at the left of this piece. This is the hole the cylinder tailpiece fits into. The tailpiece is a thin, flat brass rod that extends from the back of each of the two cylinders. Bear this in mind as you assemble the cylinder assemblies, with the guard rings in place as shown in Fig. 10-8.

Now insert the inside cylinder, tailpiece first. The tailpiece must fit into the slotted hole mentioned above in the latchbolt mechanism. If the tailpiece is in the wrong position, turn it with a key in the cylinder. The keyway must be at the top of the cylinder. Now check operation of the deadbolt by turning the key.

Step Seven: Insert the key in the outside cylinder. In case you don't know which cylinder is inside and which outside, the outside cylinder is the one on the left of Fig. 10-8. Insert the outside cylinder in the latch or deadbolt mechanism, following Step Six above. You may have to jiggle the key a bit to line up the tailpiece so it will fit alongside the rear cylinder tailpiece.

Step Eight: In the package the lock came in you will find two ¼-inch heat-treated steel bolts. These are used to bolt the inside and outside cylinders together. Insert each bolt through the hole in the inside cylinder housing (Fig. 10-8) and tighten with the Allen wrench furnished.

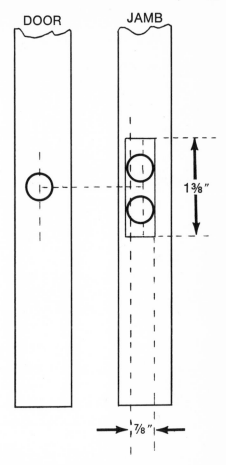

Fig. 11-8 / *Location of strike in door frame, for tubular deadbolt lock. Note that two holes are drilled in jamb (frame) to make chiseling out wood to recess strike easier.*

Put cap bolts over bolt heads in the inside cylinder (also furnished).

Step Nine: Install the strike. Mark a point on the door frame jamb, exactly opposite the center point of the deadbolt hole. From this point, draw a vertical line on the jamb, 1¼ inches above and below that center point, as shown in Fig. 11-8. The strike has two parts, the strike box and the faceplate, Fig. 12-8. You will need to cut a hole in the jamb, exactly opposite the bolt as noted above,

Fig. 12-8 /   *Top, strike box; bottom, strike plate. Both for tubular deadbolt lock.*

1 ⅜″ x ⅞″ x 1″ deep, to receive the strike box. The easiest way is to drill two ⅞-inch holes as shown in Fig. 11-8, and with a small sharp wood chisel, carefully chip out the strike box hole. When finished, blow out all wood chips and insert the strike box in the jamb. Install the strike plate with the two wood screws provided. Close the door and, with the key, open and close the bolt. The bolt should slide easily and accurately, without binding, into the strike box, when the door is in its normally closed position. You should never have to tug or

shove on the door to get the lock to open or close easily. You might check condition of the door hinge screws. If the door sags because hinge screws are loose, remove these screws where they go into the frame, fill the holes with polyester resin and, using slightly longer wood screws, reinstall them before the resin has a chance to cure and harden.

How to Add Security to Your Present Locks

If you have just moved into a new house, apartment, office, or store, how certain can you be that the previous owner still hasn't a key to your premises? How do you know for sure that the former occupant has not lost a key to your new abode, or that for this or a hundred other reasons a criminal now has possession of one of these keys? The best way to be absolutely positive that you and only you have possession of the keys to your new quarters is to have a locksmith change the pin combination of your lock cylinders, and cut new keys to the old locks. Then, and only then, can you rest assured that any keys former occupants may have in their possession, or have lost, will not fit your own locks.

Or you may have a perfectly good lock, properly installed (see Chapter Nine). Chances are this good lock does not have "mushroom" pins. The older pin-tumbler locks (see Chapter Thirteen, How Locks Work) have small round spring-loaded pins. These pins are of different lengths, corresponding to the depth of "cuts" in the key. When the key is inserted in the locks, these pins are lifted up out of the way, the key can now turn and the lock can be opened. An experienced burglar can also pick open plain pin-tumbler locks; in seconds

if he's lucky, in minutes if he has time. Mushroom pins (Fig. 13-8) are much harder to pick open, because the shape of the mushroom pins is such that these pins tend to bind in the lock when a lock pick is inserted in the keyway and pushed up under the bottom pin, as shown in Fig. 13-8.

For key security and new mushroom pins, it is necessary to remove the lock cylinder. The locksmith can come to your house, remove the cylinders, take them back to his shop, remove the old top pins, install new mushroom top pins, change the bottom pin combination and cut new keys for you. Sometimes a good locksmith will have a key cutter and the right size new pins and key blanks with him in his truck, if you tell him what make and model lock you have (or he can make a good guess if you just tell him the type of lock and the make). However, this involves at least one trip, if not a round trip, from his shop to your place; and it could cost you a lot of money.

You can remove the lock cylinders yourself, do some shopping or business and come back in a couple of hours and pick up your rekeyed and more secure cylinders. Be sure, though, to make a date with the locksmith and that he understands you want the work done by a specific time. And be sure to have someone in the house or store while you're gone (which you should do if the locksmith takes the cylinders). Now all you need to know is how to remove and install lock cylinders. It's simple.

How to Remove Lock Cylinders (and put them back)

If you have installed one of the rim-locks mentioned in Chapters Three,

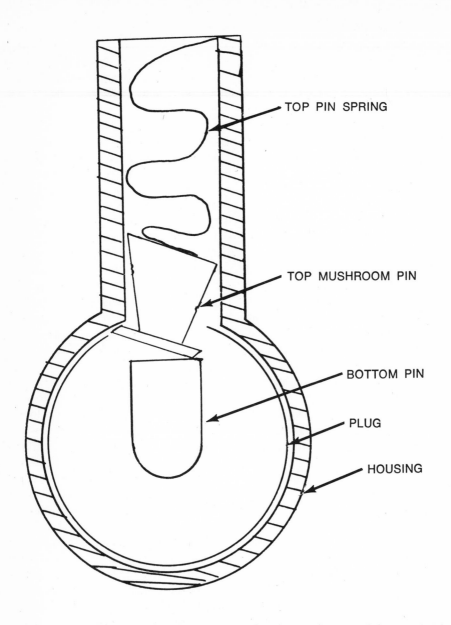

TOP PIN SPRING

TOP MUSHROOM PIN

BOTTOM PIN

PLUG

HOUSING

Fig. 13-8 / *Strong locks already installed can be made harder to pick open by adding one or two "mushroom" pins to the cylinder. Remove cylinder, bring it to a locksmith, ask him to install the high-security pins. Mushroom pins "catch" at cylinder plug housing when the lock-pick tool tries to push them up to open lock.*

Four, or Five, cylinder removal is simple. A rimlock is any lock that is fastened to the surface of the door; for example, the interlocking deadbolt in Chapter Five. Just remove the lock body from the inside of the door, remove the two screws that hold the front cylinder to the backplate and pull the cylinder out. Remove the inside cylinder from the lock body (if you have a double-cylinder lock).

Remove cylinders from a tubular deadbolt lock by reversing installation instructions for this lock in this chapter.

To remove the cylinder(s) from a mortise lock, remove the lock faceplate (Fig. 14-8) by removing the two screws that hold it to the lock body. Underneath this plate you will find a small brass setscrew, near the top of the lock (Fig. 15-8). Turn this screw counterclockwise as far as it will go (about six to eight turns should do). This setscrew fits into a slot or groove the length of the cylinder and prevents it from turning. Otherwise a burglar could simply apply a pipe wrench or pliers and unscrew the cylinder (Fig. 16-8). When the setscrew is turned far enough to remove it from the cylinder housing, you should be able to remove the cylinder by turning it counterclockwise, as shown in Fig. 17-8.

Now that you have removed the cylinders, take them down to the locksmith and tell him you want the pin combinations changed, new keys made and one mushroom pin installed. You can have the keys cut alike, so one key will open any lock, provided the locks are all of the same make, with the same make cylinders.

I take this opportunity to give you a word of caution about who cuts your keys. If you take the cylinders to a good locksmith, you will have no problem with the new keys. There will be deep cuts interspersed with shallow cuts, so that there is little chance a "foreign" key could work in your cylinder.

Beware, though, of part-time "locksmiths" who are really amateurs. These sometime lock "experts" can rekey locks, and cut new keys with key cuts that have relatively little variation in depth. Keys where the cylinder pin combinations have been changed by a full-time professional locksmith should always have depth of cut spacings on the key that make the lock hard to pick open. Let me illustrate. Look at Fig. 18-8. I consider this key poorly cut. Cuts B and C are the same depth. Cuts D and E are the same depth. Cut A is at the tip and very deep, which means a weak key tip easily bent, especially if the key is aluminum. More important is the fact that with pins and cuts of the same depth the lock picker has a much easier time. Often he can pick the lock with one rake of the pick across the pins.

A much harder lock to pick would be one with pins and key cuts as in Fig. 19-8. Note that in this key the cuts are of different depths. Cut A is high, which means a strong tip and a long first pin that poses an obstruction to the lock pick probing for pins further in. Cuts B, C, and D are progressively higher, and matching pins progressively shorter toward the rear of the lock. An ideal combination of pins in a five-pin tumbler lock would be pin numbers 1, 3, 6, 4, and 2. Pins are numbered according to standard lengths. For example, a No. 1 pin is .263 inches, a No. 2 pin is .249 inches. The difference between the two is only .014 inch. Don't tell your locksmith to space pins

Fig. 14-8 / *First step in removing cylinder from a mortise lock is to remove the lock faceplate, located in edge of the door.*

Fig. 15-8 / *With faceplate removed, unscrewing the cylinder lockscrew will permit cylinder removal.*

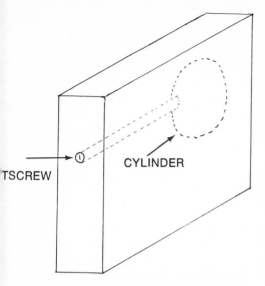

CYLINDER

TSCREW

Fig. 16-8 / *Drawing shows how set-screw fits into barrel of mortise cylinder. This is why mortise locks need cylinder guards. A wrench on the cylinder face could twist brass cylinder past the steel setscrew, cutting a groove in the brass housing.*

according to the ideal formula above, though. I'd hate to think that all my readers have the same keys. By now, too, I hope, you have realized that the number of possible pin combinations in even a five-pin tumbler lock can be well up into the thousands, and with a seven-, ten-, or twelve-pin lock up into the hundreds of thousands.

For more detailed information on lock cylinder construction and function, please skip ahead to Chapter Thirteen. You don't really need to know all this much about locks, but there will be readers who want more technical background. Thus I have included some simple drawings and explanations of how the various types of locks work, as well as some details as to their relative security.

Fig. 17-8 / *With setscrew removed, mortise lock cylinder can be removed.*

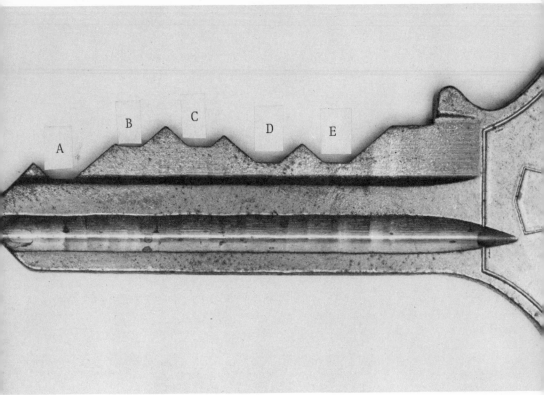

Fig. 18-8 / *Example of a poorly cut key. Cuts "B" and "C" are same depth. Cuts "D" and "E" are same depth. "A" is cut too deeply, weakening key.*

Attack Prevention for Locks

If a burglar can get a pair of pincers on your lock cylinder (Fig. 20-8), he can probably pull the cylinder right out of the lock body. All he needs to open your door, once the cylinder is out, is a screwdriver to turn the bolt mechanism open.

There are two ways to make it virtually impossible for a burglar to get a grip on your lock cylinder. One way is to buy a lock with a free-wheeling, hardened-steel smooth tapered guard. Actually Fig. 20-8 shows such a cylinder guard, normally a part of an Adams-Rite lock. The notches cut into the cylinder guard in this photo were made by the pincers. Then it is extremely difficult, if not impossible, to get enough of a grip on such a guard with any tool. If the pincers don't slide off and do grip, nothing happens because the guard turns freely around the cylinder itself. Fig. 21-8 is a close-up of such a cylinder guard. When you buy a lock, ask the locksmith about one with a built-in lock guard such as the one I have described. The Weiser tubular deadbolt lock mentioned in this chapter has such cylinder protection.

Another excellent lock guard is a heavy, thick aluminum cover that fits over the lock (Fig. 22-8). This guard is bolted right through the door. Nothing is showing to get a grip on. It's available from your locksmith; if he doesn't have it, ask him to order the H.P.C. Armor-Plate guard from his distributor. Another lock guard, Fig. 23-8, is solid hardened steel, and is designed for narrow aluminum doors. This type of guard is available for either round or conventional flat-key-type locks, and to fit over a wide variety of rimlocks such as interlocking and ordinary deadbolts. The mere appearance of these guards is enough to keep a burglar out. The guard in Fig. 23-8 is made by Scotsman Products, Inc., Campbell, California 95008, and is also available through your locksmith. This guard also bolts through the door, and has no projecting parts or bolts to grip.

Aluminum doors are soft and easy to rip open with a pry bar (Fig. 24-8). A hard steel strike guard (Fig. 25-8) adds security to these doors. This type of guard is available through your locksmith. Another protection against this kind of attack is to install a lock with a longer deadbolt *plus* the strike guard. (See Chapter 3 for a discussion of superlock deadbolts). Figures 26-8 and 27-8 show two other varieties of strike guards for aluminum doors.

Key Control, or, Who Has the Key?

A business establishment, institution, or other type of building with hundreds of locks is asking for trouble without some form of key control. All keys as-

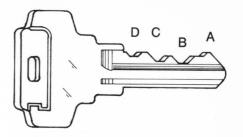

Fig. 19-8 / *Well-cut key, with greatly varying key cuts, means a lock much harder to pick open.*

(Right)
Fig. 20-8 / *Hardened-steel cylinder guard. Note that the guard is beveled to make gripping more difficult. Guard also rotates freely, so even if it could be gripped, pulling the cylinder would not be easy.*

Fig. 21-8 /   *Close-up of same cylinder guard in Fig. 20-8. At right is the retaining snap-ring washer.*

Fig. 22-8 / *Heavy, thick aluminum lock guard fits over rimlock cylinders on outside of door. Keeps burglars from pulling lock cylinder out of lock.*

signed to personnel should be coded and registered. People with keys should be warned to report a loss so that lock combinations can be changed quickly. Keys not in use, or keys that must be returned after each use, should be kept in a locked key cabinet, such as the one shown in Fig. 28-8, made by Tel-Kee, Inc., Glen Riddle, Pennsylvania 19037.

Master Keys . . . a Threat to Security

Master keys are a great convenience. They give the holder a sense of superiority. Master keys can also be one of the weakest links in security in any building. Whenever you add master keying to any building you make the lock that much easier to pick open. And the more gradations of master keying you have, the easier the lock is to pick, or even to be opened with the wrong key. One level of a master-key system is a change key that permits a hotel maid to unlock guest rooms on a given floor. A grand-master key lets the hotel house dick unlock all guest rooms. A great-grand-master key lets the regional manager open all the locks in a group of hotels and a great-great-grand-master gives the big boss access to his corporate universe. Every one of these gradations of master keying involves descending security. I would urge any business executive to think twice before indulging in the luxury of a master-keyed system beyond an absolutely required minimum level.

Apartment Dwellers, Beware!

The building superintendent (janitor) of your apartment building very probably has a master key to your apartment. Your lease most likely says you

Fig. 23-8 / *Hardened-steel cylinder guard for narrow-style aluminum doors, such as found in office buildings. This type of guard is available for both flat and tubular key locks.*

Fig. 24-8 / *All aluminum door frames are soft. A pry bar can easily tear this metal out past the bolt so the door can be opened, as shown.*

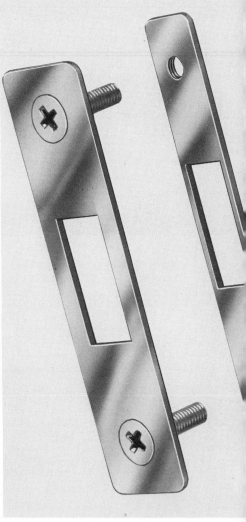

(Above)
Fig. 25-8 / *To prevent an attack such as in Fig. 24-8, a hardened-steel strike should be installed in aluminum door frames.*

(Left)
Fig. 26-8 / *Another type of aluminum door-frame strike reinforcement.*

►
(Opposite)
Fig. 27-8 / *A stronger strike guard is the two-piece hardened-steel fixture shown here, for aluminum door frames.*

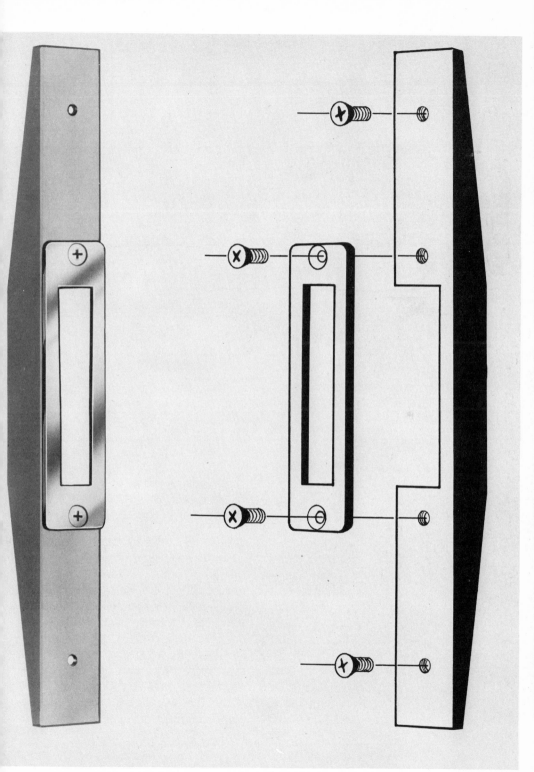

Fig. 28-8 / *Key control in large buildings can be a problem. Keys must be kept out of unauthorized hands. One way to do it is with a key control cabinet, such as shown.*

can't change your lock combination, so that in case of fire or some other disaster while you're away, the janitor can get in. The trouble is, the janitors can be crooks. Very few apartment building owners screen new janitors for a criminal history, or require them to take a polygraph test. Janitors have been known to have extra master keys cut in case they lose the original, and then lose the original without notifying the tenants. For all these reasons, and more, I urge you to remove the cylinder, take it to your locksmith and have him change the combination. Then if the janitor argues about it, ask him why he tried to enter your apartment. It's better to argue about this minor lease violation than it is to lose your valuables or even your life because some building employee turned crooked or was careless about his master key.

If you're interested in how master-key systems work and the technicalities of why they weaken lock security, please read the section in Chapter Thirteen on master-key systems.

9

THE *DOOR* FOR YOUR *LOCK!*

Hollow-core doors . . . thin wood-panel doors . . . doors with weak, spongy frames, aren't worth the installation of good locks. The best lock in the world is useless if a criminal can hack his way around it right through the door. Here is what you should know about doors, door frames and viewers . . .

UNTIL BUILDING CODES caught up with them, a lot of contractors saved money by installing cheap hollow-core exterior doors in new homes.

These doors can be kicked or chopped through in seconds. Most of them have a thin sheet of plywood veneer glued on over an egg-crate or cardboard shell interior (Figs. 1-9 and 1-8).

You can tell if your exterior door is hollow core. Just rap on it. If it sounds hollow, it probably is. Or drill a small hole in it. If the drill bit hits air after about ⅛ inch of penetration, you have

a door that will keep out the birds and the bees and the rain, but not much else. Depending on your security risk, you should replace such a door with a solid particle-board door, a solid wood-core door or a steel door.

For a high-crime-rate area I would use a steel door. For medium crime areas, an exterior solid-wood-core door offers strong protection. For low crime areas an exterior particle-board door is adequate. Table 1-9 compares all of these types of doors in terms of security and cost.

Fig. 1-9 /   Hollow-core door with flimsy eggcrate interior is easy to kick or cut through.

Steel Doors for High-Crime Areas

A steel door, if it's thick enough, is highly resistant to forcible attack by cutting, punching and pressure. The steel frame holds well against attempts to spread it with a pry bar or automobile bumper jack, so as to push the strike out of the bolt.

There are steel doors and there are steel doors. Some are excellent, some little better than much cheaper wood doors. No matter which steel door you buy, though, I cannot recommend it if it has glass windows (Fig. 2-9). Nor can I recommend any steel door made of steel thinner than 16 gauge. Thinner steel is just too flimsy and vulnerable to attack (see Table 1-9).

Some steel doors come with locks already installed. Unfortunately, these locks are usually the key-in-knob kind that are useless in terms of security (see Chapter Two). I would have the locks

►
(Opposite)
Fig. 2-9 /   *Steel doors are a good idea, but not if they have windows and a key-in-the-knob lock in them.*

installed at the factory, when you order the door. I would suggest the M.A.G. mortise lock with double cylinder be installed, for maximum security.

Acceptable steel doors are made by Curries Manufacturing Co., Mason City, Iowa, and by Ceco Corp., Cicero, Illinois. Both are available from lumber yards, and can be installed, along with their matching steel frames, by any competent home mechanic or carpenter.

If you are extremely vulnerable to crime, as you would be if you own a jewelry store, I would install a 12 gauge steel door (Fig. 3-9). On that door I would install a good bar lock (Chapter Thirteen).

All of the better steel doors are filled with polystyrene or other insulation, and have magnetic weather stripping.

Tips on Steel Door Installation

It costs about $50 to have the average steel door and frame professionally installed. No matter who does the job, here are a few things you should know about.

If the door and frame are to be installed in a brick wall, make sure the frame is well grouted and anchored in cement. Otherwise the frame could be pushed out of the wall with a pry bar.

In a wood-frame house, the steel door frame should be anchored to the rough frame. See the discussion later on in this chapter on reinforcing frames.

Reinforcing with Steel

You can save a lot of money by installing a steel plate on a strong, solid wood or particle-board door (instead of buying a steel door). The steel plate should be installed on the inside of the door to prevent attempts to pry it off the door from the outside.

Fig. 3-9 / *Here is a strong steel door and frame ideal for areas of high crime, such as the back door of a jewelry store.*

TABLE 1-9

COMPARATIVE COSTS AND SECURITY RATINGS
FOR WOOD AND STEEL DOORS

Door or Panel	Security Rating*	Cost †	Weight	Size
Hollow Core	5	$ 57	NA	3′ x 6′8″ x 1¾″
Solid Particle	15	70	NA	3′ x 6′8″ x 1¾″
Wood Core	17	84	NA	3′ x 6′8″ x 1¾″
Steel (16 ga.) ‡	100	250	NA	3′ x 6′8″ x 16 ga.
Steel Panels, Full Door Length				
7 gauge	95	112	150	3′ x 6′8″ x ³⁄₁₆″
12 gauge	90	80	100	3′ x 6′8″ x ⅛″
13 gauge	85	54	75	3′ x 6′8″ x ³⁄₃₂″
16 gauge	80	48	50	3′ x 6′8″ x ¹⁄₁₆″
20 gauge	60	32	25	3′ x 6′8″ x ⁷⁄₆₄″
Steel Panels, Partial				
7 gauge	50	15	15	12″ x 20″ x ³⁄₁₆″
12 gauge	45	12	10	12″ x 20″ x ⅛″
13 gauge	40	10	7.5	12″ x 20″ x ³⁄₃₂″
16 gauge	35	8	5	12″ x 20″ x ¹⁄₁₆″
20 gauge	30	5	3	12″ x 20″ x ⁷⁄₆₄″

* Based on a scale of 0 to 100, relative resistance to steel saw, cutting, hacking, chopping forces.

† Includes warehouse cutting charge. You can save money by shopping around in scrapyards for pieces of steel you can cut up to fit your door yourself.

‡ Includes frame.

A steel sheet on the inside of the door will prevent attempts to saw around a good lock, or to cut a panel out of the door big enough to crawl through.

The size of the plate, and the thickness of the steel, should be determined by your own evaluation of your exposure to crime. The bigger the steel plate, and the thicker it is, the more protection you have. For most doors, though, be warned that there is a limit as to how much weight the hinges will support. Most residential doors should be able to carry an extra load of about 150 pounds. Table 1-9 gives weights and gauges of various sizes of steel panels.

Steel Panel Installation

The best way to install a steel panel on a wood door is to use "breakaway" bolts (Fig. 4-9). These bolts have a double head. When you tighten them to a certain point the hex head breaks off and leaves a rounded head underneath. The remaining rounded head has no place where it can be gripped by a tool and, of course, is the end that should be outside the door. Just the view of a half dozen or so of these heads should be enough to discourage a burglar. If you can't locate these bolts in a locksmith's shop, write to the manufacturer, Folger-Adam Company, 700 Railroad St., Joliet, Illinois 60436. If you don't want to bother tracking down these bolts, you could use ¼-inch machine screws with round heads. Use lockwashers under nuts on the inside.

Doors for Low- and Medium-Crime Areas

For medium-crime areas I would use a particle-board door (Fig. 5-9) or a wood-core door (Fig. 6-9). There's not much difference between them in terms of strength. Both types come with veneer wood facing in a variety of woods and finishes. I would use either type of door to replace the hollow-wood-core door.

Reinforcing Wood Doors

A simple and inexpensive way to add cutting resistance to a wood door is to install ¼-inch cold-rolled steel bars around the lock area (Fig. 7-9). All you do is bore ¼-inch holes about eight inches deep, two inches apart, into the edge of the door. Cut rod sections 7½ inches long, push the rods all the way into the bored holes, and fill the ends with wood paste. A little paint over the wood paste filler and you have hidden the reinforcement. Now a burglar is going to be in for a big surprise if he tries to cut or saw his way around your good lock. If he uses a saber saw, the rods

Fig. 4-9 / *Break-away bolt for installing security steel-plate reinforcement on a wood door.*

will roll under the saw blades, and the blade will not cut them.

Warning: Panel Doors Are Useless!

Exterior doors with thin wood panels are no better, really, than hollow-core doors. Older apartment buildings in particular use paneled doors that can be kicked through quickly. These panels are usually big enough to permit a burglar to crawl through, once they are

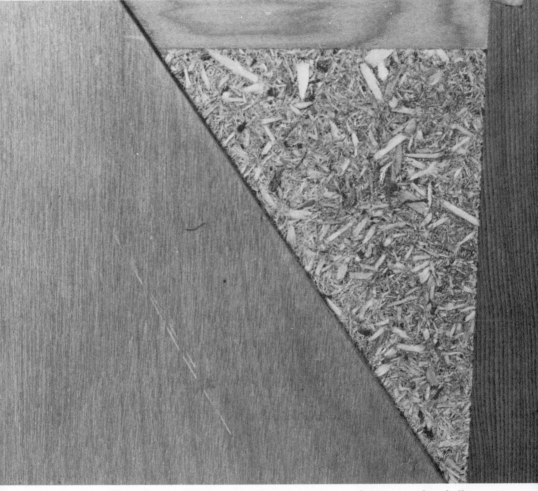

Fig. 5-9 / *Wood-particle board door is much stronger than hollow-core door.*

kicked out. A typical attack (successful, I might add) is shown in Fig. 8-9.

If you are stymied in replacing a paneled door because you merely rent the place, you can at least give yourself some protection by installing a steel plate over each panel. Since the landlord will probably scream if he sees boltheads outside the door, use wood screws on the inside. Nothing will show on the outside. Drill small guide holes for the screws, and fill the holes with polyester glue before installing the screws.

Aside from the door and locks, the door frame is the weakest link in security in most buildings. Most door frames in modern homes, for example, are made of flimsy ¾-inch-thick soft wood. The chunk of wood knifed out of these frames for the lock strike leaves very little wood at this vulnerable point (Fig. 9-9) to resist the burglar's pry bar.

Worse yet, there is nothing but two

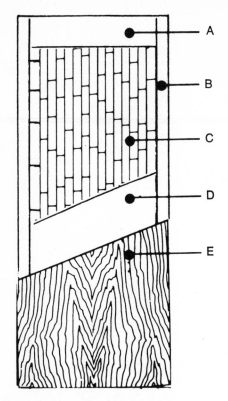

A

B

C

D

E

Fig. 6-9 / *Solid-wood stave door also offers resistance to forcible attack.*

inches of air between the average finish frame and rough frame (Fig. 10-9). All a burglar need do is insert his pry bar between the door and the frame and pull. The frame will "give" enough, in most cases, so that the strike moves away from the bolt. This would be like moving the strike away to open the door, instead of moving the bolt away by turning the key in the lock. In the first case the strike is shoved out of the bolt. In the second case, the bolt is moved out of the strike. In both cases, the door will open.

Older Apartment Buildings Vulnerable

The lobby and individual apartment front doors in older apartment buildings are very easy to get through without a key. The doors and frames are wood that has been softened and weakened by years of rough, slamming usage. Lobby doors in particular can usually be quickly opened with the ubiquitous pry bar, or by slipping a thin piece of metal under the latch.

The typical older apartment front door is spongy and soft. Fig. 11-9, for example, shows a mutilated apartment door frame after a successful burglary. You can see that the lock strike was ripped out of the door frame. It is obvious that the wood of this door frame is weak and softened at this critical point.

As for the aluminum doors and door frames in modern high-rise apartment and office buildings and other multistory structures, these I have discussed at length in Chapter Eight. All I can say is that unless precautions are taken, as described in Chapter Eight, these doors are not at all difficult to get through. You just need to know where to apply the pressure.

How to Beef up Your Door Frame

Most houses built during the past fifty years have an inch to a two-inch air gap between the finish and rough door frames. To prevent a burglar from spreading the weak finish frame with his pry bar and defeating your lock, you will need to reinforce the frame at the strike area. This you can do by installing two metal braces behind the strike. One metal piece goes behind the strike, and the other takes up the air gap between the rough and finish frames. An alternative way, though not as good, would be to fill the gap with a piece of plywood. Either way, here is how to do it.

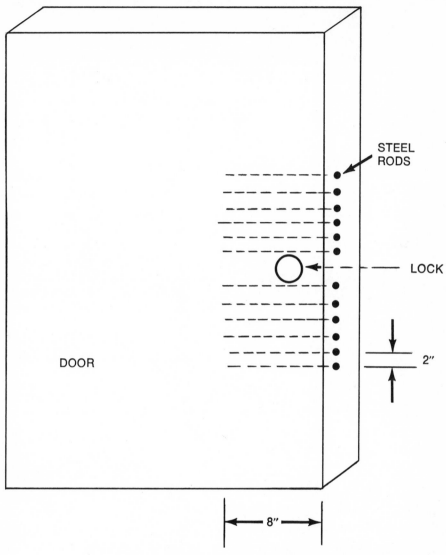

Fig. 7-9 / *Method of reinforcing a wood door. Steel rods are inserted through edge of door, around lock area, to slow down attempts to cut door out around the lock.*

Step One: Break the contact between the wallpaper and the door casing with a sharp knife, to prevent tearing the wallpaper when you remove the casing (Fig. 12-9).

Step Two: Pry the door frame trim (casing) off. Be careful not to split the casing wood. Use a few thin pieces of metal to protect the casing from tool marks as you pry (Fig. 13-9). Use a nipper to cut any nails that won't come out easily (Fig. 14-9).

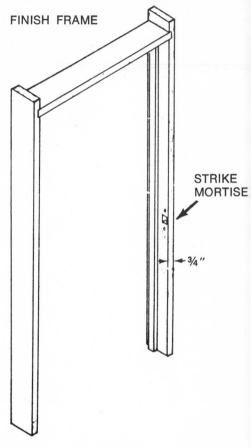

FINISH FRAME

STRIKE
MORTISE

¾"

Fig. 9-9 / *Door frames are often of thin, soft wood and are easily pried apart, especially at the strike area.*

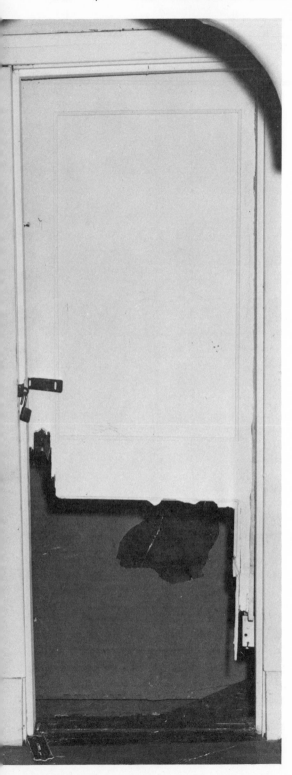

◄

Fig. 8-9 / *Exterior doors with thin wooden panels are easily kicked in, as was this one in an actual burglary.*
COURTESY CHICAGO POLICE DEPARTMENT

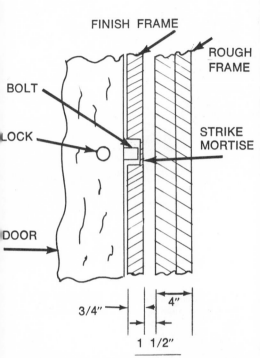

FINISH FRAME

ROUGH FRAME

BOLT

LOCK

STRIKE MORTISE

DOOR

3/4"

4"

1 1/2"

Fig. 10-9 / *Drawing shows air gap between finish and rough door frames. A pry bar between the door and the finish frame can bend the frame. When the frame is bent, the strike can be moved far enough away from the lock bolt to open the door.*

▶

Fig. 11-9 / *Older apartment buildings have weakened, rotted door frames. Here is one that was ripped open in a burglary attack.*

Fig. 12-9 / *First step in removing door trim is to break the seal between the trim and the wallpaper or paint.*

Fig. 13-9 / *Now the casing (trim) can be removed with a chisel. Note the protective pieces of metal that keep gouge marks off the trim and frame.*

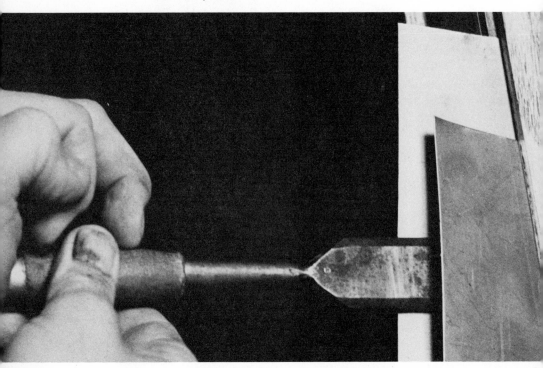

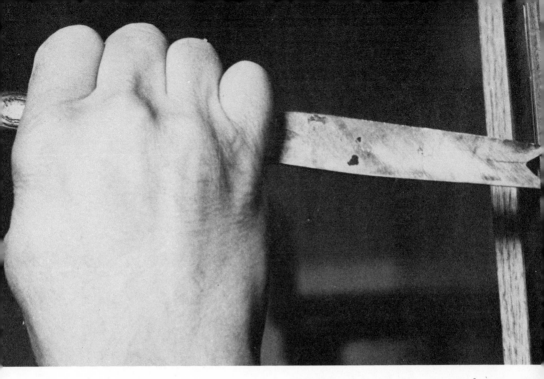

Fig. 14-9 / *If finish nails holding trim do not come out, cut them off with a tool like this.*

Step Three: Remove the lock strike (the part the lock bolt goes into when the door is locked).

Step Four: You now have the choice of filling the air gap between the rough and finish frame with plywood or metal. Plywood will do for low and moderate crime areas. I would use two metal pieces for high crime areas. For the plywood fill, use a .piece of ¾-inch-thick outdoor-grade plywood and tap in as many thicknesses as you need to fill this gap (Fig. 15-9). Screw two-inch-long wood screws (No. 10 or 12 screws) into the finish frame, plywood filler and rough frame (Fig. 16-9). Use longer screws if necessary to get them to penetrate into the rough frame (Fig. 17-9).

Alternate Step Four: In this step we will use two pieces of steel instead of the one or two pieces of plywood to fill the gap between the finish and the rough frame.

You will need two pieces of steel cut and bent to fill the gap. Fig. 18-9 shows the two pieces in place, to give you an idea as to how the reinforcement is made. One piece (Fig. 19-9) fits behind the strike area of the finish frame. The other piece (Fig. 20-9) butts up against the first piece and is screwed to the rough frame.

Mortise (cut out) the strike-reinforcing metal piece into the finish frame so the metal section fits flush against this frame. You should have matching holes drilled through both of the pieces of steel plate so long wood screws will go all the way through the strike, the finish frame, both metal pieces, and into the rough frame. With the strike in place, you can now screw all the pieces together as noted above. Note also that the rough frame is mortised to receive the metal reinforcing plate, so when the casing or trim is reinstalled it will fit properly.

Step Five: Reinstall trim around the

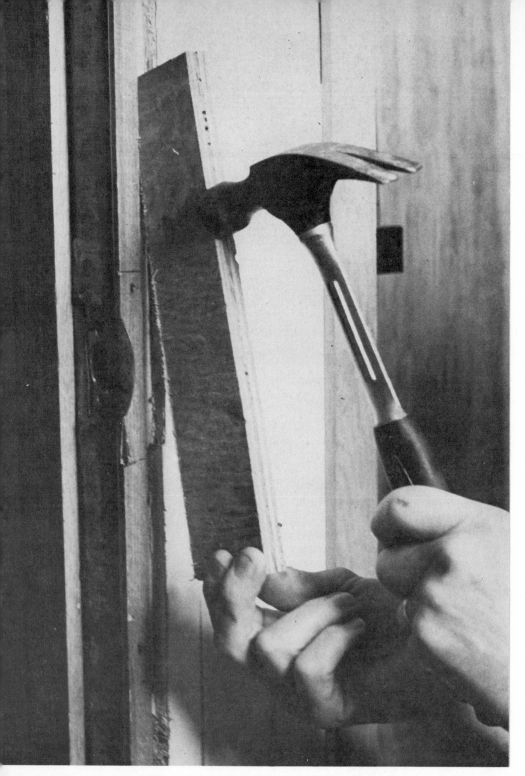

Fig. 15-9 / *You can use a piece of plywood to fill any gap between the finish and rough door frames.*

Fig. 16-9 /   *The plywood should be screwed in place with long wood screws that go into the rough frame.*

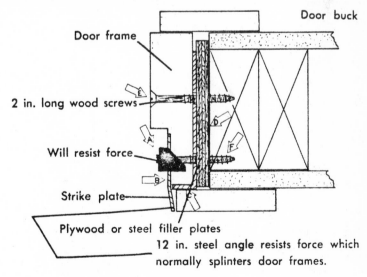

Door buck

Door frame

2 in. long wood screws

Will resist force

Strike plate

Plywood or steel filler plates

12 in. steel angle resists force which normally splinters door frames.

Fig. 17-9 /   *Or two steel angles can be used to add spread resistance to the door frame, installed as shown.*

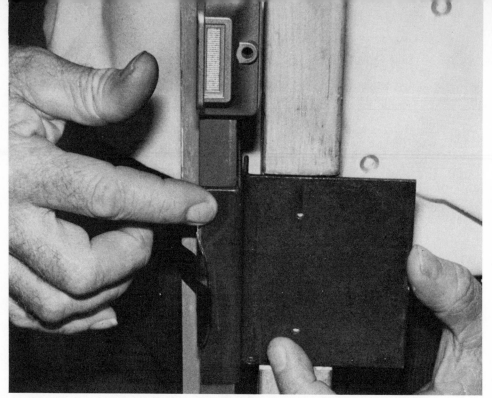

Fig. 18-9 / *Here are the two door-frame reinforcing plates, held in place to illustrate how they should be installed.*

Fig. 19-9 / *The finish-frame steel reinforcing plate. Note that strike holes in the plate should meet strike holes in the frame, so wood screws will go through both the strike and the plate.*

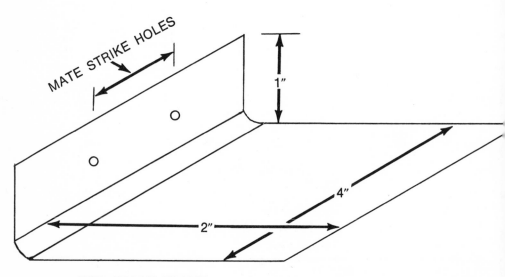

MATE STRIKE HOLES

1"

4"

2"

FOR FINISH FRAME

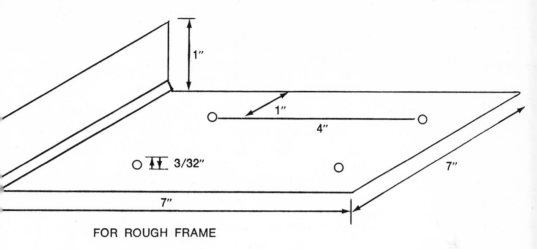

FOR ROUGH FRAME

Fig. 20-9 / *Plate for rough frame.*

door. Now you have a beefed-up door frame that will resist a burglar's pry bar.

Keep Doors From Being Lifted Out

Another inexpensive way to add strength to a door is to "pin" the hinges. Time aside, your cost for pinning door hinges would be about fifteen cents.

By pinning hinges I mean installing a metal pin in one hinge so it fits into a hole in the facing hinge section when the door is closed (Fig. 21-9).

All you do is remove both door hinges completely. Then you put one complete hinge in a vise and drill a hole about where shown in Fig. 21-9, all the way through both sides of the hinge. Repeat for the second hinge set. Reinstall the hinges. Then screw a steel wood screw into the door frame, through the drilled hole, leaving about one inch outside the hinge. Cut off the head of the screw. Drill a hole about $\frac{7}{8}$ inch deep through the other hinge section into the door to receive the pin. Now when the door is closed pins will hold the door in place

against any attempt to lift it out, even if someone has removed the hinge pins.

If hinge pins are outside, put a steel cap over them. One such cap (Fig. 22-9) screws into the wall or finish frame to prevent the hinge pin from being removed. This pin cap is distributed

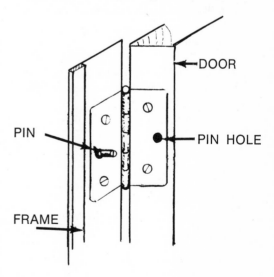

Fig. 21-9 / *If you "pin" hinges as shown, door will be harder to lift out, even when hinge axle pins are removed by a burglar.*

Fig. 22-9 / *You can put a steel cap over hinge axle pins to slow down their removal. This is important if these pins are on the outside, where they could be removed in an attempt to lift the door out of place.*

Fig. 23-9 / *An optical viewer such as this one lets you see who's out there, even if a person stands flat against the wall next to the door.*

by Scotsman Products, Inc., 491 Mc-Glincey Lane, Campbell, California 95008.

Peeping Toms Live Longer

For safety's sake, be a Peeping Tom whenever anyone comes to your front door. If your door does not have a window so you can see who is out there and check the identity of a stranger, you need another way to see through the door.

One good way is to install a window peeper, an optical viewer you can peek through to see who is banging on your door or ringing your bell.

The better optical viewers give you a 180° view of the outside, so you can see a person even if he is hugging the wall next to your door. These viewers also have several optical elements, so the view is clear enough that you can read identification held up in front of it.

Viewers I can recommend are the type made by Home Protector Manufacturing Company, P.O. Box 425, Pico Rivera, California 90660 (Fig. 23-9) and the 180° viewer from Loxem Manufacturing Corporation, 5110 Mercantile Row, Dallas, Texas 75247.

Before you stick your eye up to any viewer, though, make sure the lens has not been removed from the outside. Crazies have been known to poke wires through viewers at people inside. The better viewers cannot be removed from outside the door.

10

PRACTICAL WAYS TO KEEP YOUR POSSESSIONS FROM "WALKING OFF"

How to lock up bicycles, motorcycles, trailers, outboard motors, boats, skis, office equipment, and other highly salable merchandise. Recommended padlocks and special locks for specific goods . . .

As I WAS having lunch and watching the sidewalk scene from a restaurant window in Cambridge, Massachusetts, I saw a little scenario of crime that is repeated often throughout the country.

A man (it happened to be a policeman) pedaled his bicycle up to the sidewalk in front of me and dismounted. He chained and locked the bike to a lamppost and walked away. A few minutes later a young man walked by, carrying a large paper shopping bag in one hand. He stopped and looked at the bike, but walked on in a few seconds. He walked a few yards, turned, and came back. As he approached the bike

I noticed the paper bag was now held by both hands. He stopped a moment in front of the bike, leaned toward it and seemed to snap his hands together. Another second or two and he walked on. I saw the chain lying on the ground. Before I could get to the door, the bicycle thief had returned, obviously after waiting to see if anyone had noticed anything, and was riding off down the street.

An uncommon scenario? Not at all. Inside the bag was a bolt cutter, the working tips of which were pushed through a hole in the bottom of the bag. The lock in Fig. 1-10 and the chain

Fig. 1-10 / *The shackle of this inexpensive padlock was easy to cut with a bolt cutter.*

were all that was left of the policeman's bicycle.

The lesson here is that it pays to spend the few dollars it takes to prevent valuable merchandise from being stolen. In this chapter you will learn how to tell a weak padlock from a strong one, and all about special locks for specific possessions such as bicycles, motorcycles, outboard motors, skis, and office equipment.

What You Should Know About Padlocks

The first thing you should know about padlocks is that they can *all* be defeated. Stronger padlocks merely buy you time. It's time that's the crime stopper, not the padlock. No thief wants to risk jail over a boat or a bike or a motorcycle by having to spend a lot of time sawing through a strong lock. He'd rather spend the time ripping off somebody else's poorly locked goodies. Time is of the essence, and one lock supplier counts it in seconds. Skid-Lid furnishes a bicycle lock it claims is "almost worthless" and they are right. The lock has a very thin, stranded steel cable and cheap padlock. The cable could almost be cut with a pair of scissors. The point here is that the lock will add a few seconds to a theft attempt. The lock is not to be used to leave the bike totally unguarded. You are supposed to have one eye on the bike at all times. But you may be in a restaurant, close to the door and a window where you can see the bike. With no lock on it, a kid could hop on the bike and be a half block away before you got out the door. With the Skid-Lid el cheapo, you could nab the bike before the lock chain was cut. The lock only weighs 3¼ ounces, so it's fine for the touring cyclist who wants to travel light. The manufacturer guarantees the lock to be impervious to attack by fingernail clippers, dull knives, and sharp teeth. From Skid-Lid Mfg. Co., Box 243, La Jolla, California 92083.

At the other extreme are hundred-dollar padlocks used to lock up warehouses containing bonded liquor, nuclear devices, and other high-value merchandise. Somewhere in between is the padlock for you, and if you will check Table 1-10 you will find it. But first, let's quickly look at what constitutes a strong padlock, so you can pick one out of the morass of junk in a hardware store.

Padlock Shackles

The shackle of a padlock is the part that opens and closes (Fig. 2-10) and holds a chain or hasp together. The shackle should be at least ⁷⁄₁₆ of

SHACKLE

Fig. 2-10 / *Padlock shackles should have the word "hardened" engraved on them, as shown, to indicate a surface-hardened steel shackle.*

Fig. 3-10 / *An example of an excellent padlock. The thick hardened-steel shackle resisted cutting. Even the tungsten carbide rod saw attack took five minutes to cut as far as shown, about halfway through.*

an inch (almost a half inch) thick, and should be case-hardened to resist cutting attack. Case-hardening is simply a surface hardening a few thousandths of an inch, so that once the very hard skin is cut, the softer metal underneath is easy to saw away. Look for the word "hardened" on the shackle. A thick, hardened-steel lock shackle is almost impervious to an ordinary hacksaw, but can be cut with a tungsten carbide particle-embedded "rod saw" available for a few dollars from any hardware store. The "rod saw," when time permits, is a burglar's true friend. Time, though, is the secret word. The shackle in Fig. 3-10, for instance, is shown cut about halfway with a rod saw. You can see the saw in the picture. It took me just five minutes to cut this far, even though the lock was held in a vise. If the lock is flopping around on the ends of a chain or on a hasp, cutting time will be a lot longer. Every second's delay in cutting such a shackle means that much greater chance of a crook's getting caught. If you have a good padlock, a strong one, the crook is going to pass up your bike or whatever and go after an easier target.

The shackle should be double locked at both "heel" and "toe," that is, at both sides of the shackle, as shown in Fig. 4-10. This double locking helps defeat a forcible attack such as one by the padlock "popper" shown in Fig. 5-10. This little tool will bust open cheap padlocks, such as the padlock in Fig. 6-10, which is the dime-store variety, and the warded padlock in Fig. 7-10. The warded padlock is also easily

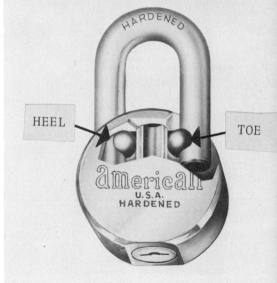

(Right)
Fig. 4-10 / *Padlock shackles should be locked at both "heel" and "toe" ends, as shown.*

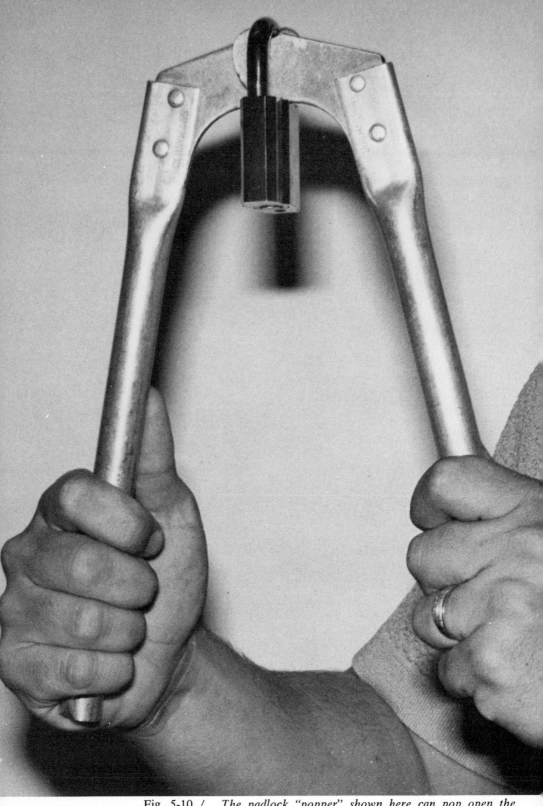

Fig. 5-10 / *The padlock "popper" shown here can pop open the shackle of any padlock that is not locked at heel and toe.*

Fig. 6-10 /   *This dime-store padlock can be opened in seconds with a screwdriver. Note that shackle is not locked at the open end.*

Fig. 7-10 /   *A weak padlock. Any time you see a flat, stamped key like this you know the padlock is a poor security device. Such a lock is easily picked open.*

Fig. 8-10 /   A "shrouded" shackle padlock. The shackle is recessed
when closed to make it inaccessible to bolt cutters or a hacksaw blade.

picked open (Chapter Thirteen, How Locks Work, tells why). Just remember, if you see a flat key like that in Fig. 7-10, you have a terrible lock. To be fair, these locks are made to a price bracket, and there are uses for them, such as keeping the kids out of a toy closet or darkroom.

A shrouded shackle, such as in Fig. 8-10, makes use of the shackle "popper" difficult, if not impossible. A fully shrouded shackle is shown in Fig. 9-10, but be warned: this padlock costs upwards of $90 and is for high-security applications, obviously. The lock body is of hardened-steel laminations, almost impossible to saw or hack apart and the lock cylinder is highly pick-, pull- and drill-resisant. A good way to shroud a shackle is to use a locking device such as the Kryptonite bicycle lock, Fig. 10-10. A bike was locked like this to

Fig. 9-10 / Here is a very strong shrouded shackle padlock used for ultra-high-security needs.

Fig. 10-10 / *Bicycle padlock with another approach to a shrouded padlock shackle. Note that the front wheel has been removed and is locked along with the rear wheel.*

a post in Boston's worst neighborhood. After two weeks the bike was still there, but the stainless steel padlock holder was nicked by bolt cutters and scarred by hacksaw cuts. (Good thing no one there knew about the rod saw; that bike would have disappeared in the first sixty minutes.) Sometimes the lock itself is part of the locking device and there is nothing showing, such as the locks in Figs. 11-10, an improved version of the Kryptonite lock, and the Citadel, another very fine bike lock, Fig. 12-10. While I'm talking about bicycles, look at the clunker in Fig. 13-10. This monstrosity was padlocked a year ago at this writing to a post at the corner of Fifty-seventh Street and Seventh Avenue in New York City. I went back six months later and it was still there. The padlock and chain cost about $25, which is a lot more than the bike is worth. If

Fig. 11-10 / *This clunker bike has been locked in place for months on a busy New York City street. The heavy chain and good padlock have prevented it from being stolen.*

you do lock your good bicycle, be sure to put the chain (see below) around something that can't be cut, such as a stop-sign post. Don't lock the bike to a parking meter; the bike, chain and all can be lifted up and over the meter post. Personally I would *never* lock a good bike to anything, with any lock. My bikes cost upwards of $750, and there's just no way I am going to risk that investment. Just the saddle and handlebars

together cost over $50, and how can you lock them up? If you commute to work, school, or whatever, use a cheap bike, a good lock and chain, and pray a lot. Drape the chain through the back wheel and frame, remove the front wheel and drape the chain through it too, and then around something that can't be cut. This takes a five-to-six-foot chain.

Fig. 12-10 /   *Another excellent bicycle padlock, with integral lock.*

Fig. 13-10 /   *This thick hardened-steel bicycle lock has a built-in lock cylinder.*

Combination Locks

Inexpensive combination locks, such as you use on lockers in schools, should never be used for even moderate security applications. I suppose it's unlikely a kid in high school will use a shackle popper (Fig. 5-10) or try to cut the shackle. But these locks are so flimsy the sheet metal bodies can be hacked open with a cold chisel and hammer in a minute or less (Fig. 14-10).

Chains Are Able, Cables Aren't

To lock up anything such as a bike, motorcycle, or lawnmower, you will need some sort of chain. Right away, I want you to forget about stranded *cable* of any practical thickness. The cable, for example, in Fig. 15-10 is $\frac{7}{16}$ of an inch thick (almost a half inch), yet I cut it almost through in one minute flat. For pull strength, cable can't be beat; they suspend mile-long bridges with cable. But for cutting resistance, they are bad news.

Much better than stranded cable is case-hardened steel chain. True, a bolt cutter can snap $\frac{1}{8}$-inch chain in a few seconds, about as quick as the same diameter stranded cable. But $\frac{3}{8}$-inch case-

Fig. 14-10 / *Cheap combination padlock is easy to cut open with a cold chisel and hammer, or with a hacksaw.*

hardened welded-link steel chain is something else again. Bolt cutters can't cut it, and even with a tungsten carbide embedded rod saw it took me five minutes to get halfway through a ⅜-inch chain. Do not use security chains for towing, and vice versa. A five-foot length of ⅜-inch security chain weighs eight pounds and costs $13.20. You might leave it, and the lock, at your destination, if you commute by bike or motorcycle regularly.

Hasps for Garages, Chicken Coops, and Atom Bombs

A hasp that's wood-screwed onto a garage or barn door, the thin, ordinary garden variety hasp, that is, may keep the kids out of the closet. But a burglar would have no trouble ripping it out of the woodwork. Use ordinary dime-store padlock hasps for nonsecurity purposes such as locking up the chicken coop or a child's toy chest.

Fig. 15-10 /   *Stranded steel security cables can also be quickly cut open. Chains are better.*

For real security you need a hardened-steel hasp such as shown in Fig. 16-10, in which a good padlock is an integral part. Another such hasp is shown in Fig. 17-10. These hasps are *bolted* all the way through the woodwork (or metal door) and bolt heads are concealed behind the lock.

If you want the ultimate in security, a padlock-hasp combination used by the AEC and for Federal and industrial ultra-high-security applications, use the BMR lock shown in Figs. 18-10 and 19-10. These locks are the BMR Tufloc, BMR Products Corporation, 425 North Third Street, Reading, Pennsylvania 19601. The lock body is made of ¼-inch-thick hardened steel. This hasp uses the super drill- and pick-resistant Medeco cylinder. The Tufloc costs a bundle though—around $85—but worth it if you have a warehouse full of bonded liquor or plutonium waste or jewelry. The Tufloc is fastened with ¼-inch hard

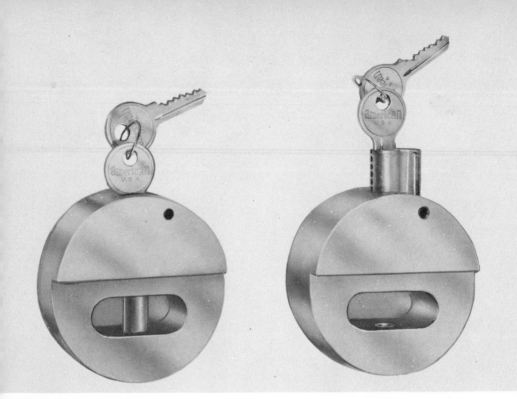

Fig. 17-10 /   *For wider doors, this hasp and padlock combination is of hardened steel.*

steel bolts and can in addition be welded, as to a steel truck door.

Door Chains, an Illusion

There isn't a door chain on the market that is worth two cents in terms of security. Worse still, they may foster the belief that you are safe. When you open the door with the chain fastened, all it takes is one good heave to rip this contraption out of the woodwork. Even the kind you can lock in place (Fig. 20-10) is just about useless.

For Motorcycles

Motorcycle locks are a laugh in terms of security. They are, first of all, right out there where they can be picked. Or, the ignition lock can be "jumped" or by-

◄
(Opposite)
Fig. 16-10 /   *Padlock and hasp combination has a hidden shackle.*

passed by a "hot wire" from the battery to the coil.

The only lock that's built into the motorcycle that's worth much as a theft deterrent is the fork lock. Even that won't keep the motorcycle thief from hoisting the machine into the back of a pick-up truck and driving away. Chain the motorcycle through both wheels, the frame, and to something that can't be ripped off, such as a telephone post. You can make the crook work twice as hard if you use two shorter chains and two padlocks, one on each wheel and through the frame as well. And even then you're not completely safe. Crooks these days are getting exotic in their methods; they use Freon gas, available from any refrigeration supply house, or even liquid nitrogen, to chill lock or chain metal until it's so brittle it can be snapped with a hammer blow. I might also point out that in big cities the public just doesn't give a damn. A thief can ride away on your bike or motorcycle, and

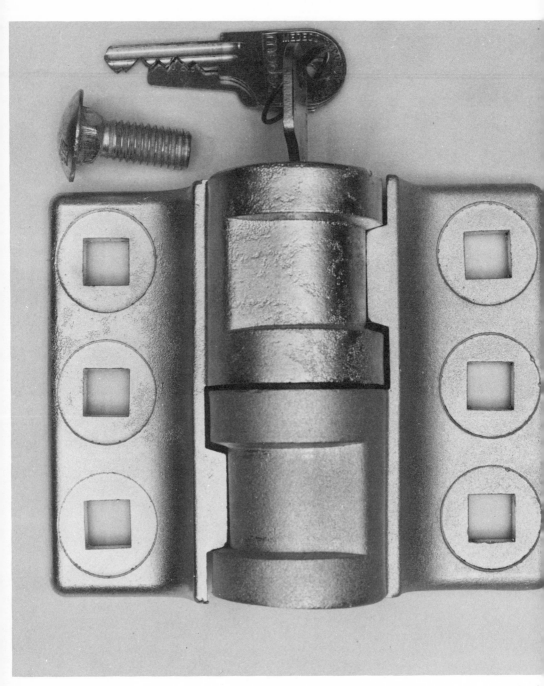

Fig. 18-10 / *Super-high-security hinge-type lock has integral pick- and drill-resistant Medeco cylinder. Lock is shown in closed (locked) position.*

Fig. 19-10 / *Same lock as in Fig. 18-10, in unlocked position. Lock body is of thick, hardened stainless steel. Lock is fastened with machine bolts.*

Fig. 20-10 / *Door chains, even ones with a key lock, are virtually useless because they can be ripped out of the woodwork by a determined shove on the door.*

nobody would turn a hair. The bike could even be ridden up a ramp into a panel truck without attracting any attention. For example, I once spent ten minutes sawing away at a good lock shackle. A friend of mine had lost her key to her bike lock. The bike was chained to a bike rack in front of a store. As I was sawing away a police car passed by. I waved to the police officers, they waved back, I kept sawing away, they drove on. To be fair, the police may have had more urgent business elsewhere, but who knows?

To Keep Skis From Being "Lifted"

Never leave your skis unattended while you go in to warm up, even for a moment. There is an excellent light-

weight lock and cable you can use, specially designed for skis and ski poles (Fig. 21-10) made by Master Lock Company and, like all their specialty locks, available from hardware or sporting goods stores.

Lock Outboard Motors Aboard

Outboard motors are a favorite target of thieves. You should lock outboard motors with a special lock (Fig. 22-10) such as that made by Master Lock Company. You tighten transom clamps well, then apply the lock over the clamps so they can't be untightened.

Lock boat cabins with a stainless steel or brass lock. If brass, make sure it is forged. Cast brass locks are brittle and can be shattered by a hammer blow.

To Keep Trailers Truckin'

Trailers of any type are easy to steal. You can lock the hitch with a hitch lock (Fig. 23-10). This is especially important if you park your trailer and car while you are out boating for the day.

Boatnapping Tips

- *Paint boat name and registration numbers* on bow and stern. Stick-on or screw-on letters are easy to remove; it takes several coats of paint, probably over the entire boat, to mask painted-on letters and numerals.
- *If boat is stored on a trailer,* remove one wheel and block it up. Park a locked car behind the trailer.
- *Remove identification papers* from the boat.
- *Engrave your social security number* on all valuable removable

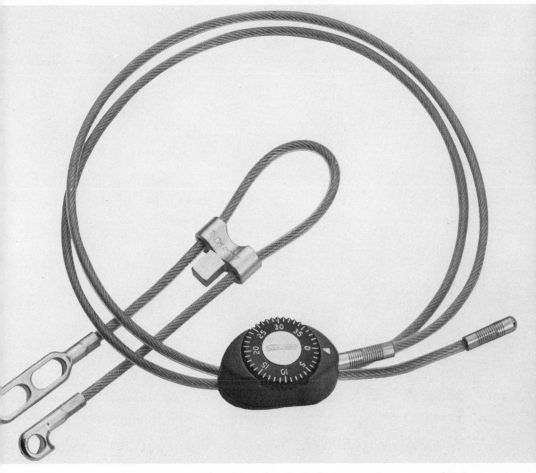

Fig. 21-10 / *This ski and pole lock set can keep your skis from being stolen while on the ski rack.*

parts, such as motor, compasses, winches, radios, depth and direction finders.

- *Move connector plug* from car-to-trailer lights back aft far enough so any other car would have trouble making this connection.
- *Replace all screwed- or bolted-* down equipment screws or bolts with one-way screws or break-off bolts.

Keys to Your Car . . . Anybody Can Get Them!

The driver climbed out of his new Cadillac Coupe de Ville and went into a nearby restaurant. A passerby stopped and looked for a moment at the Cadillac's rear license plate holder, which bore the name of the local dealer from whom the car had been purchased.

The passerby, who was a professional car thief, stepped into a phone booth and made two calls. The first was to the nearest police station. He identified him-

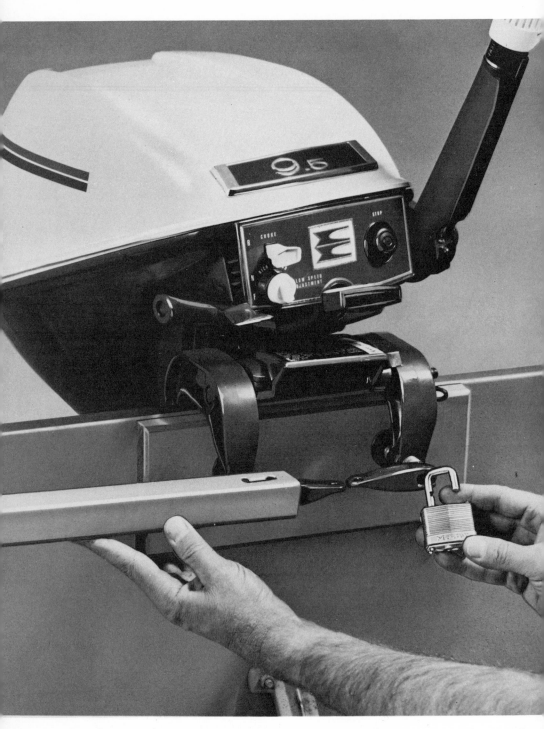

Fig. 22-10 / *Protect your valuable outboard motor with a special lock that prevents access to motor clamps.*

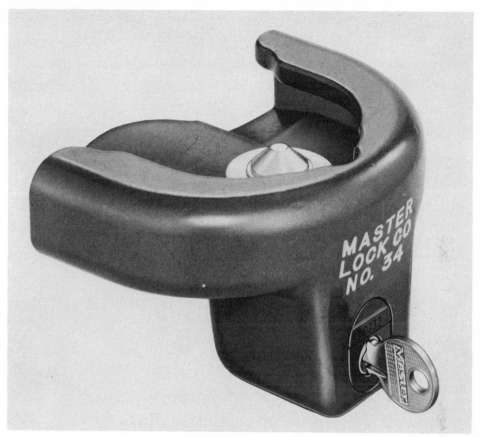

Fig. 23-10 / *Lock your trailer on the car with this trailer hitch lock.*

self as the owner of the restaurant and stated that a car was blocking the fire zone in front of his place. He gave police the license plate number and asked for the owner's name as probably being in the restaurant. The police, after a quick check by computer, came up with the owner's name and address.

The car thief then phoned the automobile agency that sold the car, identified himself as the owner, explained that he had lost his keys and had urgent need for the car. He asked that the clerk look up the key code to the Cadillac keys so new keys could be cut. The clerk obliged. Armed with the code, it

was the work of a few minutes to cut new keys with a portable key cutter.

An alternative to this scenario could have been a peek inside the car to see if the car registration was in sight, perhaps draped around the steering column. Or the thief could have followed the car owner into the restaurant and discreetly wormed the car owner's name from the head waiter, if the man was well known.

In any case, the two obvious steps to take to eliminate this easy way to obtain your car keys are:

- Make sure the new car dealer has removed all trace of your car key

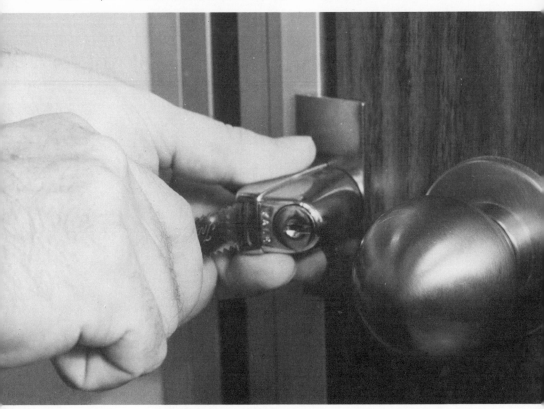

Fig. 24-10 /   *Portable lock that can be used to lock your hotel or motel room at night, from inside.*

code. (The code is a series of numbers indicating the depth of cuts to make in a key blank.) Keep a record of this code yourself.

• Do not carry around free advertising for the car dealer. Remove his decals or license plate holder bearing his name and address.

• A third precaution would be never to leave the license plate registration where it can be seen from outside the car. In fact, keep this registration in your wallet (or purse).

For Truck Trailers

Hijackers often back up their own truck to a trailer, hitch it in place and drive off with a trailer load of marketable goodies. To prevent such theft, you can use a "Fifth Wheel" trailer lock, such as that made by American Lock Company, Chicago.

Hotel Security

There's no way you can be sure no one else has a key to your hotel or motel room. Key security in these institutions is almost nonexistent. For this reason do not leave valuables in the room when you are out. Take them with you, or check them in the hotel safe, if there is one. If not, you will have to take any valuables, such as cameras and jewelry, from the room when you leave for a time.

At night, you can protect against an intruder, armed with an extra guest key, entering the room. Just use a Yale Travelok (Fig. 24-10). This portable lock should be stuck between the door and door frame, where it's wedged in place when locked to keep the door from being opened from the outside.

Lock That Gun!

A handgun should have a trigger lock, especially if there are children in the house. Any handgun in a store showcase should also have a trigger lock (Fig. 25-10) in place.

Locks for Office Equipment

As I write this book on my IBM Correcting Selectric II (which cost about $850) a letter arrived from the local IBM service people warning me to double check the identity of anyone claiming to be an IBM serviceman. It seems there has been a rash of bogus IBM servicemen who cart these costly typewriters off for "repair."

Another way to prevent theft of expensive office equipment is to anchor it to the desk with a locking device. Two such devices are on the market. One uses a special locking tool (Fig. 26-10) to bolt the equipment in place. Without the tool, the bolt would be extremely difficult to remove. The tools

Fig. 25-10 /   *Lock gun triggers with this special trigger lock.*

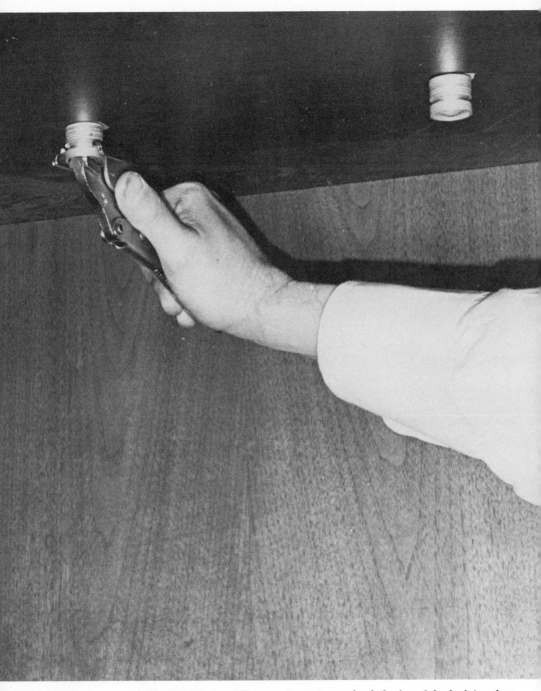

Fig. 26-10 / *Office equipment can be bolted and locked in place. Bolts cannot be removed except with special tool, registered at the factory.*

TABLE 1-10

RECOMMENDED PADLOCKS

Make	Model	Cost	Features
Medeco	1	$40	Double-acting six-pin pick- and drill-resistant cylinder, hardened-steel shackle. An excellent padlock.
American	2000	$31	Combination hasp and padlock. No shackle to cut. Fig. 19-10.
Abloy	3061	$36	Shackle of hardened steel resists 22,000 lbs. pull. Excellent pick-resistance. Keys duplicatable by factory only.
Master Lock	15	$12	Shackle is hardened steel, resists 10,000 lbs. pull. Very tough lock indeed, a lot of padlock for the money.
Abus	24/ST/70	$12	Stainless steel case and hardened shackle, mushroom pins.
American	825	$ 5	Hasp only, but a good one, of hardened steel.
Fort	PK1200	$11	Tubular cylinder, round key, seven pins for good pick-resistance.

are registered with the factory that makes them, and only bona fide owners are supposed to have one. But disgruntled employees have been known to steal, so to that extent, at least, this type of lock is vulnerable. This lock is made by Protexall.

A key lock for office equipment is available from Bolen Industries, Inc., 789 Main Street, Hackensack, New Jersey 07601. Both types should be available through a competent locksmith.

Padlock Recommendations

There are thousands of padlocks on the market today. Some are made in Europe, others in Japan, many in America. In terms of quality they appear to follow the normal curve; a few are terrible or ultra-high-security, most are adequate. Table 1-10 gives a few sample selections from these locks which will, at various prices, offer reasonably good security. In general, the more you pay for the lock the better it is in terms of pick-, drill-, force- and corrosion-resistance. There are other equally high-quality locks on the market; these are representative of them.

11

PROTECTION WHERE CRIME BEGINS!

All about decorative but tough window and glass door bars and grilles . . . fences to keep crooks at yard's length . . . lights that scare them off . . . super-tough glass for special security needs . . .

IF YOU LIVE in a high crime area, or have a lot of windows at ground (grade) level, you will be a lot safer behind bars. The kind of bars I have in mind are decorative grilles that provide both security and peace of mind.

For example, older apartment dwellings, with windows over rear porches, are sitting ducks for attack through the window. Homes with windows at or below grade level can be entered by breaking the glass. Even sliding glass doors are not immune to being broken through, if the building is isolated so the noise will not disturb or alarm a neighbor.

Windows that can be reached by climbing a tree, or from the roof of an adjoining building, should also be considered for the protection afforded by bars and grilles.

Bars Do Not a Prison Make

Window bars and grilles can be quite decoratively styled, as shown in Fig. 1-11. At least one window in a room should have openable bars, with a key lock, for emergency exit (Fig. 2-11).

For total window-length protection, sliding "scissor" gates can be installed, although these are not very esthetically pleasing (Fig. 3-11). A better application for scissor gates is over sliding glass doors (Fig. 4-11).

Note that in all the illustrations, the

Fig. 1-11 / *Protective bars and grilles can be an attractive security feature for residences where there may be a high crime risk.*

bars or scissor gates are installed on the *inside,* where they are a lot harder to reach to rip out or cut through.

Bars Must Be Well Anchored

Window bars and grilles should be anchored to resist the pry bar. Poor examples of bar anchorage are shown in Figs. 5-11 and 6-11. In Fig. 5-11, burglars found the bars anchored by wood screws in window woodwork, where bars were obviously easily ripped out. In Fig. 6-11, the scissor gate was poorly anchored at one end, and at the bottom was not fitted into a track.

One good way to anchor window bars is shown in Fig. 7-11. Several nuts are threaded on ¼-inch steel machine screws. The screw fits into a ½-inch hole which is filled with cement grouting. The head of the bolt is welded to the metal frame of the bars.

How To Make Your Own Window Bars

I made up enough window bars for my six basement windows, following the design in Fig. 8-11. I spent about $125 for the round and flat bar stock, which I bought from a local steel-supply firm. I already had a MAPP gas welding outfit (Fig. 9-11) which I had used for making bicycle frames and other hobby work. The MAPP gas outfit, with a

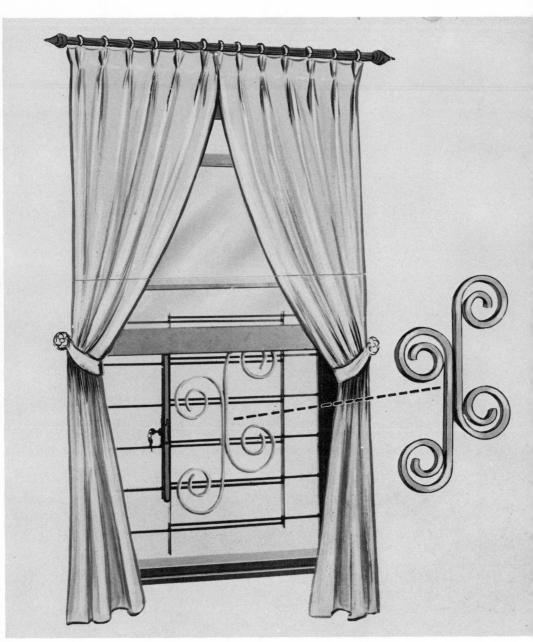

Fig. 2-11 /   *At least one window grille should be openable. Here is one model that can be opened and can also be locked in the closed position.*

Fig. 3-11 / *Scissor gates offer good security, particularly for the rear windows of older apartments and the back door of stores. Note that this gate slides in a track at top and bottom. Note too it is installed on the* inside *of the window where it is tougher to get at to defeat.*

MAPP tank and an oxygen tank, cost about $150. It is made by Airco Welding Products.

Cutting the bars and drilling the holes in the flat stock is simple. The only precaution I would suggest is to tack-weld or braze the pieces together, before finishing-welding or brazing them. This way the frame won't distort, and the job will come out straight, and in line.

Fences to Keep Them at Yard's Length

Burglars like to have a clear escape route in case you or the cops trap them. That's why they hate a fenced-in yard with a locked fence gate. One way of escape is blocked to them. Fences also keep criminals from getting away with bulky merchandise. They also help keep kids out of the pool and away from other potentially harmful objects in your yard.

For a home, I would install a wire-woven or mesh fence something like that in Fig. 10-11. Note that this fence has a smooth pipe top, and that the wire ends are crimped over so as not to have any sharp-pointed edges on top. This is the kind of fence a child could climb and not get hurt, as opposed, for example, to the fence in Fig. 11-11 with sharp upward-pointing wires. This latter type of fence is more suitable for industrial yards, as is the taller fence with barbed wire top in Fig. 12-11.

Lights Stop Crime

When Rensselaer, Indiana, city fathers turned off streetlights to conserve energy, assorted criminals exerted theirs and the crime rate in this small city jumped 40 percent. When the lights were

Fig. 4-11 / *A scissor gate over a sliding glass patio door adds intrusion protection.*

Fig 5-11 / *Even strong bars are useless if they are not well anchored. These husky bars were fastened to wood, with wood screws. Burglars had no trouble at all in prying the bars loose.*

COURTESY CHICAGO POLICE DEPARTMENT

▶

(Opposite)
Fig. 6-11 / *This scissor gate was easy to defeat because it was poorly anchored at both ends.*

COURTESY CHICAGO POLICE DEPARTMENT

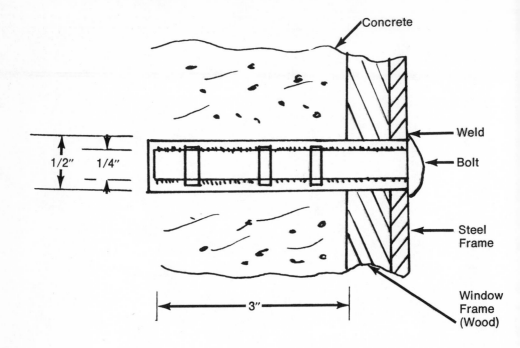

Fig. 7-11 / *Steel window bars should be anchored in cement, held by steel machine bolts, as shown. Rounded tops of bolts should be welded to bar frame.*

Fig. 8-11 / *Use this drawing to make up your own set of bars for basement windows. Change dimensions to fit your own windows. Remember, basement windows are usually a very weak link in security. Install bars inside the windows.*

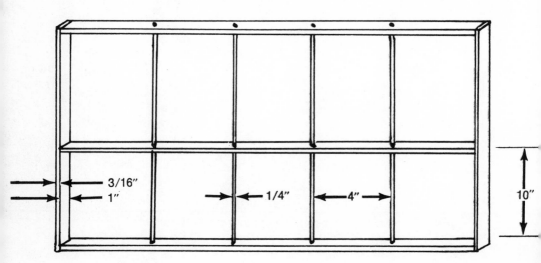

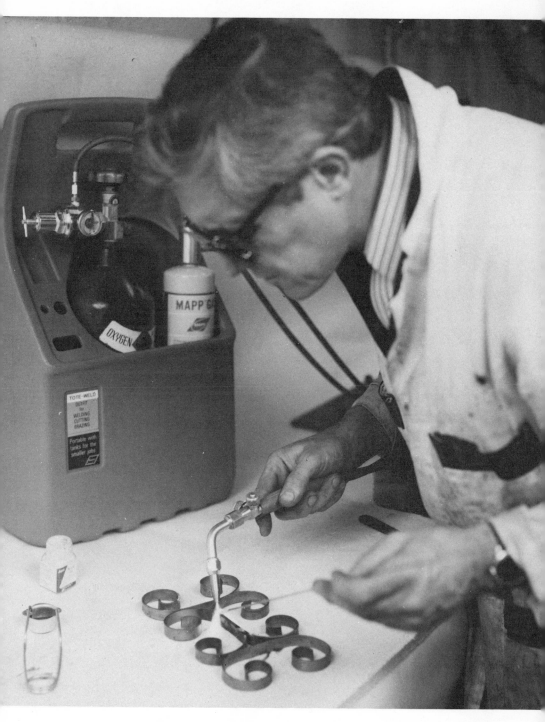

Fig. 9-11 / *Airco Mapp gas outfit makes welding your own bars and grilles easy.*

Fig. 10-11 / *This is an excellent residential yard fence. The top of the fence is smooth pipe and links of fence are curled over. There are no sharp edges to hurt a child who might climb the fence.*

turned back on, crime in Rensselaer returned to normal.

Burglars tend to stay away from homes with room lights on during normal evening hours. That's why it is a good idea, if you are going to be out of town, to use a timer to turn the lights on and off during the evening. Use two or three timers to confuse the enemy. A living room and kitchen light should go on at sundown. A bedroom and bathroom light should go on about 10:00 P.M. All lights should go out around 11:30 P.M.

Yard lights to flood the front and back yard and the alley or garage area should be used to make any attempt at a break-in at night visible to neighbors. To save electricity (in case you forget to turn off the lights during the day) you can use photoelectric cell switches.

Some yard lights, such as the one in Fig. 13-11, have such a switch built in to them. This light is made by Thomas Industries, 207 East Broadway, Louisville, Kentucky 40202. Another model is made by Perfect Line Manufacturing Corporation, Lindenhurst, New Jersey 11757. These yard lights can also be wired into the burglar alarm system so they blink when the alarm is triggered.

Tips on Industrial Lighting

High intensity lights can create almost daylight conditions around a large building. However, these lights should be located at the outer perimeter of the building and shine *inward* to light up the yard and the building walls and entrances. With lights shining inward, they will not blind passing police cars

Fig. 11-11 /   *This fence is fine for industrial use but the sharp edges at the top make it unsuitable for residential yard use.*

Fig. 12-11 /   *Barbed-wire-topped industrial fence can keep criminals out of the yard.*

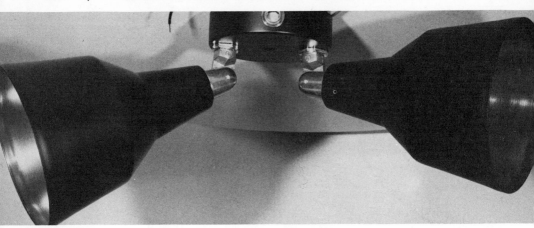

Fig. 13-11 / *This lamp has a photoelectric switch that automatically turns it on when the sun goes down, and off when the sun comes up.*

or a guard patrol. If the lights are mounted on the building and shine outward, it is more difficult to see an intruder through the glare. Lights should silhouette an intruder. Coverage should overlap, without blind spots between lamp coverage.

Burglar-Resistant Glass

Burglar alarms can't stop the smash-and-grab attack of a brick thrown through a plate glass window. The uses of impact-proof or bulletproof glass in stores, banks, prisons, schools, and the like are endless. I will only give you a quick review of what's on the market so you can decide whether you want it or not.

"Lexan" is a polycarbonate material made by General Electric that will resist pounding with baseball bats, sledge hammers, and other heavy objects. But this material can be penetrated with a blow torch, drilled, and cut with a saber saw. "Secure-Lite" is another type of plate glass with a shatter-resistant coating. This "sandwich" of glass comes in $\frac{5}{16}$-, $\frac{7}{16}$- and $\frac{9}{16}$-inch thicknesses and is

approved by Underwriters' Laboratories. The UL sanction means the glass survived the drop of a five pound steel ball from a height of ten feet, repeated five times, and one drop of the same ball from a height of forty feet, both drops without penetration of the glass.

The Secure-Lite glass is not cheap, but it can reduce burglary insurance premiums up to 40 percent. Cost of a typical forty-square-foot storefront installation, with another twenty square feet of entryway glass $\frac{7}{16}$ inch thick, would run about $510 installed. This glass also resists burning and drilling and is virtually impossible to cut with a saber saw.

Both makes of glass come with bullet resistance for banks and other institutions requiring this type of protection. There are various grades of bullet resistance. For example, Secure-Lite $1\frac{3}{16}$-inch-thick bullet-resistant glass is UL approved for resistance to bullets from revolvers and pistols developing 1,397 feet per second and 490 foot-pound energy at the muzzle. The three-inch-thick glass withstands machine gun and rifle bullets.

12

THE RIGHT SAFE
FOR YOUR VALUABLES

How to select the best safe to protect your valuable records and documents from fire . . . cash and belongings from burglars.

WHETHER OR NOT you should have a safe at home, and if so, what kind, is not an easy matter to decide. At the office, store, or commercial enterprise, you have no choice; your insurance company will decide for you, unless you want to see coverage premiums go sky high. In this chapter we will cover the basics of the two broad types of safes, fire-resistant and burglar-resistant safes. I use the word "resistant" because there is no such thing as a fireproof or burglarproof safe. Given time enough, a fire can destroy the contents of any safe or a burglar can break into any safe.

Fire-Resistant Safes

Do you have any records at home or at the office you should not lose? If so, you need a fire-resistant safe unless the documents are not used often and can be kept in a bank safety deposit box (which is not fire resistant, although the bank has sprinkler systems and elaborate smoke and heat alarms in the vault).

For example, if all your tax records went up in smoke, could you remember *all* the deductions you are entitled to? And if you could remember them, could you prove their existence if the Internal Revenue Service questioned the deductions in an audit?

As a businessman, how about accounts receivable? If those records were lost in a fire, would your customers' honesty and goodwill insure that they would pay every nickel they owe you?

And how about accounts payable and records of bank deposits, sales contracts, taxes, payroll, and all the other vital documents you need to preserve? Could you afford to lose them? Computer tapes can stand only 150° F., so you need a special safe that will hold inside safe temperature below that level, as well as holding relative humidity down to around 50 percent. Paper chars at 400°, so fire-resistive safes keep inside temperature down around 350° in a fire. The difference between a computer safe and a document fire-resistive safe, temperatures aside, is that after the fire you need to be able to run the tape or the disc through the computer but you need only be able to read the documents. The criterion in a document safe is legibility; that is, will the documents be readable after a fire that has leveled the building?

Underwriters' Laboratories Ratings

Never buy any safe without a UL rating label on it, and never buy a safe without a label that meets your needs. You would not need, for example, a fire-resistant safe that could fall three stories, and remain intact at white-hot heat, for a simple home safe. But you would need such a safe for an office building. Here are the basic UL ratings and what they mean in terms of fire resistance. None of these labels has anything to do with burglar resistance, and a fire safe is not even remotely burglar-resistant. Such a safe does offer some protection against amateur burglars, but a pro could peel one open as fast you could open a can of sardines. UL fire-resistive safe ratings are:

- *UL 350° F.—Four Hours:* This is the highest UL classification. To

qualify, a safe must pass three very tough tests; fire up to 2000° F., a drop and impact test and an explosion-hazard test. In this test, the safe is "soaked" in a furnace for four hours, during which temperatures reach 2000° F. outside the safe but temperatures inside the safe must not exceed 350° F. When the safe has cooled, papers inside must be soft and legible. Another sample safe is heated to 2000° for thirty minutes, during which time it must not explode (from steam pressure inside). While still white-hot, this safe is dropped thirty feet onto brick and rubble (simulating three-story fall), then reheated upside down to 1700° F. and allowed to cool to room temperature. Specimen documents inside must be legible, and thermocouples inside must not have registered over 350° F.

- *UL 350° F.—Two Hours:* The safe is heated to 1850° F. over a two-hour period, during which inside safe temperatures must not exceed 350° F. and specimen papers must be soft and legible. Another sample safe is heated to 2000° F. for thirty minutes during which time it must not explode. The same safe is cooled to 1550° F., reheated to 1640° F. and held there for forty-five minutes, after which, while still hot, the safe is dropped thirty feet onto brick and rubble. The same safe is reheated upside down to 1700° F., cooled to room temperature, and opened. Documents inside must be legible.

- *UL 350°F.—1 Hour:* Basically the same test as above, except that the safe stays in the furnace for only one hour with temperature reaching only 1700° F. Explosion and drop tests are the same.

• *UL 350° F.—1 Hour-D:* Same as 350° F.—1 Hour except that the drop test is eliminated. This label is for fire-resistive filing cabinets.

Fire-resistive safes have a lining of moisture-impregnated insulation. Under the extremes of heat in a fiercely burning building, this moisture is driven off as steam into the inside of the safe. Vents in the safe let some of the steam escape to prevent explosion, as in a pressure cooker. So long as steam not under pressure fills the safe, inside safe heat does not get much above 212° F. That's the theory, anyway.

About Used Fire-Resistive Safes

Do not buy a used fire-resistant safe. It may have been in a fire. Even a mild fire, which does little more than singe the paint on the safe, can drive off enough moisture from the insulation to reduce its protection substantially.

If *your* safe was in a fire, scrap it, even though it looks as though a paint job would restore it. If it's an expensive safe, still scrap it because its fire resistance is now only cosmetic.

After a Fire

If you do have a fire, it's very important you have the fire department find the safe as soon as possible and cool it off with a fine water spray. The longer the safe remains hot, the more likely all the moisture protection will have been driven off by the heat. Open the safe as soon as it has been cooled and remove the contents. Locating the safe can be a problem in a large building,

especially if the safe has fallen several stories into the basement and is covered with rubble. This is why you should have a map of the safe's location you can give to the fire department to help in locating it after the fire.

Never open a hot safe because then you let out the steam that may be all that's keeping its contents from flashing into fire. When you do open the safe, have a bucket of water, a hose or a CO_2 extinguisher on hand in case documents are burning. And stand the cooled safe upright as soon as possible.

A New Safe Can Be Damp

Some makes of fire-resistant safes, such as those made by Diebold, have moisture sealed into the insulation in such a way that it cannot escape unless fire melts the low-temperature-melting insulating material. Other safes do not have this feature, and, especially when new, can "sweat" inside. Beads of moisture can form on the walls, and damage documents or other valuables such as jewelry, guns, or coin collections.

A new safe should be opened two or three times a week to let the interior dry out. If the dampness problem persists, use silica gel bags to absorp the moisture. Do not install a fire safe in a damp basement, or where it is subject to flood. Fire safes are not air- or watertight by nature or designed to avoid explosion from steam pressure. So if water rises far enough, it may leak into the safe.

If moisture can damage valuables, they can be wrapped in a plastic bag, preferably a heat-sealed bag. Do not locate the safe near a heat register or radiator, the heat from which can drive off some of the moisture in safe insulation.

Combination Fire- and Burglary-Resistive Safes

You can buy small home and office safes that are UL-rated for both fire and burglary resistance. However, because the safes are small and fairly light (about one hundred pounds) they can be carried off by a burglar. I would never keep much money or jewelry in such a safe, or anything else of intrinsic value. If you use equipment daily, such as cameras and lenses, a burglar-resistant safe can be a convenience. If you do buy such a safe, anchor it in some way to the wall or to the floor in a cement slab so it is difficult to remove and cart away.

Combination Protection

I refer to the combination of the lock on the safe in this context. Keep a record of the combination in a safe place, and scramble the numbers backward on the record. Be careful someone nearby is not watching when you spin the dials; it's easy to pick up the combination visually, even with binoculars from a distance. Shield the dials with your body as you spin them. When locking the safe, spin the dials well past all the combination numbers. Crooks know that some people are so lazy they don't spin the dial more than one digit. In this case the safe combination is easy to find, sometimes by luck, sometimes by trying each number, sometimes by sensing a slight tightness as tumblers align at the combination number.

Keeping Vital Records

If you live far from a fire department, as on a farm, or your business is located in an older building not rated as fire resistant, you should store vital records in a fire-resistive safe. Here are some of the documents you should keep there:

Bank books	Seven years
Bank statements	Seven years
Check stubs	Seven years
Canceled checks	Seven years
Income tax records	Seven years
Insurance records	For life of policy plus two years
Birth certificate	Permanently
Marriage records	Permanently
Will	Permanently
Sales slips and receipts	Seven years

Don't keep bonds, stocks, or anything else of value in a fire safe. These safes are far too easy to open. A skilled burglar could do it about as fast as you could open a tin can, as I said earlier.

Apropos of fire safes, take a look at Fig. 1-12. This drawing appeared in a Chicago magazine. The body copy, on behalf of a local jewelry firm, read: "They built them strong back in 1870. So strong that safes like ours lasted through the great (Chicago) fire and the contents were hardly scorched at all." All I can say is that the "contents" must have been bricks and rocks. This is an old-fashioned safe with absolutely no fire resistance and almost no burglar resistance. I only hope this jewelry firm has graduated to a better and more attack-resistant safe; otherwise the manager is going to be in for an expensive surprise one of these mornings.

Computer fire safes are rated to hold the inside temperature below 150° F. If you use an outside computer service make sure they store your tapes and discs in such a safe.

Not even the Chicago Fire could crack a safe like ours.

Fig. 1-12 / *This ad appeared in a Chicago magazine on behalf of a local jewelry firm. Every safecracker in Chicago must have spent about two minutes of fantasy, hoping this safe is still in use. A skilled safecracker could peel it open in a few minutes.*

Money Safes

First, as I said a while back, there's no such thing as a burglar*proof* safe, only varying *degrees* of time-rated attack resistance. Safe burglar resistance is time-rated by UL because time is of the essence in such an attack. The longer it takes to "crack" the safe, the greater the risk of capture, so far as the burglar is concerned. There's no way I can cover,

in this short chapter, everything there is to know about safes and vaults. I can steer you in the right direction, though, and after that it's between you and the safe manufacturer and your friendly burglar and, oh yes, your insurance company, who will insist on a safe commensurate with the risk.

How Safes Are "Cracked"

This book isn't a school textbook for burglars; these people learn safe cracking in prison. Anytime you don't think so, ask any prison warden to show you the unbelievably sophisticated and talented shop drawings and notes of methods crooks leave behind as they leave jail to start a "new life." I only mention in very brief detail some of the safe-cracking methods burglars use so you won't get entranced by a gilded and engraved steel monstrosity such as that shown in Fig. 1-12.

Perhaps not the newest but surely the most dangerous safe-cracking tool is the thermal lance, or "burning bar" as it is called in police parlance. It's dangerous for two reasons; first because the Underwriters' Laboratories offer no safe rating that protects against the thermal lance and second because the lance can burn through six solid inches of tempered steel in an unbelievable fifteen seconds and through three to three-and-a-half feet of concrete in five minutes, at a working temperature of 10,000° F. The thermal lance is so hot and goes through steel so fast that nearby heat sensors don't pick up the heat. That's why better safes have a thin layer of copper lining on the safe or vault door, to conduct heat to heat sensors that will trip the burglar alarm system. As I said, UL does not test safes with the thermal lance, so you should install heat and smoke sensors on and near the safe. The thermal lance emits dense quantities of smoke, which is why the smoke detector is needed. The danger of the thermal lance is its simplicity and compactness. A complete outfit can be carried in a large briefcase. The lance itself is simply a one- to two-inch-diameter piece of common pipe stuffed with aluminum, steel, and magnesium alloy wire. One end is supplied with oxygen, the other, the working end, is ignited by a small oxy-acetylene torch, which is removed after ignition. The pipe is from six to ten feet long, and can be in several lengths to fit into the briefcase.

Other tools used include diamond-core drills, air hammers, and explosives, against which safes *are* UL rated as shown below. Vibration sensors, tuned to the frequency of drills and hammers, should also be installed around safes. Proximity detectors, which pick up the presence of a human body at a preset distance, as well as ultrasonic and microwave motion sensors, can also be used to detect an intruder before he gets close enough to the safe to work on it. The safe itself can also be wired with a contact switch on the door and wires in the safe body. I would use the hard-wire door-and-wire system, plus one of the intrusion detectors, to protect a safe, particularly if the safe is located out of sight from the street. Money safes for the day's receipts from a store should if possible be located and spotlighted in the front window, or near it, for obvious reasons. For more data on the specialized sensors for safes, please see Chapters Fourteen, Twenty, and Twenty-two.

Any safe that weighs less than five-hundred pounds should be imbedded in concrete, because burglars can, and have, converted boat trailers to safenap

large safes. Once in *their* garage, an attack can be carried out in relative safety and with all the time in the world.

UL Ratings for Burglar-Resistant Safes

These are Underwriters' Laboratories basic safe ratings, in order of burglar resistance, beginning with the least resistant rating:

- *TL-15:* Resists tool attack for fifteen minutes.
- *TL-30:* Resists tool attack for thirty minutes.
- *TRTL-30:* Resists tool and torch attack for thirty minutes (does not include thermal lance).
- *TRTL-60:* Resists tool and torch attack for sixty minutes (does not include thermal lance).
- *TRTL-60X:* Resists torch, tool, and explosive attack for sixty minutes (does not include thermal lance).

The TL-15 safe is OK for home use. It should be anchored to the floor or well-concealed. The TL-30 tests do not include attack by hammers over eight pounds and pry bars over five feet long.

Recommended Safe Manufacturers

Excellent safes are made by the following manufacturers:

Diebold, Inc., Canton, Ohio 44702

The Mosler Safe Company, 1561 Grand Boulevard, Hamilton, Ohio 45012

Meilink Steel Safe Company, P.O. Box 2847, Toledo, Ohio 43606

John D. Brush & Company, Inc., 900 Linden Ave., Rochester, New York 14625

John Tann, Ltd., England (see local safe distributor).

13

A BRIEF HISTORY OF LOCKS
AND HOW THEY WORK

From the early Egyptians to modern times, a quick review of lock development. Plus a layman's guide to the inner mysteries of locks.

ABOUT A THOUSAND YEARS before Christ was born some smart Egyptian breathed a sigh of relief, because he had found a way to keep crooks from stealing his possessions. As with all such sighs, however, the relief can only be temporary. For all lock developments are merely stages in the battle between the designers of locks and the equally clever (if misguided) criminals who figure out ways to defeat these innovations.

Modern man found the first ancient lock in the excavations that revealed the palace of Sargon II, who ruled Persia from 722–705 B.C. The site is an archeological excavation on the banks of the Tigris River. The lock was a typical Egyptian pin lock (Fig. 1–13), the lineal descendant of which is the modern pin-

Fig. 1-13 / *Replica of an Egyptian pin lock, from the palace of Sargon II, King of Persia from 722 to 705 B.C. The principles of this lock are still used in modern pin-tumbler locks.*

THE BRITISH SCIENCE MUSEUM

3-13) shows that when the key is inserted, the pins of the key raise the pins in the lock upward. With the lock pins raised, the lock bolt (the part that protrudes into the strike in the door frame) can now be moved and the lock unlocked.

Warded Locks

An even simpler lock than the Egyptian pin lock, the warded lock was in use as early as the first century B.C.

The simplest warded lock has only three moving parts; the bolt, an arm that moves the bolt, and the key that actuates the bolt arm. An ancient warded lock made of wrought iron and attributed to a sixteenth-century Flemish lockmaker, is shown in Fig. 4-13. The key is at lower left. It has only two "cuts" or indentations in it. The key fits into the keyhole "A". The cuts of the key match the fixed, raised "wards" or tiny fences at the top of the keyhole and at "B". When the lock is turned, the cuts in the key permit it to pass over the two wards. When the key is turned far enough, it hits the "gate" "C" or projection of the bolt "D". When the key contacts the bolt gate and pushes against it, the bolt is moved inward and the lock opens. When the key is moved the other way, it hits the gate and pushes the bolt outward, and locks the lock. A spring at the end of the bolt keeps it in the locked position.

I am sure you can see at least two ways to defeat this simple lock. The easier way would simply be to insert a thin steel blade in the bolt and push it back. Another way would be to reach into the lock case with a simple pick and again push the bolt back.

Warded locks on this very same prin-

Fig. 2-13 / *Keys to ancient pin locks had to be carried over the shoulder.*
THE BRITISH SCIENCE MUSEUM

tumbler lock. The key (so large it had to be carried over a shoulder) looked like a crude comb (Fig. 2-13). Actually, the pins of the key mate with pins in the lock. A view of one of these locks (Fig.

Fig. 3-13 / *An early Egyptian-type pin lock from the Faroe Islands. When the key, at bottom, is in the lock, the wooden pins drop out of slots in bolt at top, and the bolt can be moved to open the lock.*

ciple of design are still being made and sold, mostly as dime-store-type padlocks. A similar such lock (and key) from the seventeenth century is shown in Fig. 5-13.

Lever-Tumbler Locks

The next basic lock improvement was the introduction of tumblers, moveable devices between the key and the lock bolt. The tumblers added one more degree of security and attack resistance, because now the key could be more complex and the lock harder to pick open.

An early version of the lever-tumbler lock, made in 1844 by Chubb (England) is shown in Fig. 6-13. The key is hollow. When inserted in the keyway, the hollow barrel of the key fits over the post "A". The oval-shaped pieces of steel "B" are the lever tumblers. The bolt "C" has a fixed, raised pillar or "post" "D". When the key is turned in the lock, its cuts fit over the tumblers at "B". Cuts of the key are matched to the bottom oval cuts of the tumblers. When the key is turned, the tumblers are raised just far enough so the tumbler gates "E" allow the bolt post "D" to pass through. When the key is turned still further, it contacts the bolt and moves it.

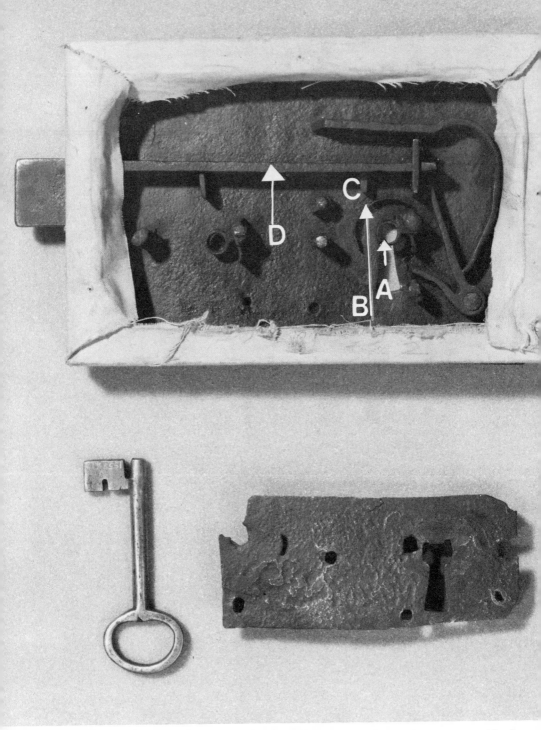

Fig. 4-13 / *A 16th-century Flemish warded lock. Cuts in the key pass over fixed, raised "fences" "A" and "B", permit the key blade to open and close the bolt "D" by pushing against a post "C" on the bolt.*

Fig. 5-13 / *A 17th-century warded padlock and key.*

THE BRITISH SCIENCE MUSEUM

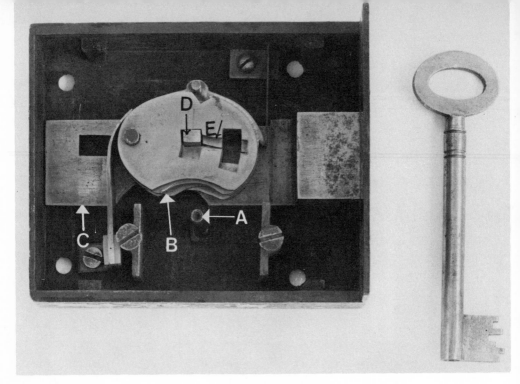

Fig. 6-13 / *Chubb lever-tumbler lock, circa 1844.*

Fig. 7-13 / *Wafer tumbler lock. "A" shows wafers recessed in plug. "B" shows cam at end of plug.*

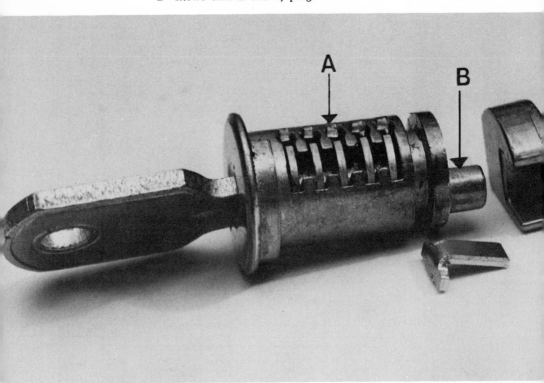

Fig. 8-13 / *Wafer-tumbler lock with key withdrawn. Wafers pro-trude out of plug. If plug were in housing, the protruding part of the wafer tumblers would be in matching slots in the housing and the plug could not turn.*

Fig. 9-13 / *Parts of a wafer-tumbler lock are: "A", cylinder hous-ing; "B", plug; "D", tailpiece; "E" through "K", wafer tumblers; "I", key.*

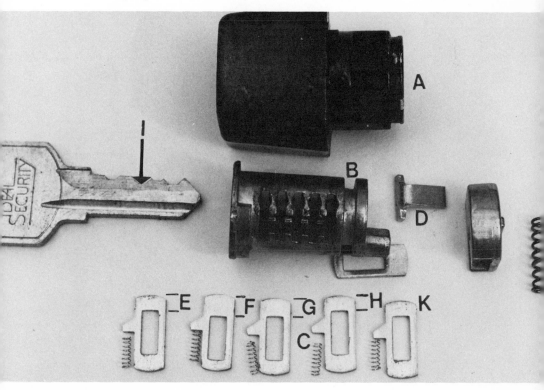

The lock in Fig. 6-13 is in the unlocked position, with the bolt post "D" in the left rectangular opening in the tumblers.

The cheaper and simpler lever-tumbler locks have been and still can be found on the back doors of older homes and apartment buildings in this country. They are easy to defeat by lockpicking, and as I have said earlier, master keys for them can be purchased in hardware stores.

However, there are also highly complex lever-tumbler locks, often used on bank safety deposit boxes, and these do offer a high degree of security.

Wafer-Tumbler Locks

Wafer-tumbler locks (or disc locks as they are also called) can be simple or very complex and highly secure. The simpler wafer-tumbler locks, such as shown in Fig. 7-13, are fairly easy to pick open.

Here is how they work. Small wafers (Fig. 7-13) "A" fit into slots in the cylinder plug. When the key is inserted in the plug, cuts of the key pull the wafers down to the surface (shear point) of

the plug, as shown in Fig. 7-13. Now the key can turn the plug. The cam at the end of the plug "B", moves the lock bolt mechanism.

When the key is removed from the plug (Fig. 8-13), the spring-loaded wafers "A" pop up out of the plug "B". The wafers now fit into slots in the fixed position cylinder housing. Now the wafers are partly inside the plug and partly inside the housing. The plug cannot turn and the lock is in the locked mode.

If you will examine Fig. 9-13, showing the working parts of a simple wafer-tumbler lock, you will note that the wafers ("E" through "K") have varying lengths of rectangular holes cut or stamped out of them. The lengths of these holes correspond to "cuts" in the key "I". You can see the wafer slots in the plug "B" but of course not in the cylinder housing "A" because these slots are inside the housing.

Pin-Tumbler Locks

Pin-tumbler locks work on the same basic principle as the wafer-tumbler

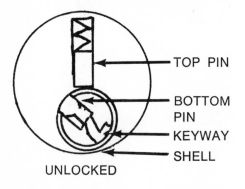
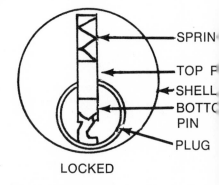

Fig. 10-13 / *Pin-tumbler lock showing one typical pin tumbler. Left, key is in lock. Cuts of key have lifted pins to the "shear" point so plug can turn and lock can be unlocked. Right, with key out of the lock, the top pin has dropped so it is partly in the plug and partly in the housing. Now the lock is in the locked position.*

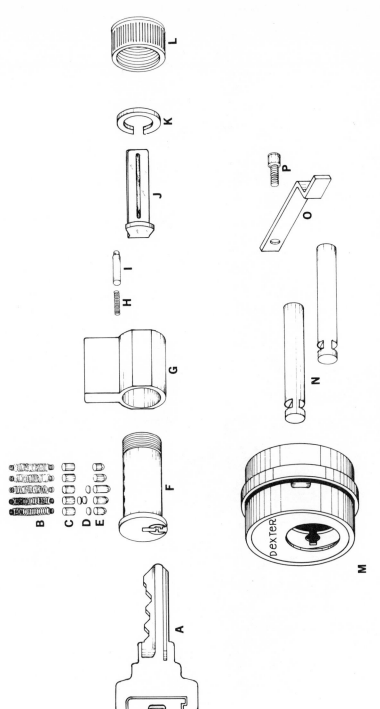

Fig. 11-13 / Exploded view of typical pin-tumbler cylinder. Parts are: "A", key; "B", bottom pins; "C", top pins; "D", master pins; "E", bottom pins; "F", plug; "G", shell; "H", spring; "I", pin; "J", tailpiece; "K", tailpiece circlip; "L", cap; "M", housing; "N", tie rods; "O", strap; "P", screw.

Fig. 12-13 /   *Two views of a round key. You can see that cuts in the barrel of the keys vary as to depth.*

Fig. 13-13 / Round key lock, showing bottom pins. "A" points to shear line between plug and cylinder housing.

lock. The only difference is that instead of wafers, the pin-tumbler lock uses tiny round brass pins. This type of lock offers more security than most wafer-tumbler locks because it is more difficult to pick open.

When the key is inserted in the keyway of a pin-tumbler lock (left, Fig. 10-13) the cuts of the key match the length of the bottom pin. The pin is raised flush with the top of the plug (the shear line) and the plug is now free to turn. When the key is withdrawn, the spring-loaded pins are pushed down into the plug, so they are partly in the plug and partly in the cylinder housing, as shown at the right of Fig. 10-13. You will also note that there are actually two pins in each pin slot. At the top there is a top pin. Top pin lengths are the same. Below the top pin there is a bottom pin, the length of which varies. These bottom pin lengths match the depth of the cuts of the pin. In the locked position, with the key removed, the bottom pin is pushed below the top of the plug, and the top pin is partly in

the plug and partly in the housing, blocking the plug from turning.

You can tell how many pins a pin-tumbler lock has by counting the number of cuts in the key. Working parts of a pin-tumbler lock are shown in Fig. 11-13. The small round discs between the top and bottom pins ("D") are master-key pins. A master key has cuts that match both the bottom pins and the extra master pins. The lock in Fig. 11-13 is a very simple pin-tumbler lock. High-security cylinders such as the Medeco and Illinois Duo are much more complicated.

Round Key Locks

A variation of the pin-tumbler lock was introduced some years ago, using a round key. This key (Fig. 12-13) has cuts in its barrel that match the length of the pins (Fig. 13-13). The shear line of the plug is shown at point "A" in Fig. 13-13. You can't see the top pins in Fig. 13-13 because they are inside the plug, underneath the bottom pins which are showing.

14

HARD-WIRE BURGLAR ALARMS, YOUR FIRST LINE OF DEFENSE!

As ROME lay sleeping early one morning during the year 390 B.C., Gallic soldiers began a stealthy attack against the Imperial City. Surprise seemed to be on the side of the invaders, for there was no sign that their presence had been detected. Suddenly the stillness of the dawn was shattered by the piercing shrieks of the burglar alarms. Roman guards sprang to life, Roman soldiers to their arms. The Gauls were driven off.

What burglar alarms? What piercing shrieks? Why, geese, of course. Geese had been used as early warning alarms at least since the start of Rome's rule by the Sabines years earlier. Geese are still used as alarms in Southeast Asia. They have a strong sense of territoriality, rotten dispositions, keep the lawn trimmed, and can be eaten if they fail to alarm or give too many false alarms.

There are today other burglar-alarm systems a good deal more sophisticated

than geese. The alarms I will discuss in this chapter are called "hard-wire" systems because all the alarm components are linked together by electrical wire (as compared with wireless systems and microwave and ultrasonic motion detectors to be covered in later chapters).

Basically, a hard-wire burglar-alarm system consists of magnetic contact switches on doors and windows, a control box to which they are wired, a loud siren or bell, and batteries.

The magnet half of the switch is mounted on the door or window. The switch half is mounted on the door or window frame (Fig. 1-14).

As long as the door or window remains closed, the magnet is next to the switch, and the switch contacts stay closed. With all switch contacts closed (Fig. 2-14) the electrical circuit loop to all such contacts is complete right up to the control box.

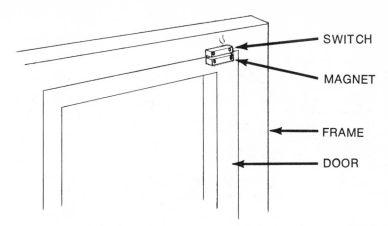

SWITCH

MAGNET

FRAME

DOOR

Fig. 1-14 / *Magnetic switches can be installed on doors and windows to trigger the alarm if an intruder breaks in.*

But let a burglar come in the house through the door or a window and within seconds the howling, piercing shriek of the alarm siren, or the loud clanging of the bell, will signal his presence for blocks. When the door or window is opened, the magnet is moved away from the switch, and the switch contacts open. Now the circuit to the control box is broken (Fig. 3-14). Relays in the control box "latch" shut and keep the alarm going until someone shuts it off at the control box, or until a time-delay switch shuts it off automatically and rearms the system, ready for the next burglar.

The hard-wire system is positive in nature. Very little can go wrong with it, it is virtually false-alarm free (provided you know how to use it) and it has limitless application to every type of security problem.

Hard-wire systems do require, as noted earlier, that thin wires be strung between the magnetic switches on windows and doors, and to the control box. However, these wires can be hidden behind walls, run behind baseboards or under rugs and floors.

Alarm Accessories

Accessories that increase the chances of a police response can be wired into the alarm system. For example, if the alarm does no more than produce an earsplitting sound in a residential neighborhood, someone is bound to call the police sooner or later. Sound is funny, though, and there may be echoes off nearby buildings that may make it hard for the police to find the right house quickly. An extremely bright blue flashing strobe light can be mounted over the front door that will start flashing as soon as the alarm sounds. This light is highly visible even during the day.

If you live in the middle of a crowded city, or you have a store in a neighborhood that is not occupied at night or an apartment high up in a high-rise building, it's possible no one will hear or respond to the alarm. The alarm is merely a "local" device to scare away a burglar. It is hoped a Good Samaritan citizen will call police when he hears your alarm. One way to make sure police get the message is to install a telephone dialer.

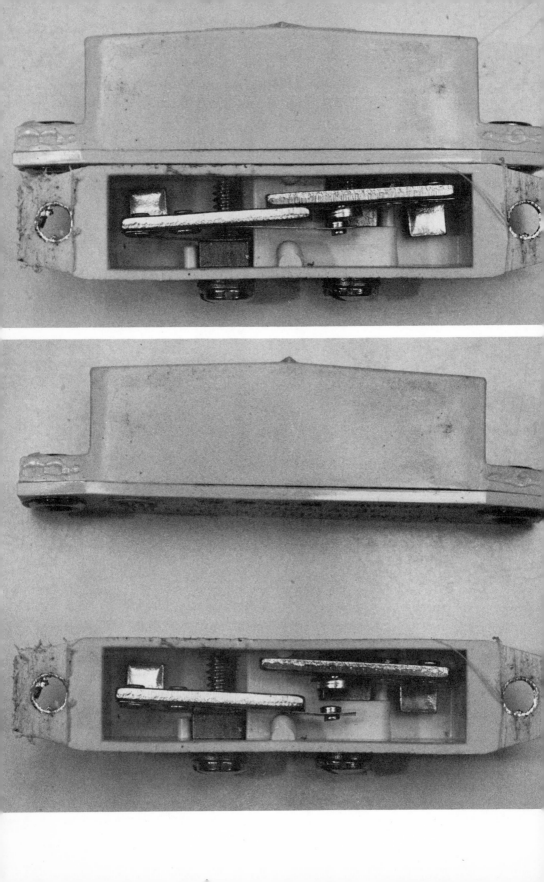

◄
(Above)
Fig. 2-14 / *When the magnet half of the switch, top, is next to the switch contact half, the contacts stay closed and the protective circuit remains intact.*

◄
(Below)
Fig. 3-14 / *When the magnet half of the switch, located on the door or window, is moved away from the contact half, the switch contacts open, breaking the protective circuit and causing the alarm to sound.*

We will discuss dialers at greater length in Chapter Eighteen. Right now all you need know about them is that they can be used with any type of burglar-alarm system.

Dialers have a built-in tape message. When the alarm sounds, the tape starts. The dialer plugs itself into the telephone, dials the police and gives its message. The message tells police that there is an emergency at the residence of ———— and gives your name and address.

Police Connect

Dialers are not always reliable, however, for a number of reasons (see Chapter Eighteen) and so are not approved by Underwriters' Laboratories and insurance companies for use with commercial and industrial alarm systems. In a jewelry store or bank at night, for example, you want to get to the police directly and immediately. These systems use a leased telephone line that goes directly into the police station communications room. This is known as a "police connect" system. Since the telephone line is leased, the alarm system is more expensive to operate. Further, police can't and won't supervise the lines for sabotage and trouble, so the reliability of these systems is limited.

Central Station

For the most reliable alarm system, the central station connect offers greatest security. Here the alarm system is wired, via telephone lines or radio link, to a professional guard service with its own electronic recording devices in a central receiving station. All incoming alarms are monitored, recorded and hard-copy printed for a permanent record. The subscriber's alarm system is continuously monitored (see Chapter 23) for failure or sabotage. The central station itself is heavily guarded, and is under the tightest security to prevent being disabled by criminals.

Smoke and fire sensors can also be wired into the hard-wire system, and these I will discuss in detail in a separate chapter (Seventeen). Right now all you need know is that for very little more money, you can add the security of early-warning smoke sensors, and fire and heat sensors, to the hard-wire alarm system. Should any of these sensors detect smoke, fumes, or a rise in air temperature to a danger level, the alarm will sound. If the alarm is a siren, the sound will be steady for burglary and pulsating for fire. If you use a bell, the bell will be steady for burglary and intermittent for fire. Not all hard-wire system control boxes will give a dual tone, one each for burglary and fire. You should specify this dual tone, though, because it is important you be able to distinguish between these two emergencies. You would not want to lock yourself in the bedroom because you think there's a prowler in the house, when you should be getting out of the house as fast as possible because the place is on fire.

Dialers are available that will dial the fire department in a fire emergency and police in an intrusion situation. Police-connect alarm systems can also provide these dual alarms, as can the central station system. In the central station system, patrolling guards can be alerted by radio of any emergency, and police or fire departments alerted at the same time.

When To Install

The best time to install a hard-wire alarm system is when the building is under construction. During this period, wires can be run behind partitions, and magnetic contact switches can be recessed into door and window frames (Fig. 4-14).

Hidden wires and magnetic switches provide greater security than exposed wiring and switches. For example, all a burglar need do to defeat a hard-wire system is to wrap a short piece of wire over the switch contacts. Now he can open the door without sounding the alarm. His little piece of wire has kept the alarm circuit loop intact, even though the open door has caused the switch to open and break the circuit. The control box can't tell whether or not the switch has been compromised. All it cares about is whether or not the alarm loop is, in effect, one continuous wire from switch to switch and back to the control box.

Wiring during the construction stage is also considerably less expensive because it is less time-consuming than hiding wires in an existing structure.

Control Box Options

Here is what you should look for in a control box. First, you need some way to get in and out of the place without setting off the alarm. You *could* (and many people do) install a key-operated lock switch somewhere near the front door. When you turn the key you, in effect, drop a piece of wire across the door magnetic contact (shunt it out). This switch is called a "shunt switch." Now you can enter the house without the alarm going off. However, I don't like shunt switches outside the house. First, the lock can be picked open, thus defeating your alarm system. Second, it can be pulled out of the wall, exposing its wires, and again it can be defeated.

Shunt locks can have a tamper switch to make defeating them from outside the house or building tougher. A tamper switch is simply a spring-loaded switch. In use, the switch is placed against something to hold it closed. In this case (Fig. 5-14) the switch ("B") is pushed against a stud or the wall. If the shunt lock face-

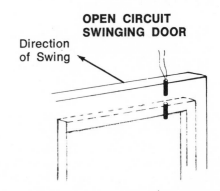

Fig. 4-14 / *Magnetic switches (and the wiring to them) can be recessed out of sight in door and window frames. Wiring can be run behind walls or baseboard.*

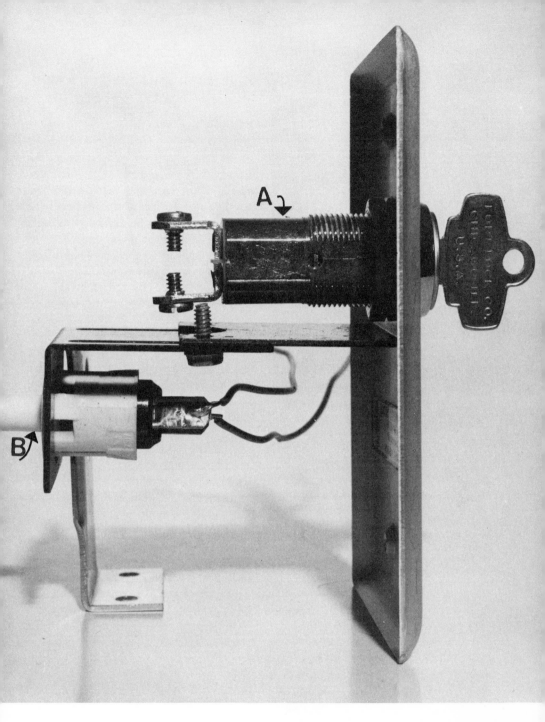

Fig. 5-14 / *This switch is for installation outside (near doorbell button, for instance). It uses the key switch to turn the alarm off so it won't sound when you open the front door. "A" is the key shunt switch, "B" is a tamper switch that also turns on the alarm if the lock is pried away from its mounting.*

Fig. 6-14 / *Typical residential-type burglar alarm system control box. Box contains relays and circuitry to initiate alarm if a protected door or window is opened. Note key switch and the five alarm modes it provides, the test lights and the emergency panic button that can also sound the alarm when pushed.*

plate is pulled away, the tamper switch contacts open and the alarm will sound.

A more secure approach to the exit/entrance problem is to use a control box (Fig. 6-14) with a built-in automatic timer. The timer should be adjustable from zero to one minute. Now you can go to the control box, usually located in a closet, turn on the alarm, and have time to get out of the house before the timer arms the system. On return, the timer gives you time to unlock the door, put down whatever you may be carrying,

go to the control box and, with a key, turn the alarm off or to standby.

Control Box Controls

Besides an exit/entry delay timer, the control box *must* have a key-actuated switch. Otherwise the burglar can run to the nearest closet or wherever he thinks you have located the control box, and just turn off the alarm himself.

Some packaged alarm systems incorporate an inside siren or noisemaker in the control box. This sound makes it a lot easier for the burglar to get right to the control box. Even if the box is key-switched, he may be able to disable it if he can find it. A noisemaker inside the house (as well as outside) is a good idea to alert you to an intrusion or fire. But not if it leads an intruder to the box. Locate the inside noisemaker as far from the control box as possible.

A control box should also have a test switch that will check condition of any batteries, all switches, and smoke and fire sensors and their connections. The test should be done without turning on outside audible alarm horns or bells.

The control box should also give you an "Instant" alarm mode that bypasses the exit/entry delay. If you are at home, perhaps taking a nap during the day, you don't want to give a burglar even ten seconds to get into the house before the alarm sounds. You want that alarm to go off the second the door (or the window) opens a half inch.

Another handy option is to have a shunt switch wired into the control box that will shunt out the front door magnetic switch. Now the kids can come and go all day, but you will still have all the other door and window switches, and the fire and smoke sensors, armed and

Fig. 7-14 /   *This loud, clanging alarm bell says "Burglary in progress" when it rings. Note weather-protecting two-directional louvers in steel box, and the two tamper switches. Tamper switch "A" sounds the alarm if box cover is removed, switch "B" if the entire box is pried from the wall.*

ready to go. This is a handy feature. For example, you don't want a lot of false alarms. This does not make for happy neighbors, and if too many occur they may not respond quickly. Your children may not be old enough to be reliable about getting to the control box before the time delay expires. Yet the kids come and go all day. If there is a lot of child activity on the street, a burglar won't use the front door. He may sneak in the back door or through a rear window and make off with your purse or other valuables, even while you are outside talking to a neighbor on the sidewalk. It happens every day—it happened to one of my own neighbors. But with the standby feature, the front door can be removed

from the alarm system, while all other door and window switches and the fire sensors, are "armed."

Panic Buttons

Another valuable adjunct to a hardwire (or any other type) of alarm system is panic buttons. These are merely switches wired into the protective alarm loop. When you press the button, the protective alarm loop is broken (as if a door or window were opened) and the alarm will go off. Panic buttons can be located anywhere. Convenient locations are the kitchen, master bedroom, living room, and basement workroom.

Fig. 8-14 / *This alarm siren is in a protective steel enclosure that also has two tamper switches, one on the rear of the box, one on the box cover.*

Alarm Timers

Before you buy any alarm system, check your local ordinances governing their installation. You may find, for example, that the alarm may not sound for more than a specified period of time (usually from four to fifteen minutes). After that time the alarm must shut off automatically. At that time the alarm system must also automatically rearm, ready for the next intrusion. The timer is a good idea; if you are out of town when the alarm goes off, it could howl all night or until police break in and shut it off (probably by destroying the control box).

There are other features to look for in a control box, and these will be discussed at the end of Chapter Fifteen (How To Install Your Own Alarm System).

Bells or Sirens?

One more point and we can go on to installing hard-wire alarm systems. Should your alarm system have a bell or a siren? If it's in a store or other commercial establishment, it will have to be a bell. For a home you have a choice of a bell or a siren.

Personally, I prefer a loud, clanging bell. We have all heard one of these, usually as the store owner closed for the day and opened for the day, when the bell clanged for a few seconds before he shut the alarm off.

The loud bell says "burglary in progress" to most of us. The siren could be anything from an ambulance to a cop chasing a speeder. There are too many sirens sounding every day in our major cities as it is. I'd stick to the bell.

But siren or bell, either should be installed in a protective steel box, with a tamper-switched cover. The siren or bell should be located high up under the eaves where a burglar can't reach up and fill the box with styrofoam or even shaving cream from a spray can. The bell in Fig. 7-14 has two tamper switches, one on the back of the box where it triggers the alarm of the box if pulled off the wall, and the other on the bell box cover where it sets off the alarm if the cover is removed. The siren in Fig. 8-14 is similarly tamper-switched.

15

HOW TO INSTALL
YOUR OWN BURGLAR ALARM
AND CUT TOTAL SYSTEM COSTS
IN HALF!

IF YOU CAN hook up hi-fi components you should be able to install your own burglar-alarm system. Half the cost of an alarm system is labor, so if you do the work you save half the cost. Furthermore, since there is a shortage of skilled alarm installers, there are a lot of untrained people out there installing alarms. You may thus wind up with a lot better and more reliable alarm system if you give it your own tender loving care.

There's also the fact that it is not a good idea to have people out in the world who know the intimate details of your alarm system. An installer who did your job would have this information. I well recall the time I took a course in burglar-alarm installation from a trade school, just to see what they taught. To enroll we all had to take a polygraph examination (lie detector). About half the class flunked the polygraph exam. It seemed that the flunkers either had a criminal record, or were about to have one. Yet I know of very few burglar-alarm installers who require the installing crew to take a lie detector test.

Preview

In this chapter, I am going to discuss the installation of a hard-wire system only. Installation tips for pulsed infrared, ultrasonic, microwave, and proximity alarm systems will be given in Chapters Twenty, Twenty-two, and Twenty-three. Because smoke and fire sensors are part of a hard-wire alarm system, their installation will be included in this chapter.

However, I urge you to read Chapter Seventeen on the need for fire sensors if you are not sold on them now. Most hard-wire control boxes have provisions for wiring in smoke and fire sensors; if not, you can insist on such a control box when you shop for components.

As for components, I will discuss parts selection at the end of this chapter, and give you some idea as to their cost at that point. I will also review packaged alarm systems now on the market that provide all the components you need for your particular building.

Parts You Will Need

In a high crime area or for a vulnerable building (a high-income-bracket home, for example) I would install magnetic contact switches on every point of entry; that is, on all doors and windows, even upper story windows to protect against entry with ladders at those points.

You will need a control box and an inside and an outside horn or bell. You will also need two six-volt lantern batteries, one for the intrusion loop and one for the bell or siren loop. I would prefer you use gel-cell batteries with automatic recharger instead of the lantern batteries, though. Lantern batteries can run down, whereas the gel-cell batteries with automatic recharger will assure you of greater reliability of standby power.

You will also need enough 22 gauge two-conductor coded wire for the protective circuit switches; 16 gauge or 20 gauge two-conductor wire for smoke sensor power-supply wiring and 22 gauge two-conductor wiring for smoke and heat sensor contact wiring. The smoke sensors require a six-volt power supply. Both

smoke and heat sensors have switches that stay open until the sensor senses smoke or heat rise. So you need two sets of connections to smoke sensors, one for the power supply and one for the sensor contacts. Heat sensors do not require a power supply, so all you need is wire for the sensor contacts.

If the control box does not have a siren pulser, you will need one. This is a separate module (if needed) that connects to the siren and makes it sound. The pulser also provides a steady tone for intrusion and a pulsing tone for fire.

If you prefer a bell (I do; please see Chapter Fourteen as to why), the control box should have a bell pulser. (Bell and siren pulsers are not interchangeable, the siren pulser won't pulse the bell and vice versa.) The bell pulser provides a steady bell ring for intrusion and an intermittent ring for fire.

Most control boxes come with a 110-volt AC stepdown transformer to provide power to the box. The battery is standby in case power fails (or power lines to the house are cut).

Tools You Will Need

- Drill with flexible ⅜″ x 54″ and ¼″ x 18″ bits
- Wire stripper
- Staple gun and staples
- Screwdriver
- Volt-ohm-ammeter (cheap one, about $18) or six-volt test lamp
- Fish tape and reel for pulling wire
- Wood chisel and one-inch putty knife for lifting baseboard and molding
- Soldering iron and rosin-core solder
- Five-inch square of masonite to protect walls when prying up baseboard and molding

1050 SERIES	1070 SERIES
Drill Mounts	Flange Mounts

Fig. 1-15 / *Magnetic-contact intrusion switches for recessing out of sight in windows and doors.*

COURTESY SENTROL, INC.

- Patching putty for gouge marks and for filling in over wires run along baseboard

Locating Magnetic Sensors

If you are installing a burglar- and fire-alarm system in a building under construction, recessing sensors in window and door frames is no problem. Wires can be strung behind studs and around the building with ease, and you won't need the fish tape and reel for pulling wire behind walls.

If you are wiring up a home under construction you really should recess and hide all magnetic switches to eliminate the possibility of their being compromised by a "jumper" wire laid over switch contacts. For recessed sensors you will need to order special types of switches, such as those shown in Fig. 1-15. These are installed in holes drilled in the window or door frame. I prefer the drill mounts since the switches can be totally hidden from view by a thin layer of paste wood filler, painted over. The magnet part goes in the window or door, the switch half in the frame.

Where to Install Magnetic Switches

Installation of magnetic switches is quite simple. On doors, the switch can be located as shown in Fig. 1-14 (Chapter Fourteen). On overhead garage doors you will need a wide-gap magnetic switch, mounted as shown in Fig. 2-15. The magnet is on the top door section, the switch part on the bracket.

Instead of a magnetic switch on tilting overhead garage doors you could use a mercury switch (Fig. 3-15). If you use the mercury switch, it will have to be mounted on the door and you will have to have a flexible connector to wire it up (Fig. 4-15). This arrangement can also be used on any tilting door.

On windows, install two magnets and one switch, as shown in Fig. 5-15. The second magnet should be located high enough so the window can be opened for ventilation but not so high a person could crawl through.

On sliding glass windows install the two magnets and one switch as shown in Fig. 6-15, using the drill mount switch shown in Fig. 1-15 and epoxy glue to fasten the switch and magnet in place.

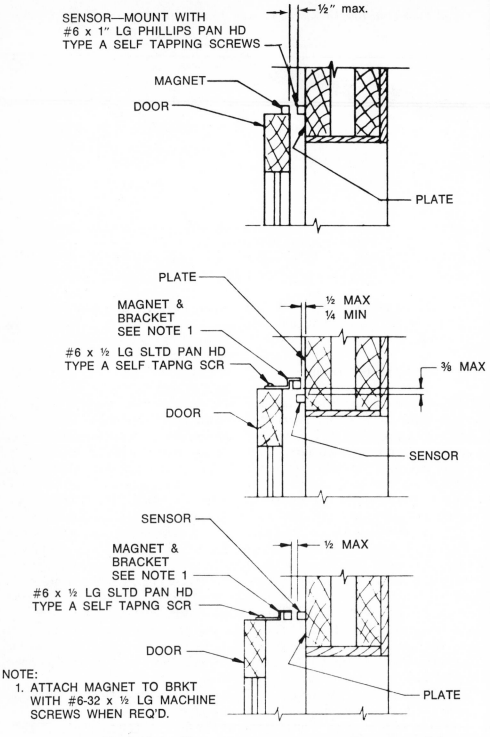

SENSOR—MOUNT WITH
#6 x 1" LG PHILLIPS PAN HD
TYPE A SELF TAPPING SCREWS

½" max.

MAGNET

DOOR

PLATE

PLATE

MAGNET &
BRACKET
SEE NOTE 1

#6 x ½ LG SLTD PAN HD
TYPE A SELF TAPNG SCR

DOOR

½ MAX
¼ MIN

⅜ MAX

SENSOR

SENSOR

MAGNET &
BRACKET
SEE NOTE 1

#6 x ½ LG SLTD PAN HD
TYPE A SELF TAPNG SCR

DOOR

½ MAX

NOTE:
1. ATTACH MAGNET TO BRKT
WITH #6-32 x ½ LG MACHINE
SCREWS WHEN REQ'D.

PLATE

Fig. 2-15 /   Three ways to mount a magnetic contact switch on a
garage door.

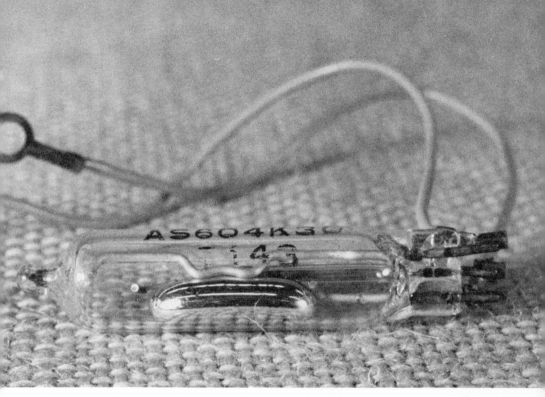

Fig. 3-15 / *Mercury switch can be used on overhead garage doors.*

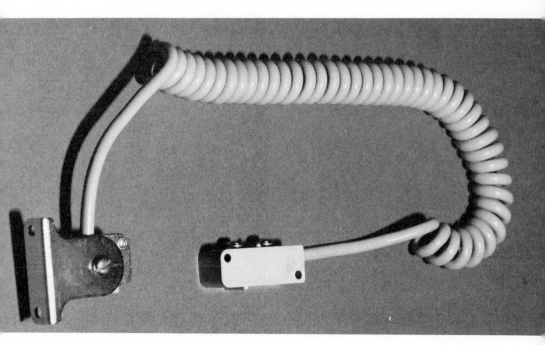

Fig. 4-15 / *Flexible connector should be used with mercury switches on overhead garage doors.*

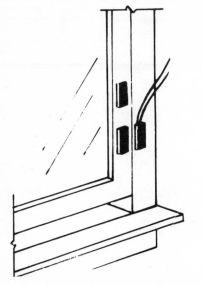

Fig. 5-15 / *So window can be opened for ventilation, use two magnets on the window and one switch on the frame, as shown.*

When installing magnetic switches, make sure the two pieces are correctly positioned, as in Fig. 7-15.

As an added precaution I would use a floor-mat switch under the rug or on the first one or two steps of any stairway leading to upper floors from the first floor. It's possible a burglar could defeat a hard-wire system by cutting a large hole in a window and crawling through. If he stepped on the floor mat, the alarm would still go off. These hidden switches can also be hidden under rugs anyplace in the home (Fig. 8-15). The switches come in a standard width of thirty inches, in five-foot rolls for $18 per roll, and a twenty-five-foot roll for $77. Individual sections can be cut out from the roll to fit. These switches can also be installed on window sills. A window sill model, 151-BBW, costs

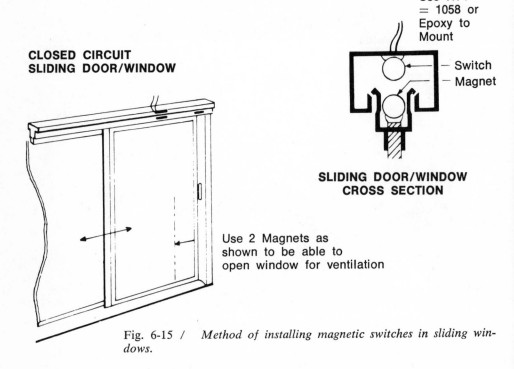

CLOSED CIRCUIT SLIDING DOOR/WINDOW

Use RTV = 1058 or Epoxy to Mount

— Switch
— Magnet

SLIDING DOOR/WINDOW CROSS SECTION

Use 2 Magnets as shown to be able to open window for ventilation

Fig. 6-15 / *Method of installing magnetic switches in sliding windows.*

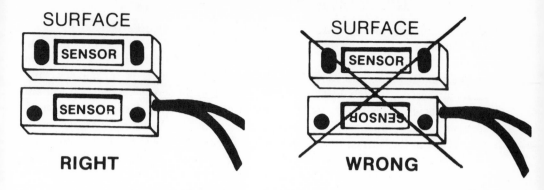

RIGHT

WRONG

Fig. 7-15 / *Right and wrong way to install magnetic switches and their magnets.*

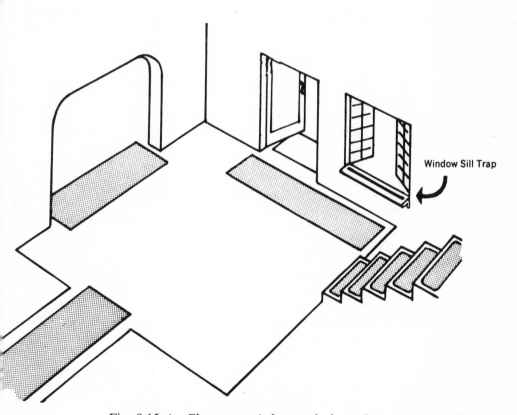

Window Sill Trap

Fig. 8-15 / *Floor-mat switches can be located in a variety of places to trigger the alarm when stepped on.*

TAPESWITCH CORPORATION OF AMERICA

about $5.50. The switches are made by the Tapeswitch Company (see Appendices).

The standard magnetic contact switch and the mercury switch have normally closed contacts. This means switch contacts are closed when the alarm system is switched to the "armed" position, with all doors and windows closed. The floor-mat switches, on the other hand, are "normally open" (NO). When an intruder steps on the floor-mat switch, its contacts close and trigger the alarm. Smoke and fire sensors are also "normally open" switches. A fire sensor, for example, is a bimetallic element, very much like the element in your furnace thermostat. When the heat element senses heat it begins to bend. When heat reaches a certain point (usually 135° F. or 190° F.) the thermostat element closes its contacts and triggers the fire alarm.

I mention the difference between the normally closed (NC) state of magnetic contact switches and the normally open state (NO) of floor-mat switches and smoke and fire detectors because they are wired differently, as we will now discuss. But first, one more word about floor-mat switches. If your control box does not have NO contacts, you can buy a converter for around $9 that converts these switches to NC. If you have a dog, you will have a false alarm every time it steps on the Tapeswitch. You can eliminate false alarms from anything under fifty pounds by installing a small plastic bridge under each switch section. Use Tapeswitch KT-205 bridge; $18 for a sixteen-piece set.

For jalousie windows, magnetic switches are impractical. The answer is a very special screen (Fig. 9-15) that has tiny wires woven into the screen.

Should the screen be pierced the alarm will sound. The wires are normally closed, in effect. You can't see it, but in addition there is a mercury "tilt" switch in the screen's frame that will also trigger the alarm if an attempt is made to remove it. As noted, both the woven wire and the mercury switch are "normally closed." I mention this because the control box has both NC and NO connections, and you should know which set to use for what type of sensor. The screens come from Imperial Screen Company, Inc. (see Appendices).

Wiring Up

The normally closed magnetic switches are simply wired in series, one after the other, as shown in Fig. 10-15. You should use 22 gauge two-conductor wire for connecting the switches. When you cut the wire, you will notice that one wire is colored silver, the other copper. Use the copper wire for the positive loop (Fig. 10-15) to connect the switches as shown. The silver wire should be used as the negative loop. Then both wires wind up connected to the normally closed connections in the control box.

Since every control box connection panel is located in a different position, I can't tell you where to make the connections in the box for the protective loop. A typical control box connection panel looks something like Fig. 11-15. The normally closed magnetic contact switches are connected to the two terminals marked "Intrus. N/C" at the upper left of the drawing. Running the positive and negative sides of the loop together makes troubleshooting a lot easier. You could run just the positive loop as a single wire from the battery and from

Fig. 9-15 / *Window screen for jalousie-type windows has thin wires that trigger alarm when cut, and mercury "tilt" switch hidden in bottom of frame.*

Fig. 10-15 / *Typical wiring diagram for hard-wire alarm system. "A" is alarm bell or siren, "B' is alarm relay; "C" is bell battery; "D" is key-lock-function switch; "E" is intrusion-loop relay and circuitry; "F", magnetic contact switches; "G", switch magnets; "H", intrusion-loop battery.*

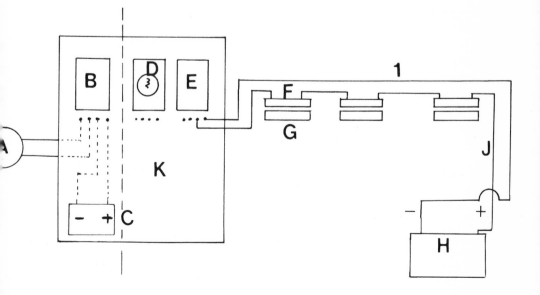

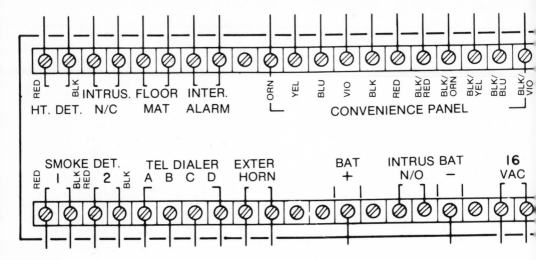

Fig. 11-15 / *Typical connection panel in control box. Note connections for intrusion switches, fire and smoke sensors, floor mats, telephone dialer, external horn, and battery inputs.*

switch to switch and finally to the control box. You would then run just one wire directly from the battery to the control box for the negative loop. You may save wire and time that way, but this shortcut could be a very long cut indeed if you had a defective switch or open circuit someplace caused by a broken wire. One mark of a quality installation is the dual wiring job with the positive and negative loops side by side.

In Fig. 10-15, you will see that the positive intrusion loop starts at the battery and goes from switch to switch and to the control box. The negative loop goes from the negative side of the battery to the control box, paralleling the positive loop (but not, of course, connected to it; the word "parallel" in this instance means "next to"). The positive loop wire is "J", the negative loop is "I"

The switch is "F" and the magnet used with each switch is "G". The intrusion loop six-volt lantern battery is "H".

Going to the control box, you will note that it is divided by a vertical dotted line (for convenience in this explanation only). The right hand side of the dotted line contains the control box key switch "D" and the circuitry and relays "E". When a switch opens (a door or window opens) and the system is "armed" a relay "locks on" and causes the bell or siren to sound. Closing the switch won't cut off the alarm because now the relay itself is "latched" and can't be shut off except by the control box key switch or automatic shut-off timer.

The bell (or siren) battery is located inside the control box, where it is (or should be) under lock and key to keep a burglar from disconnecting the wires to the bell and thus turning it off.

The intrusion-loop battery should be located as far away from the control box as possible. It should preferably be hidden in a closet. However, disconnecting a wire from this battery will cause the alarm to sound, because the protective loop circuit will be broken. The intrusion relay, held open by current from the intrusion-loop battery, will close, causing the bell "latching" relay to lock into position and start the bell clanging.

Floor-mat switches, being normally open, should be connected in parallel to the NO contacts in the control box. In Fig. 10-15, these are located at the lower right. Instructions for some control boxes say to connect the NO contacts across the intrusion loop. That is, one wire from the floor-mat switch goes to the negative-intrusion loop, the other to the positive loop. Then when a person steps on the floor switch, the momentary closure of that switch triggers the alarm.

Panic switches are NO devices and should be wired in parallel to the NO connections in the control box. Locate panic switches in the kitchen, master bedroom, front door hallway, and any other place you feel you need one. To

trigger the alarm, just press the panic button. The alarm can't be reset from the panic switch, however. You will have to go to the control box and use the key switch to do this.

You can install remote-alarm-system key-operated reset switches in convenient places around the house. They will save a lot of running to the control box if you need to reset the alarm system often, as you probably will if you have children who cause a lot of false alarms. If the control box has provisions for a remote-reset switch, it will also have instructions as to how to wire this switch. You will need four-conductor wire for this connection. When more than one remote-reset switch is used, connect them in parallel. Also, if you use remote-reset switches, you should also use tamper switches with them. Otherwise a burglar could remove the cover of the switch and

Fig. 12-15 / *Smoke and fire sensors should be connected in parallel, as shown. Some control boxes do not require end-of-line resistor. Smoke sensor also requires power input from control box.*

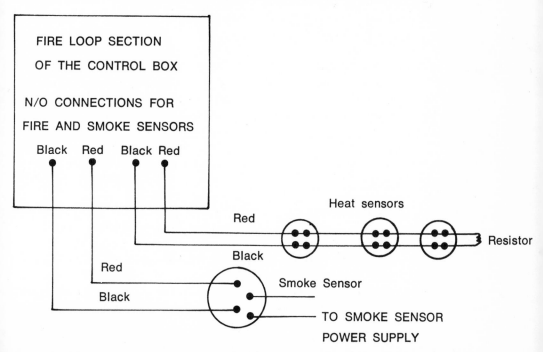

do his own "reset" by jumping the wires. You should find very explicit wiring instructions with any control box, because the alarm installer usually needs them as much as you do.

Wiring Fire Sensors

As you will see from Fig. 12-15, the heat sensors and smoke sensors are wired in parallel to the control box. Smoke sensors, in addition, require a power supply which should be available at the control box panel. For example, Fig. 11-15 shows heat-sensor connections at the upper left of the panel. The smoke-detector inputs and power-supply outputs are at the lower left of the same panel.

I won't get into the various types of heat sensors here because this subject is thoroughly treated in Chapter Seventeen. I will say that these sensors detect heat at a specific temperature. Living zones usually use 135° F. and attics 190° F. heat sensors. Rate-of-rise sensors detect a rise in temperature above a certain speed, usually 15° per minute, as well as at a specific temperature and will thus respond to a flash fire where heat builds up rapidly. Rate-of-rise sensors should be installed in the kitchen, basement, and garage. The pros and cons of photoelectric versus ionization smoke sensors are also detailed in Chapter Seventeen, and before you select one or the other I urge you to read that chapter.

Where to Install Fire Sensors

First you have to know that all heat sensors (Fig. 13-15) have an effective range of coverage of a radius of fifteen feet out from the sensor. Imagine a circle, with the sensor (which is about

2½ inches round) in the middle. If you had a piece of string fifteen feet long, with a piece of chalk at one end and with the other end fastened to the center of the sensor, you could mark a circle on the ceiling by walking around the room with the string tight. If you did this you would see that in a thirty-square-foot room the corners would not be protected. In a smaller room, say 20 feet x 20 feet, you would have complete coverage if the heat sensor were centrally located, as at left in Fig. 12-15. For a 25 foot x 20 foot room, you would need two heat sensors, located to give overlapping coverage. If you put one heat sensor in a room 20 feet x 20 feet over in one corner, as at right in Fig. 14-15, you would have an uncovered area in which heat could rise past the alarm point of the sensor without triggering an alarm. These little sensors are well under $5 each, and if you install them properly, you won't have blind spots.

If you have an open-beam ceiling, locate heat sensors *under* the beams, as shown in Fig. 15-15, at ten-foot intervals for overlapping coverage. Avoid placing heat sensors on walls. In rooms with cathedral (sloping) ceilings, heat tends to concentrate at the apex of the slope. In such a room heat sensors should be placed lower, on the bottom of a cross beam or joist.

Do not place heat sensors near air-conditioning or ventilating outlets, because air from these outlets can "mask" any heat rise from a fire.

Locating Smoke Sensors

Smoke and fume sensors "sniff" the air continuously and trigger the fire alarm if smoke or other harmful fumes reach it. These sensors (see Chapter

Fig. 13-15 / *This heat sensor triggers the fire alarm when it senses air temperatures at 135° F. It automatically resets when temperature drops below 135° F.*

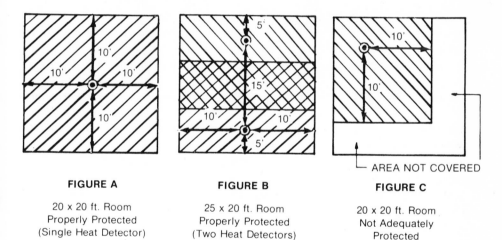

FIGURE A

20 x 20 ft. Room
Properly Protected
(Single Heat Detector)

FIGURE B

25 x 20 ft. Room
Properly Protected
(Two Heat Detectors)

FIGURE C

20 x 20 ft. Room
Not Adequately
Protected

Fig. 14-15 / *One incorrect and two correct locations for fire (heat) sensors. "A" and "B" show correct locations. "C" shows an area not covered and so not protected.*

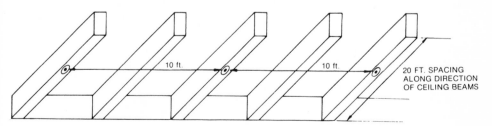

Fig. 15-15 / *Heat sensors for an open-beam room should be located on bottom of beams as shown.*

Fig. 16-15 /   *Test smoke sensors every month by blowing smoke at them.*

17) should be installed in the basement stairwell, in stairwells to upper floors, in upper-floor hallways in the bedroom area and in the living room.

Do not install them near heating and air-conditioning outlets or near fans or open windows where the products of combustion can be driven away or diluted. You want the smoke and fume sensor to measure any products of combustion or build-up of potentially lethal fumes long before they reach the killing point. Ionization-type smoke and fume detectors should not be installed in the kitchen, garage, shop, or any other area where fumes normally are created. Otherwise you will be plagued with false fire alarms every time you cook, or drive into the garage or do any soldering or brazing or welding in the basement workshop.

Test All Sensors Before Installing

Nothing in this world is completely perfect. This includes security products. You will save a lot of time and trouble-shooting headaches if you test every intrusion, smoke, and fire sensor before installing it. Check magnetic contact switches, floor-mat switches, and panic buttons. Use the ohmmeter part of the volt-ohm-ammeter, or a test lamp and battery, to make sure contacts open and close properly. You should also hear a slight click as the magnet leaves and is brought near the magnetic switches. Test smoke sensors right after installation (Fig. 16-15) and monthly thereafter.

You may find that the smoke sensor will trigger the fire alarm if you have a party with a lot of guests who smoke. That's one way to inform your guests how you feel about smoking. Certainly if the smoke sensor causes the fire alarm to sound off when the room gets full of tobacco smoke, it is only doing its job in giving you early warning of a potentially dangerous situation.

Running Wire

Because residential frame construction varies somewhat from decade to decade and framing-type to framing-type around the country, it is not practical to cover all the variations in this chapter. I can give you some practical hints about running wire that will be of value, though.

You can use electrician's fish wire to pull the snared ends of wire through stud spaces in walls, as shown in Fig. 17-15.

It may be easier to fish wire up through the attic and run it down through studs to individual doors and

FISHING WIRES AND CABLE HOOKUP

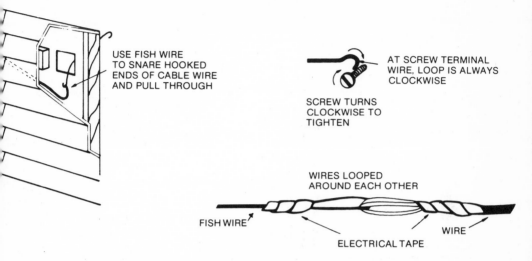

USE FISH WIRE
TO SNARE HOOKED
ENDS OF CABLE WIRE
AND PULL THROUGH

AT SCREW TERMINAL
WIRE, LOOP IS ALWAYS
CLOCKWISE

SCREW TURNS
CLOCKWISE TO
TIGHTEN

WIRES LOOPED
AROUND EACH OTHER

FISH WIRE

WIRE

ELECTRICAL TAPE

Fig. 17-15 / *Use this electrician's fish wire to pull alarm-system wires through walls, behind plaster or plasterboard and between studs and joists.*

COURTESY BOWMAR, INC.

windows, as shown in Fig. 18-15. Or it may be simpler to go up through the basement, if it does not have a finished ceiling (Fig. 19-15).

I can recommend two books that will help in fishing wire through a residential frame house. One is *Wood-Frame House Construction,* U.S. Department of Agriculture, Forest Service, Agriculture Handbook No. 73, 1970, $2.60, and *Wiring Simplified,* by H. P. Richter, 1975 (rev.), Park Lane Publishing, Inc., P.O. Box 8527, Minneapolis, Minnesota 55408, $1.39. The first book gives details on frame construction, the second on wire pulling. The Richter book covers only 110-volt wiring, but alarm-system wiring must follow the same route to get to doors and windows.

Mounting the Outside Noisemaker

To keep a criminal from defeating the alarm system by cutting wires to the bell or siren, you should mount whichever one you use as high as possible on the outside wall of the house. A simple way would be to install the noisemaker just underneath or, better yet, above the attic window.

As noted in Chapter Fourteen, the horn or bell should be in a weatherproofed steel cabinet, with louvered slot openings on the outside door facing downward and on the inside door facing upward. This keeps out the rain and resists poking with sharp objects and filling the metal enclosure with styrofoam spray and other gunk. There should be no visible wiring; all wires should come through the wall. The box should be tamper-switch protected on the back of the housing, between the box and the wall, and on the inside cover (Fig. 7-14).

Attic Installation

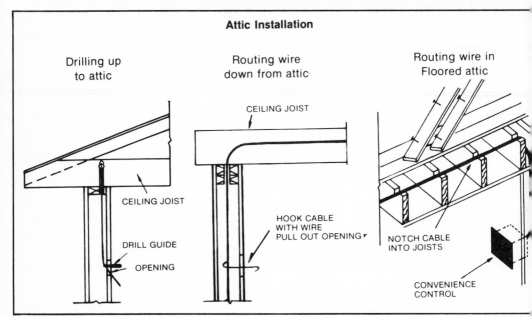

Drilling up to attic

CEILING JOIST

DRILL GUIDE

OPENING

Routing wire down from attic

CEILING JOIST

HOOK CABLE WITH WIRE PULL OUT OPENING

Routing wire in Floored attic

NOTCH CABLE INTO JOISTS

CONVENIENCE CONTROL

Basement Installation

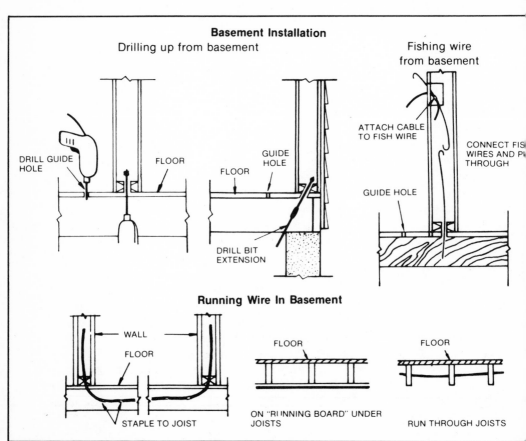

Drilling up from basement

DRILL GUIDE HOLE

FLOOR

FLOOR

GUIDE HOLE

DRILL BIT EXTENSION

Fishing wire from basement

ATTACH CABLE TO FISH WIRE

CONNECT FIS WIRES AND P THROUGH

GUIDE HOLE

Running Wire In Basement

WALL

FLOOR

STAPLE TO JOIST

FLOOR

ON "RUNNING BOARD" UNDER JOISTS

FLOOR

RUN THROUGH JOISTS

◄
(Above)
Fig. 18-15 / *Alarm system wires can be pulled up to attic and dropped down to individual doors and windows.*
COURTESY BOWMAR, INC.

◄
(Below)
Fig. 19-15 / *Or alarm system wires can be pulled up to windows and doors from basement, if basement ceiling is not finished.*
COURTESY BOWMAR, INC.

Troubleshooting

Here are typical problems that crop up in burglar-alarm systems and their causes and solutions:

Problem: Alarm sounds when system is switched on at the control box. Exit/entry delay does not delay.

Cause: An open circuit or defective magnetic switch.

Solution: Check all switch connections. Check wiring between control box and battery, between control box and switches, and between switches with your test lamp or ohmmeter. Disconnect one lead to intrusion-circuit battery first. Check operation of all switches, make sure magnet is not too far away from switch.

Problem: Intermittent false alarms. Could be on either intrusion or fire circuits.

Cause: A loose connection or broken wire that "swings" open and closed at irregular intervals. This situation is known as a "swinger" and can be infuriating to locate because it is not always defective in that it works sometimes, and at other times it does not.

Solution: Check all wiring and connections for integrity immediately following a false alarm. You may find a

broken wire inside apparently unbroken wire cover insulation.

Problem: Alarm does not go off on test mode, or when exit/entry delay has expired.

Cause: No voltage to control box or to bell or siren.

Solution: Check bell battery and intrusion-circuit battery, and fuse box on circuit-to-control box stepdown transformer. Replace defective batteries. Another solution would be to use gel-cell batteries and automatic battery charger so batteries would not go dead.

Problem: Fire alarm sounds and cannot be reset.

Cause: A closed or short circuit in the fire-alarm loop.

Solution: Check each fire and smoke sensor for shorted wiring. Use test lamp or ohmmeter. Disconnect one lead of fire loop from control box before testing. If you do not find a shorted wire, check control box fire-alarm relay and connections. Do not attempt repairs on any part of the control box. Instead, remove module, if removable, or return entire control box to dealer for repair or replacement.

Locating the Inside Siren

To make sure you and a burglar both hear the alarm signal or that you are alerted out of a sound sleep to a fire alarm, you should have a loud siren inside the house.

The inside noisemaker should be located where you will be sure to hear it. I would suggest over the front door, aimed at the stairway to an upper level. Some control boxes, including those of

RECOMMENDED BELLS

Manufacturer*	Model No.	db	Tamperproof Metal Housing	UL	Bell Volts Size	DC	Drain (Mils.)	Approx. Cost
Thomas Ind.	KBB-910-6	106	Yes	Yes	10"	6	350	$48
Alarm Device	AB	NA	Yes	Yes	10"	6-12	350	62

RECOMMENDED SIRENS

Manufacturer*	Model No.	db	Tamperproof Metal Housing	UL	Bell Volts Size	DC	Drain (Mils.)	Approx. Cost
NAPCO	ESB	100	Yes	No		6-12	NA	95
Kolin Ind.	ES-1100	122	No	No		12	1.6 (Amps)	94.50

* Please see Appendices for manufacturers' addresses.

ultrasonic and microwave residential systems, have a siren integral with them. As I said in Chapter Fourteen, a control box with a siren simply leads a burglar directly to it. If he can find the control box he may be able to defeat it. So if your control box has a built-in siren, disconnect the siren and install one someplace else, far from the control box.

Recommended Bells and Sirens

Any bell or siren should be loud enough to be heard for blocks. If used inside the house it should be so loud as to be near the threshold of pain.

Here are a few comparisons of sound, to give you an idea as to the various ratings of bells and sirens. First, though, the sound-level outputs of bells and horns should meet Underwriters' Laboratories requirements. The UL standard sound-level-measuring method measures sound levels at ten feet from the device in outside air conditions. Remember too that sound level falls off rapidly in intensity with distance from the siren or bell. For example a device that emits 137.2 decibels (a unit of sound measurement) will emit only 99 decibels ten feet away.

A noisy subway is about 120 decibels (db), an air hammer chopping up concrete is about 97 db; the threshold of pain is between 120 and 130 db.

Recommended Control Boxes

Table 1-15 gives my recommendations for control boxes. Of all the features listed, you should have as a minimum:

• Separate alarm sounds for fire and burglary.
• Automatic alarm shut-off and reset.
• Exit/entry delay.
• Fire alarm override that sounds even though the burglar alarm is on. The burglar sound should shut off and the fire alarm should take precedence.
• Panic signal override no matter what mode the system is in.
• Test capability, preferably without turning on the outside siren or bell.
• Error resistance and false-alarm resistance.
• Key-lock switch on control box.

TABLE 1-15
CONTROL BOX COMPARATIVE ANALYSIS

Feature*	AMF 2800	Kwikset 390	API 2008	NAPCO BFC 200	Pyrotronics CRC	Rittenhouse S 7619	Sentrol 1734	Thomas T-150
Dual alarm sound	Yes	No	Yes	Yes	Yes	No	No	No
Alarm shut-off and auto reset	Yes	0	0	Yes	0	No	No	No
Outside and Inside alarms	Yes	No	Yes	Yes	Yes	0	No	No
Exit/entry delay module	Yes	Yes	Yes	0	Yes	Yes	Yes	No
Supervised circuitry	Yes	Yes	Yes	Yes	Yes	Yes	Yes	No
UL Listed	Yes	No	No	No	Yes	No	No	No
Telephone dialer output	Yes	No	0	Yes	No	No	No	No
Fire-alarm override	Yes	No	Yes	Yes	Yes	No	Yes	Yes
Panic-signal override	Yes	Yes	Yes	Yes	Yes	Yes	Yes	Yes
Test capability	Yes	Yes	Yes	Yes	Yes	Yes	Yes	Yes
Error resistance	Yes	NA	NA	NA	Yes	NA	NA	NA
Solid-state circuitry	Yes	Yes	No	No	Yes	Yes	Yes	Yes
False-alarm immunity (static)	Yes	NA	NA	NA	NA	NA	NA	NA
Key-lock mode switch on panel	Yes	Yes	Yes	Yes	No	No	Yes	No
Outside status light	Yes	No	No	No	No	No	No	No
Battery and charger backup	Yes	Yes	0	Yes	0	Yes	Yes	0
Exit delay bypass	Yes	Yes	Yes	Yes	Yes	Yes	Yes	Yes
Cost (approximate)	$423	$60	$160	$150	$350	$100	$100	$80

* Please see Appendices for manufacturers' addresses.

A Word About Magnetic Switches

The right contacts are just as important in alarm systems as they are in life. The switches should be sealed against dirt and moisture that would cause an open-circuit fault.

I prefer the sealed reed type of switch for use on doors that are used a lot. These switches can take hundreds of thousands of openings and closings without failure. One such switch is made by Silent Knight (Model 804) and is rated for 50 million openings and closings. If your door opened and closed one thousand times a day, this switch would last nearly 136 years!

If the switch must operate in a corrosive atmosphere (New York City, Chicago, Los Angeles, aboard ship, or in seaside cities, for example), I would use a sealed mercury switch such as that made by Preferred Security Components. An excellent UL-listed mechanical-action magnetic switch is A.P.I.'s No. 139 with silver-coated contacts. Other excellent switches are made by Conrac and United Security Products, who make a wide-gap model (No. U-402) for garage doors.

If you have a high-security problem, don't use any of the above switches because they can be defeated by "jumping" their terminals with a wire. For these applications, as in banks, currency exchanges, and jewelry stores, use a switch that prevents shunting defeat. A good one is made by Kidde. This is their No. DR-850 balanced magnetic switch that costs around $42 *each*. This ultra-high-security switch triggers the alarm if an attempt is made to defeat it by jumping it or by using another magnet.

How Much Should You Spend?

The cost of a good burglar-alarm system for the same building can vary from as little as $450 to well over $2,500. Prices depend on what you want and the extent of your security exposure.

For the average three-bedroom home with attached garage you should figure about $850 for the equipment and another $600 to $800 for installation (unless you do the job yourself).

If you want all the wires and switches concealed, add another $250. A telephone dialer will add yet another $250. Remember that all these prices are approximate; an alarm system in your particular building may cost less or a good deal more, depending on its construction and local ordinances. Add another $250 for smoke and heat sensors.

About Buying Equipment

A few of the burglar- and fire-alarm equipment manufacturers and very few of the wholesalers will sell direct to the consumer. Manufacturers sell to wholesalers only or, in some cases, to individual alarm installers. Wholesalers sell only to alarm installers. A very few mail-order firms cater to the individual consumer who wants only one system for his own home or building. The direct-to-you retail firms are listed in the Appendices separately from the major wholesale distributors and the major manufacturers. Most of the direct-sale distributors furnish catalogs with list prices. You can usually also buy equipment from individual alarm installers.

In larger cities you will find small specialty firms that cater to the do-it-yourself alarm installer. The countermen in these retail outlets can sometimes be of help in equipment selection and installation. Check the yellow pages under burglar alarms.

Packaged Systems

Several firms make complete packaged burglar- and fire-alarm systems. The beauty of these systems is that you don't have to worry about whether the individual pieces will be compatible with each other and with the control box. All the engineering and product selection is done for you. If you wish to install such a system, you would do well to consider one of the packaged systems I am about to recommend.

AMF Model 2008. My first choice in a completely integrated, high-quality residential burglar- and fire-alarm system is AMF's Model 2008. The total price of $699 retail list is very competitive with what you would pay if you selected all the components yourself and bought them piecemeal. Furthermore, the AMF system, with its ultra-deluxe control box, is highly reliable and just about as foolproof and childproof and false-alarm resistant as you can get. Table 1-5 gives you most of the features of this system, since they are all built into the control box. Some of the components of this system are shown in Fig. 20-15.

Included in the Model 2008 are the following:

- Master control box
- Remote control with keyswitch to arm or disarm intrusion circuits
- Indoor audio
- Outdoor audio. Both have high sound for actual intrusion, low-level sound for test mode.
- Outdoor indicator. Warns if an intruder has tripped alarm even if

alarm has reset after time delay, and gives other system status from outside the house.
- Three 135° and two 190° heat sensors
- Three door sensors
- Sixteen window sensors
- One end-of-line resistor
- Two warning labels

For another $90 you can get a matched smoke detector, which I urge you to do, since as I discuss in Chapter Seventeen in more detail, smoke and other chemical fumes from a fire can kill you long before the fire gets to you. The smoke detector AMF uses is the ionization type, which is the most sensitive and which will pick up other dangerous fumes such as natural gas from a leaking pipe line.

AMF's system comes with complete installation instructions and system-operating instructions you should be able to follow if you can do simple wiring, such as stringing together hi-fi components. There's actually no more mystique to following wiring instructions than there is to baking good bread. I do both and my philosophy is that if you can read you should be able to do both. That's what installation instructions and recipes are for.

If you need more door or window sensors or more fire sensors, you can buy them from AMF for about what you would pay for them from a local or mail-order alarm supply house.

Rittenhouse. A complete system with the same number of magnetic contacts as AMF costs around $235. But, as Table 1-15 shows, this system has no provisions for a fire loop so fire and smoke sensors cannot be used; there is no built-in provision for dialer or other acces-

Fig. 20-15 / *This high-quality residential burglar- and fire-alarm system is made by AMF Monitoralert Security Systems. The system includes everything you need to install burglar- and fire-alarm equipment. Size of package varies according to size of house.*

sory output. The key-lock shunt switch that Rittenhouse suggests be installed outside the house I would use on the control panel and modify this panel so the key-lock controls its function or mode settings. As it is now, the panel can turn the system on or off with pushbuttons, which means a crook need only run to the panel to turn off the alarm. If he has studied alarm systems at all, he will know Rittenhouse recommends the control panel be installed in the kitchen. Still, the Rittenhouse system is an entirely adequate burglar alarm, if you are willing to do without the fire protection and the other features built into the AMF system. For complete names and addresses of suppliers, please refer to Appendix.

Thomas Industries. An integrated fire/burglar-alarm system with the same number of fire and intrusion sensors as AMF's (but not with the same system features, per Table 1-15) costs around $350. You can also buy extra door and window sensors from Thomas, and a smoke detector for about $85. Various remote controls and panic switches are also available, and Thomas will even sell you all the wire you require, color coded and sized for the various uses you need, such as entry, fire, transformer, horn, et cetera. Since these wire sizes are basic to all alarm and fire systems, I will run these past you:

- Window and door sensor connections to control box: No. 22 gauge wire
- Fire sensor connections: No. 18/2 wire
- Horn: 18/2 gauge
- Remote control: 22/6 wire
- Bell: 20 gauge/2

16

ALL ABOUT WIRELESS BURGLAR AND FIRE ALARMS FOR YOUR HOME AND PLACE OF BUSINESS

Easy to install and take with you when you move, wireless alarms are ideal to protect existing homes, apartments, house trailers, and remote buildings such as greenhouses, garages, barns, storage sheds, and hangars.

A WIRELESS ALARM system is just that. No wires to snake through walls or tuck laboriously behind baseboard, no time-consuming and costly installation. Installation is a matter of a few hours for most systems, instead of a few days. Buildings up to four hundred feet away from the receiver can be included in the burglar- and fire-alarm protective system, as well as the main building.

Intrusion or fire sensors for wireless alarms are the same as for the hardwire system described in Chapters Fourteen and Fifteen. The only difference is

that instead of running wires from sensors to a central control box, each sensor is attached to a tiny radio transmitter, about as big as a pack of long cigarettes (Fig. 1-16).

When the guarded entrance is opened by an intruder, or a fire sensor is activated by heat or smoke, the sensor causes the transmitter to send a signal to the receiver, a "latching" relay locks the alarm, the siren or bell, to an "On" mode, and merely closing the protected entrance will not shut off the alarm until the alarm delay period is over (Fig.

Fig. 1-16 / *This little transmitter is hardly bigger than a package of king-size cigarettes. Attached to the magnetic-contact intrusion sensor, right, it sends a signal to a receiver if the sensor contacts move. Button on transmitter, lower left, is used to test transmitter battery and for panic alarm.*

2-16). In most of these wireless systems the alarm will usually sound for about four minutes, after which it will shut down and reset, ready for the next intruder, or for the one already in the house to leave.

Besides intrusion and fire sensors (Fig. 3-16), many other types of sensing devices can be attached to these little transmitters to sound an alarm for a great many conditions. For example, a transmitter can be attached to a money sensor (Fig. 4-16). In a hold-up situation the cashier can reach into the cash register and pull a pile of bills from the drawer, including the bottom bill which holds open the contacts of the money sensor. At this time the alarm will sound, either silently or loudly, at the option of the user.

Other sensors that can be attached to a transmitter include those that tell you (for example):

- Someone is using the swimming pool (See Chapter Nineteen)
- A thief is trying to steal your motorcycle

- The temperature in a freezer is too high or in a greenhouse is too low
- The water level in a basement or tank has reached a predetermined level
- Fire has broken out in a remote building
- An intruder has busted into a remote building
- Someone is climbing a fence, walking on the lawn, and/or driving up the driveway

You can also wire these transmitters into an existing hard-wire system by using a small auxiliary receiver such as Linear's (see Appendices for address) Model L-61 and wiring *that* to any unused normally closed input on the control box. The L-61 costs around $60. A sensor transmitter and L-61 (Fig. 5-16) receiver can also be used to turn on a dialer, a closed-circuit TV camera, or anything else that uses no more than 500 watts at 110 volts AC (requires Linear L-70 control at $60).

Fig. 2-16 / *Receiver control box accepts signals from fire or intrusion sensors, "locks" the siren or bell on to sound alarm.*

Remote Panic Transmitter

One of the more comforting features of a wireless alarm system is a small panic transmitter (Fig. 6-16) you can carry in pocket, purse, or belt clip. It works . . . well, let's say you're working in the back yard. You look up and there's a threatening-looking character coming at you through the bushes. You push the button on your panic transmitter and instantly the outside siren starts wailing its head off. The intruder is startled at the racket and flees. Or your daughter notices a seedy-looking character loitering in the lobby of the apartment house you live in. No one else is in the lobby so he approaches her and demands she take him upstairs to the apartment. She presses the panic button on the transmitter and the apartment building fills with the wail of the siren. She tells the man what she has done and suggests he'd better take off before the fuzz arrive. He takes her advice.

Hard-wire systems also have panic buttons, but they are fixed in place inside the home and are not portable.

Medical Emergency Alert

The panic transmitter can be tuned to a special receiver, such as Linear's L-61, that activates a two-channel telephone dialer which can automatically send a message to your doctor and to one other person, such as the police or a friend, alerting them to a medical emergency in your home. If you have a heart condition or any other physical problem that could require immediate medical attention, such as signaling device could save your life. It takes almost no effort to press the panic button, and you could call for help from your yard or car if necessary. Chapter Eighteen has more information on dialers. This is not a security alarm but I mention it because this device is a potential lifesaver for thousands.

Zoned Alarms

If the area you wish to protect is too large for one system to cover, as in a school or factory building, you can have receivers strategically located so as to

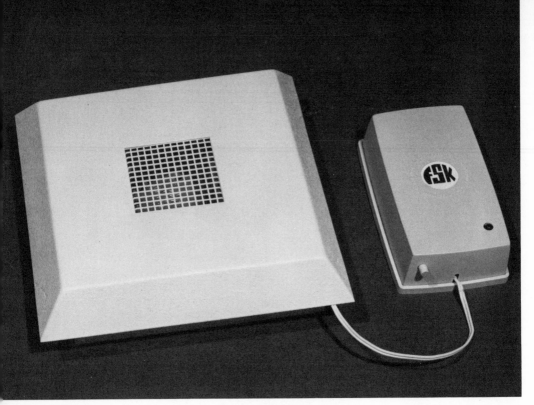

Fig. 3-16 /   *Sensitive smoke detector and transmitter can signal fire in very early stages (see Chapter 17).*

Fig. 4-16 /   *When dollar bill is removed, transmitter signals a silent alarm to a central receiver. Money transmitters like these are used as hold-up alarm in banks and stores.*

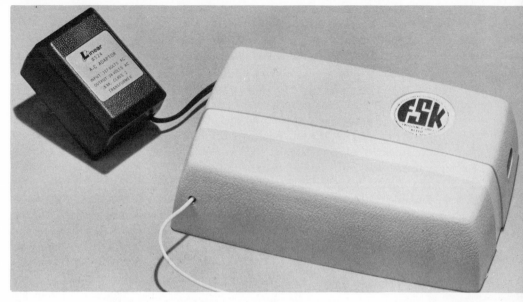

Fig. 5-16 / *Small receiver for use with separate transmitter for special uses, such as with a telephone dialer to send medical emergency message to doctor and/or hospital.*

Fig. 6-16 / *Small portable panic transmitter you can carry in pocket or purse or on belt clip; when button is pushed transmitter signals receiver to sound an instant alarm, even if you have turned receiver to "Off" mode.*

receive a signal from a sensor on a protected opening, a fire sensor, or from a panic transmitter carried by a plant guard. Each receiver can send a signal to a central guard station and activate an annunciator that tells the person monitoring the system which receiver has set off the alarm, and therefore which part of the factory is the trouble spot. Since time is of the essence in catching an intruder, the instant silent signal from a hand-held portable panic button can elicit faster help from the central guard station than would be the case if the plant patrol guard had to go to a fixed location to signal his office.

Transmitter Range

Most wireless-alarm system manufacturers claim about two hundred feet as the maximum distance their equipment will work, and one, Napco, can get up to eight hundred feet with an optional auxiliary extended-range antenna on two of their receivers, the Napco R-1 and the Napco CAU-3.

However, this range is very iffy, and the manufacturers, to do them credit, point out that effective range depends on building construction and receiver location and that range can be as low as fifty feet or as high as two hundred feet. My experience is that it is safe to rely on 50 percent of claimed maximum antenna range.

Installation Tips

Here are a few suggestions that will help you get the most from your wireless alarm system. First, always locate the receiver central to transmitters. Do not locate the receiver behind sheet-metal ductwork or a screen door, since the metal will block radio wave transmission.

Walk-test each sensor location, both intrusion and fire, using a panic transmitter at each location to make sure the receiver gets the signal and turns on the alarm. Check this out before you install the outside alarm so the neighbors stay friendly. (You might let them know what the noise means so if they hear it during the day when you're out, they will call the police.) Then, with the panic transmitter, walk-test the maximum effective distance from outside the house so you know where you can sound the alarm and be sure of a response. If at any sensor location the alarm response is erratic, the distance is very marginal. You should relocate the receiver to a more central location.

Locate all sensors, intrusion and fire, in the same place you would if installing a hard-wire system (see Chapters Fourteen and Fifteen). Try to locate transmitters where you can reach the battery test button on the transmitter (Fig. 1-16) for two reasons; one, so you can test the battery conveniently every two weeks, and, two, so you can use each transmitter as a panic transmitter, since pressing the battery test button activates the transmitter. The better transmitters have a battery test feature, such as a red light on the unit that lights when the test button is pushed to designate an OK battery.

Since transmitters are fairly expensive, around $40 to $60 each, you don't have to use one on each protected opening. For example in a room with several windows you can install magnetic contact sensors and wire them in series to one transmitter, just as hard-wire sensors are wired in series to a control box (Chapter Fifteen).

The difference is that you need be concerned only with running a wire from one window to the next in one room, and not from room-to-room-to-control box. Transmitters are also available for use with either normally open or normally closed sensors. For example, as I noted in Chapter Fifteen, floor-mat sensors are normally open devices, so that when they are stepped on their contacts will close and the alarm will sound.

Interference Protection

A sophisticated crook could (theoretically at least) jam a wireless alarm receiver with spurious signals and so keep it from working. Or if he knew the frequency to which the transmitters and receivers of such a system were tuned, he could, if the system had a remote reset transmitter, hold back an entry alarm by resetting the system.

The better transmitters and receivers of these systems have built-in protection against such clandestine attempts at defeat, as well as protection against stray signals from passing transmitters of aircraft, police, taxi cabs, CB radios, and nearby garage door openers. The better systems use enough frequencies to make it unlikely someone in range of your wireless alarm system would have a duplicate frequency.

For example, the best protection against accidental frequency duplication I have found is Linear's wireless system. This firm uses a Frequency Shift Keyed (FSK) method in which one of two frequencies in the unit is shifted one hundred times per second. The receiver will not operate unless the proper sequence of frequencies is received. By the time this book is printed, Linear should have on the market a better sys-

tem using a digital design in which the basic ultra-high-frequency carrier wave is turned on and off at specific intervals, giving a train of accurately spaced pulses. The receiver must recognize the pulse train as a preprogrammed group and reject any incoming signals not matching this digital pattern. Any combination of eight frequencies will give a choice of over 65,000 separate frequencies, so duplicates are unlikely.

Shortcomings of Wireless Alarms

Wireless alarms are not supervised, and that is their major disadvantage. For example, a battery could go dead in a sensor-connected transmitter and you would never know it. That can't happen on a hard-wire system because it is 110 volt AC connected and has automatic battery back-up if main power fails. This is why it is absolutely vital you check transmitter batteries every few weeks. If this is going to be a problem for you, then you should not install a wireless system. Another point: you could go away on a trip for a few weeks or longer. A transmitter battery may be OK when you test it, but if you forget to test all batteries one could go dead when you're gone, and that's the one opening a burglar could find. What I'm saying is that a wireless system is inherently less reliable than a hard-wire system because there are so many batteries that have to function 100 percent of the time.

On the other hand, a wireless system is one you can take with you when you move, it is easy to install and surely a lot better than no alarm system at all. And it does have the ability to protect outbuildings. I just want you to be aware of the problems basic to these systems, as well as the good points.

Equipment Selection

The quality of a wireless alarm system varies pretty much directly with its cost. The cheaper systems give you bare-bones protection without many of the features I consider desirable and in some cases essential.

Table 1-16 lists wireless system features. You will note that most of them depend on the functions built into the central receiver control box. The table features are numbered. I have elaborated on each feature in the table, by the same number, as follows:

1. One or two frequencies. One frequency means that both burglar and fire alarm transmitters use the same frequency. Thus there is no way you can have a separate audio signal for burglary, and a distinctive, different audio alarm for fire. Yet you should know which is which so you can take the correct action in such an emergency. Two frequencies permit the burglary and fire alarms to have separate sounds.

2, 3, 4. The system will accommodate both burglary- and fire-alarm sensors even with only a single frequency.

5. Panic override sounds the alarm even if the unit is in the "Off" mode or in any other mode.

6. Battery standby switches automatically to battery if the house current (110 volts AC) to the control box should fail.

7. Exit/entry delay gives you time to get out and back in the house and reset the alarm before it sounds.

8. Delay/Instant gives you the choice of exit/entry delay mode for "Day" or "Away" or "Instant" alarm for "Night" protection.

9, 10, 11. Test facilities for transmitter and standby batteries.

12. AC/On light warns you, from outside the house, that the system is armed and you must go fast to the control receiver to reset it before the delay time expires and you have a false alarm. False alarms are a no-no because they adversely condition neighbors and police not to respond, and besides they are annoying to neighbors.

13. On/Off reset key switch on control receiver lets only you, with key, turn alarms on or off or reset the system. Otherwise anybody could go right to the control receiver and turn it off by a push-button switch. This is particularly true if the control receiver has its own horn to lead a burglar right to it. A burglar could also bounce the receiver on the floor, which is why I have my own unit in a steel box, bolted to a shelf, with the key switch on the front of the box. None of the wireless-system manufacturers provide such a box, though.

14, 15, 16. The inside siren is either built into the receiver, or the receiver has an output module to power it. The outside siren also requires a built-in module. An outside bell only requires a voltage source output from the receiver control box. I prefer an outside bell and inside siren located away from the receiver to make it harder to find.

17. Special fire alarm sound tells you that heat or smoke from a fire has

TABLE 1-16

WIRELESS ALARM SYSTEM SELECTION

Manufacturer and Model Number

Feature (See Text)	Linear L-1011A	A.P.I. 2003	A.P.I. 12007	Multi-Emac	Napco R-1	Napco CAU-3	Sears 11	Transcience 400-3
1. Channels	One	Two	One	Two	One	Two	One	One
2. Burglary	Yes	Yes	Yes	Yes	Yes	Yes	Yes	Yes
3. Fire (heat)	Yes	Yes	Yes	Yes	Yes	Yes	Yes	Yes
4. Fire (smoke)	Yes	Yes	Yes	Yes	Yes	No	No	Yes
5. Panic	Yes	Yes	Yes	Yes	Yes	Yes	Yes	Yes
6. Battery Standby	Yes	Yes	Yes	Yes	Yes	Yes	Yes	Yes
7. Exit/Entry	Yes	Yes	Yes	Yes	Yes	Yes	Yes	Yes
8. Delay/Inst.	Yes	Yes	Yes	Yes	No	Yes	No	Yes
9. Burglary Test	Yes	No	Yes	Yes	No	Yes	No	Yes
10. Fire Test	Yes	Yes	Yes	Yes	No	Yes	No	Yes
11. Battery Test	Yes	Yes	No	Yes	No	Yes	Yes	Yes
12. AC/On Light	Yes	No	No	No	No	Yes	Yes	Yes
13. On/Off Key	No	Yes	Yes	Yes	No	Yes	Yes	Yes
14. Inside Horn	Yes	Yes	Yes	Yes	Yes	Yes	Yes	Yes
15. Outside Horn	Yes	Yes	No	Yes	Yes	Yes	No	Yes
16. Outside Bell	Yes	Yes	No	Opt.	Yes	Yes	No	Yes
17. Fire Sound	No	Yes	No	Yes	No	Yes	No	No
18. Dialer Connect	Yes	No	No	Opt.	Yes	Yes	Yes	Yes
19. AC/110 Module	No	Yes	No	Opt.	No	No	No	No
20. Rf Protection	Yes	Yes	Yes	Yes	Yes	Yes	Yes	Yes
21. Alarm Cut-off	Yes	No	No	Yes	Yes	Yes	No	Yes
22. Range (Ft.)	50-150	50-150	50-150	50-150	200-800	200	150	200
23. Burglary	Yes	Yes	Yes	Yes	Yes	Yes	Yes	Yes
24. Fire (heat)	Yes	Yes	Yes	No	Yes	Yes	Yes	No
25. Fire (smoke)	Yes	No	No	No	Yes	Yes	No	No
26. Panic/Emerg.	Yes	Yes	Yes	No	Yes	Yes	No	No
27. Money	Yes	No	No	No	Yes	Yes	No	No
28. Audible/Silent	No	No	No	No	No	Yes	No	No
29. Cost, Receiver	$558	$250	$270	NA	$170	$300	$70	$270
30. Cost, Transmitter	$39	$39	$39	NA	$57	$57	$17	$40

set off the alarm. Sirens can be steady or warbling for burglary, yelping or pulsating for fire. A bell can be steady for burglary, intermittent for fire. This requires dual channel receiver.

18. Dialer-connect module lets you attach a dialer (see Chapter Eighteen) that can automatically phone police, fire department, or, in case of medical emergency, your doctor.

19. AC/110 is usually an optional attachment that turns on lights, CCTV or any device using no more than 500 watts at 110 volts AC.

20. Interference protection built-in against system compromise from outside radio-frequency jamming or false-alarm trigger from stray radio signals.

21. Automatic alarm cut-off and reset. A built-in feature that shuts off alarm after time period, usually four minutes, and resets system to "armed" mode. Some cities require this feature.

22. Transmitter range in feet between transmitter and receiver. Use 50 percent of claimed maximum distance to be on safe side.

Distance varies with building construction.

23, 24, 25, 26, 27. Transmitters are available for these conditions. The money clip is for hold-up protection.

28. Audible/Silent alarm gives you a choice of audible local alarm or silent alarm if the system is connected to a police station or guard service. An audible local alarm is a "must" for residential use; silent alarm is for where no lives are at stake and where police can respond quickly to catch criminal in the act.

29. Costs are approximate retail, subject to change. Transmitter costs are average for different types of same make.

Table 1-16 that follows is keyed, as noted, to the above explanation of each item. Please refer back to this keyed explanation as you compare each make, so you know what you are buying. I can state that I have used the Linear equipment and it is excellent, with the one exception of no key switch on the control receiver. You can rewire the unit to install your own key switch, though, or your alarm supplier can do it for you.

17

ALL ABOUT FIRE (AND SMOKE AND FUME) ALARMS THAT CAN SAVE YOUR LIFE!

More people die at night, in their sleep, from invisible gases and smoke from beginning fires than from open flames. Here's how to protect yourself from this major hazard . . .

IT WAS THREE O'CLOCK in the morning. A lighted cigarette, carelessly disposed of, had dropped into a sofa in the living room four hours earlier. For these four hours the fire had at first smoldered. During this time fumes began to build up. As poisonous hydro-cyanic-acid and carbon monoxide fumes began to accumulate in the house, the sleeping family acquired a tolerance for the odors and so did not awaken. Nor did they ever awaken, because finally fumes reached a deadly concentration which killed them in their sleep. Had the fumes not been the lethal agent, the fire would eventually have reached the "flashover" stage where heat build-up causes open

flames. At that point the fume-drugged family would have had only minutes or even seconds to get out of the house before it turned into a flaming inferno.

When I mention building up a tolerance for the fumes, what I mean is the kind of experience you have after being outside in the fresh air and then walking into a smoke-filled cocktail-party room. At first the fumes are strong, but in a few moments you become used to them and the smoke is not so objectionable. My mother used to make sauerkraut, and I can tell you even the smell of boiling vinegar disappears after you are exposed to it for ten minutes or so.

A study by the National Fire Protective Association revealed that most fatal residential fires occur during sleeping hours. The study also showed that discovery of the fire is delayed and bodily reaction time to discovery is slow. Under the most optimum conditions, with a noncombustible interior finish and closed bedroom doors, occupants had only twelve minutes between ignition of the fire and lethal build-up of fumes and open flames. With a combustible interior finish and open bedroom doors the occupants had only two minutes between the ignition of the fire and the build-up of lethal conditions. The study also noted that once open flames show, they spread 1,100 percent faster in seconds.

Now for the good news. Only 6,600 Americans will have died in residential fires by year-end 1976, out of a total of twelve thousand annual fire-related fatalities. There are around 300,000 serious burn cases annually in the U.S.A. The total dollar value of fire losses is around $3.1 billion annually.

In Chapters Fourteen, Fifteen and Sixteen we discussed how to install smoke, fume, and heat detectors, so I won't repeat that information here. But I do want to elaborate just for a moment on these three types of sensors.

Smoke Sensors

Smoke sensors are based on one of two principles. The photoelectric type uses the principle of scattering of a light beam by smoke particles. When smoke occurs their tiny particles change the intensity of transmitted light, which causes the alarm to sound. The better photoelectric sensors pick up changes of obscuration of only 1 to 1.8 percent and so meet Underwriters' Laboratories requirements.

Another type of smoke sensor uses a very minute amount of radioactive substance to ionize the air around the sensing element to make the air electrically conductive. Smoke and other fumes reduce the amount of current flow in the sensing chamber and so the alarm sounds.

The photoelectric smoke sensor is far more sensitive to smoke than the ionization type of sensor, and hence can be used in the kitchen. This is also because the photoelectric unit does not pick up and react to other products of combustion such as cooking odors, or fumes from a self-cleaning oven in the cleaning cycle.

There are many lethal products of combustion other than plain smoke, such as those mentioned above, including hydrogen sulfide, hydrogen cyanide, prussic acid, ammonia fumes, and other emanations from rubber, plastics, wood, wool, cotton, furniture, wall coverings, clothing, and paint. The ionization-type sensor will smell these invisible particles and alert you to them long before they build up to lethal concentrations.

The photoelectric sensor, based on the principle of light obscuration, requires cleaning every month or so to prevent false alarms and to make sure the unit responds quickly. The ionization sensor requires cleaning less often, about twice a year.

Both types of sensors come three ways: totally self-contained, with built-in loud horn and battery powered; with built-in horn and 110 volt AC powered and with built-in horn, and wired to a central burglar- and fire-alarm system. The latter, wired to an alarm system, is by far the most reliable because when the sensor is triggered the very loud inside horn plus the outside horn or bell will be sure to wake you out of a sound sleep. But if you have just the self-contained model, either battery or 110 volt AC powered, and it sounds the alarm in the kitchen, basement, or garage, and your bedroom doors are closed and perhaps you are sleeping soundly, you may well not hear the alarm from so far away, at least not soon enough. If you have a 110-volt AC unit and the main power fails, you have no protection. The better battery-operated units have a low-sound-level beeper that warns you for as long as seven to ten days that the battery should be replaced. Never buy a smoke or fume battery-powered sensor without this feature. Batteries should last at least a year.

Table 1-17 lists a number of smoke and fume sensors and their features and prices. Since both photoelectric and ionization sensors have their own best applications, I would use both; the smoke sensor in the basement and kitchen, ionization type in the garage and bedroom hallways and living room.

A Word About Arson

Before going on to heat sensors, you should know that one reason for an increasing number of fires each year is arson. Arson has been categorized as the nation's fastest-growing crime, with 10 to 30 percent of all building fire loss attributable to arson. In one year, for example, there were 1,600 cases of proved arson in a one-square-mile area of Chicago's Woodlawn district. California was plagued by some one hundred bombings a month just a few years ago. No question about it, the crazies are out in force these days. Arson is getting to be a component of burglary, for no apparent reason other than sheer viciousness. Given our national priorities, I see little hope of curbing such crime and its

root causes. Electing people on a law-and-order platform has done nothing to change anything; in fact crime in cities such as Philadelphia has gone up under such a regime.

I wish I had an answer; all I can offer are good locks, burglar and fire alarms, and police dogs until a societally effective solution to crime is found, if one exists.

The Department of Housing and Urban Development (H.U.D.) seems to have recognized the facts of life of arson and crime by now requiring H.U.D.- and F.H.A.-insured single and multifamily dwellings to have at least one smoke detector in each living unit located near a sleeping room.

For the Hard of Hearing

If you have impaired hearing, one model smoke and fume sensor comes with a very loud 110-decibel horn. This is BRK's model SS74A combined with the external model BRK RH518A horn.

For Travelers

If you travel a lot, I recommend you take one of the battery-powered ionization smoke and fume detectors with you. You can hang such a unit on the wall or place it high up on a dresser top, where it will give you advance warning of deadly fumes creeping into the room from outside, or being generated by smoldering fumes inside the room. The average motel or hotel room furnishings are, unfortunately, too often highly combustible. TV sets can cause a fire if they are the type that light up instantly; the guest next door may have carelessly thrown a lighted cigarette into a paper-filled receptacle; a fire can break out from any one of a thousand causes.

TABLE 1-17

SMOKE AND FUME SENSOR EVALUATION

MAKE AND MODEL *

FEATURE	BRK SS717 SS	BRK SS711M	BRK SS74A	Pyr-A-Larm FB-1	Pyrotector 3040RC	Elan S-16	Elan S-14	SCAN SC-500	Pyrotronics DI-7
TYPE	Ionization	Ionization	Ionization	Ionization	Photo-electric	Photo-electric	Photo-electric	Photo-electric	Ionization
Integral Horn	Yes (85 db)	No	Yes (110 db)	Yes (85 db)	No	No	No	No	No
Power Source	Battery	12 VDC	Battery	Battery	6–9 volts DC	12 volts DC	12 volts DC	12 volts DC	12 volts DC
Low Battery Alarm	Yes	Not needed	Yes	Yes	Not needed	Not needed	Not needed	Not needed	Not needed
Integral Heat Sensor	Yes	No	No	No	Optional (135°)	No	Yes (135° & rate of rise)	No	No
UL Rated	Yes	Yes	Yes	Yes	Yes	No	No	Yes	Yes
Louder Horn Option	Yes	Not needed	No	No	Not needed	Not needed	No	Not needed	Not needed
Visual Alarm Indicator	Yes	Not needed	Yes	No	Not needed	Not needed	No	Not needed	Not needed
For use with alarm systems	No	Yes	No	No	Yes	Yes	Yes	Yes	Yes
Area Protected † (Square Feet)	1000	1000	900	900	900	2500	2500	900	900
Dialer Output	No	No	No	No	No	No	No	No	No
Cost ‡	$96	$120	$96	$90	NA	NA	NA	NA	$90

* See Appendices for manufacturer's address.
† Sensor must be centrally located for this coverage.

Heat Sensors

Since it is possible for open flames to break out before a fume sensor will detect the fire (as in a gasoline fire, for example) you should also install sensors that detect heat and trigger an alarm when the room temperature at the sensor reaches a set point.

Typical alarm temperatures are 135° F. for inside living spaces, 190° F. for attics and industrial plants. There are other types of heat sensors that sound the alarm when air temperature at the sensor rises at a rate exceeding a set limit. The rate-of-rise sensors I recommend for residential use sound the alarm if the temperature rises at a rate at or faster than 15° F. per minute. These sensors are usually combined with fixed temperature sensors, most often 135° F.

Heat and rate-of-rise sensors can be resettable or nonresettable. I recommend the resettable type for home use because they can be tested without destroying them. Resettable sensors have bimetallic elements that snap open when heat is withdrawn and can be tested with an ordinary hair dryer. For industrial use nonresetting sensors should be used, because if heat does rise in an area, say in a section of a factory, to the danger point when the sensor is triggered, it is important to locate the cause of the high temperature. Having to replace the sensor focuses attention on the trouble spot. Table 2-17 lists heat sensors.

Fire Tips That Can Save Your Life

Here are suggestions that can prevent a fire, get you safely out of the house if one occurs, and help you survive until danger passes:

- Never ignore the smell of burning insulation. Check all wiring, or have an electrician do so, if you detect these odors.
- Do not allow oily rags or other waste to accumulate in the basement. Never store combustibles near furnace or water heater. Never bring a motorcycle or other gasoline-bearing equipment inside the house, even in the basement.
- Do not use inflammable cleaning products such as naphtha or benzine. It takes very little of these substances to build up to explosive conditions in a confined area.
- If you smell fumes, never check with a match. Always use a flashlight.
- Establish a fire drill. Include escape routes and where to meet outside so you can check to make sure everyone is out of the house. This latter point is especially vital. Include the baby sitter.
- Find two escape routes.
- Use escape ladders from upper stories (Fig. 1-17).
- Do not go back for valuables; the fire may be at the flashover point and could engulf you in seconds.
- Do not waste time collecting valuables; get out of the house as fast as you can. Nothing is worth your life.
- Do not open a hot door.
- Keep a wet cloth over mouth and nose and crawl to exit if rooms are smoke-filled.
- Don't leave hot iron on ironing board unattended.
- Never use a coin or other piece of metal to replace a blown fuse; that's begging for a fire from an overheated electrical circuit.
- If you smoke, do not do so in bed. It's a good idea to be sure to

TABLE 2-17

HEAT SENSOR EVALUATION

Manufacturer *	Pyrotronics	Pyrotronics	Pyrotronics	Pyrotronics	Pyrotronics	A.P.I.	A.P.I.	Sears Roebuck
Model No.	DT-55135	DT-55175	DT-5F212	DT-LR-135	DT-IR-180	602U	601	(See catalog)
Rating ° F.	135°	175°	212°	135°	180°	135° or 200°	135° or 200°	135°
Rate-of-Rise	No	No	No	No	No	No	Yes	No
UL Rated	Yes	Yes	Yes	Yes	Yes	Yes	Yes	No
Automatic Reset	No	No	No	Yes	Yes	Yes	No	NA
Coverage † (Square Feet)	900	900	900	2500	2500	900	2500	900
Cost ‡	$19	$19	$19	$8	$8	$5	$8	$22 §

* See Appendices for name and address of manufacturer.
† Must be centrally located for this rating.
‡ Approximate retail list prices subject to change.
§ Has built-in horn.

sprinkle ashtrays before dumping them.

- Matches and kids are a lethal combination. Keep them apart.
- Be careful about Christmas trees. They are highly inflammable.
- Never use elevators to leave a burning high-rise building. Learn location of all fire escapes. And fire exits. This is vital in a strange hotel.
- Alert neighbors as to the meaning of your special fire-alarm siren or bell, so they will call the fire department for you.
- If trapped, seal cracks and vents. Go to a room with an outside window. Keep as many closed doors

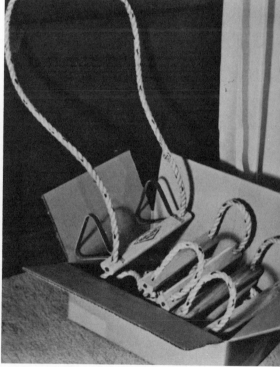

Fig. 1-17 / *Two types of home safety escape ladders. At left, a metal version that hooks over the windowsill, made by M&G Sheet Metal Co., 313 Van Sinderen Ave., Brooklyn, N. Y. 11207, and costs $20.00 for a two-story unit. Right, this attractive rope and wood ladder costs $11.00 for a two-story and $15.00 for a three-story unit. Made by Hanna Mfg. Corp., Waterville, N. Y. 13480.*

between you and the fire as possible. Open windows top and bottom for ventilation. Don't jump. Hang a sheet outside window as an emergency signal.

- If you wake up to the smell of smoke and fumes, do not sit up in bed because you could be knocked out by lethal concentrations of fumes near ceiling level. Roll over and out of bed onto the floor and crawl to an exit.

- Keep humidity as high as possible in winter. Studies have shown that a home and contents properly moisturized take longer to burn.

A Word About Fire Extinguishers

Distributors of burglar- and fire-alarm products almost always list fire extinguishers in their catalogs because they are a logical adjunct to safe living. Here are a few tips on which type of fire extinguisher to use.

First, never try to put out a grease or electrical fire with water. You will probably only make things worse. I suggest you hang a multipurpose fire extinguisher in kitchen, basement, and garage, and keep one in the car. I have had two car fires, one from a cigarette in upholstery and one from a leaking gas line or gas fumes in the motor. Both times I would have lost the car and its contents had I not had the right type of fire extinguisher handy. Believe me, I'm a believer. The motor fire was a scarer. We had one of those Ford vans loaded with camping gear and three small kids. We had stopped for a picnic lunch at a mountaintop rest area. When we were all in the car and ready to go the motor would not start. I noticed smoke pouring from the engine compartment. Sleeping bags and other gear were thrown off the compartment top so I could open it and when I did the smoke changed instantly to open fire as fresh air reached the engine. By then I had the extinguisher in hand and could douse the fire. For some strange reason the motor ran better than ever after the fire.

As to which type of fire extinguisher to buy, I recommend the type rated for A, B, and C fires. This type of extinguisher has a multipurpose chemical that is effective on medium-sized wood, paper, gasoline, oil, and electrical fires. I prefer the six-pound type because anything smaller may not have enough extinguisher to handle a medium-sized fire. Use only the type of extinguisher that has a pressure gauge so you can tell when pressure has dropped below the usable point. These extinguishers are refillable for a few dollars. The easiest type to use has a simple pin release and squeeze grip for fast action. Any extinguisher you buy should be UL rated. For boats and cars you can get by with a smaller $2\frac{5}{8}$-pound extinguisher but for marine use the extinguisher should be U. S. Coast Guard-approved as well as UL rated. Mount extinguishers on the wall in quick-release bracket holders. If you smoke, I would have an extinguisher in every room in the house you smoke in. Yes, that room too.

Finally, if this chapter has scared you, it has done its job. Fire is frightening and deserves serious consideration and use of all possible lifesaving precautions.

18

"BLACK BOXES" THAT CALL FOR HELP

Telephone dialers automatically phone for help when someone breaks into your home, a fire starts, you have a medical emergency, the basement floods, the freezer conks out, or a wide range of industrial processes go on the fritz.

ONE HOT SUMMER DAY, when you are alone in the house, three drug-crazed kids kick down the front door and come storming in. A few seconds later, after the alarm time delay has expired, the alarm sounds. At gunpoint you are forced to go to the control box and turn off the alarm manually. The alarm is silenced, but help will be called anyhow. A telephone dialer has been installed as part of the alarm system and wired into it in such a way that once that instrument begins its call for help, merely turning off the alarm siren will not stop it from calling the police department and up to nine other people for help. In a few moments three squad cars and six police converge on the house and capture the crazies.

An isolated case? Not at all, unfortunately. People are being raped, murdered, beaten, and robbed every day by home invaders. The best alarm system in the world isn't going to help much if you are forced to turn it off after it has only been sounding a minute or less. The neighbors will probably think the kids have set off one more false alarm and ignore it, thinking you caught it more or less in time and cut it off yourself.

A telephone dialer is a legal "black box" (Fig. 1-18) that can call up to ten numbers, one after the other, for help. If wired properly into the alarm system, the dialer will go through all its programmed calls even though the alarm system itself has been turned off. A good dialer, however, will have an abort

Fig. 1-18 / *This telephone dialer can automatically call for help in many types of emergencies such as fire, burglary, heart attack and other medical problems, and to alert you to other situations a sensor can detect such as low or high water levels, heat or cold as in a freezer or greenhouse.*

switch either on it or hidden near it so you can also cut off the dialer in case of a false alarm, and not every crook knows that. The crazies who invade homes for no good reason other than for enough money to buy another "bag" of dope certainly aren't going to know it.

The dialer can call for help in a burglary or invasion situation, and if it's a two-channel instrument, can call the fire department should a fire break out. In fact the dialer can call anywhere in the United States to alert those you select as to any type of emergency situation for

which there are sensors, such as heat, cold, freezer, or boiler breakdown, water levels and medical emergency.

For example, you may have a heart condition and be susceptible to sudden medical emergency, or be diabetic or epileptic or have any of a thousand other physical conditions and need to be able to call for medical assistance, yet be unable to use the telephone. A dialer can be programmed to call your doctor, an ambulance, and four or five friends in that order just in case any of the first numbers dialed are busy. The dialer can

TABLE 1-18

RECOMMENDED DIALERS

Manufacturer * Model No.	Ademco 612	Conrac 9111	Sescoa 1220/40	A.P.I. 201	Design Controls 18-200	Scan SC-8D	Napco 4000R
Channels	2	2	2–4 ‡	2	2	2	2
Fire Override	Yes	Yes	No	No	No	No	Yes
Line Seizure	Optional	Optional	Optional	Optional	Yes	Yes	Yes
Line Release	Yes	Optional	Optional	Optional	Yes	Yes	Optional
Line Monitor	No	Optional	Yes	No	No	No	No
Dial Tone Detection	No	No	Optional	No	No	No	No
Test Speaker	Yes	Yes	No	Yes	Yes	No	Yes
Voltage Protection	No	Yes	Yes	Yes	Yes	Yes	Yes
High-Quality Mechanical Features	Yes	Yes	Yes	Yes	Yes	Yes	
Key Lock							Yes
Cabinet	Yes	NA	Yes	Yes	Yes	Yes	Yes
Battery Charger	Optional	Optional	Optional	Optional	Yes	Optional	Yes
Line Coupler	Optional	Optional	Optional	Optional	Optional	Optional	Optional
Abort	Local	Local	No	Local	Remote	No	Local
Cost †	NA	$220	NA	$230	NA	NA	$286

* Manufacturers' names and addresses are in Appendices.
† Prices are suggested list, subject to change.
‡ Four channels available optionally.

be started with a wireless emergency transmitter (see Chapter Sixteen) you can carry in your pocket or on your belt. The dialer can also be started in the absence of a local alarm, to call for help silently in the event of a hold-up, as at a teller's cage or at the cash register of a store.

Not all dialers are reliable. First of all they are seldom used. But when they are needed, they must work. The cheap ones too often don't, or work so poorly the messages are garbled or sound like Donald Duck with a hangover. An emer-

gency, when you badly need police or the fire department or a doctor, is no time for the dialer to malfunction.

I have selected a few of the top-grade dialers and listed them in Table 1-18, along with the features I consider a good dialer should have to insure that when it's needed it will deliver its messages clearly and accurately.

The Taped Message

Dialers usually come with a tape that

runs for three or four minutes. Since the average emergency message takes one minute, you can call any three telephone numbers with your message. For example, for intrusion you can have the dialer call the police department and two friends in that order. For fire, the dialer can call the fire department and two friends.

Since the odds are against the police or fire department incoming phone lines being busy or out of order, you can usually count on the first message on the tape getting through to them. The dialer won't stop, though, since it can't tell whether or not anyone it calls has answered or not. It will go through all its programmed messages in sequence. The police or fire departments may have a lot of calls from your friends, but better that than not responding to the emergency. Most police departments have enough phone lines to take care of anything except a major widespread emergency situation, such as a tornado. It would be unusual for these lines all to be busy at the same time. In my own city of Evanston, Illinois, a Chicago suburb, the police department has thirteen incoming lines other than the emergency 911 number, of which they have sixteen. However, for most police departments, dialers cannot be used on the 911 number because of the false-alarm problem, which I will discuss later on in this chapter.

I suppose thirteen crooks could jam all the incoming lines but unless the "hit" is worthwhile, who would bother? This possibility of jamming police telephone lines is one reason why commercial establishments should not use a dialer; they can be defeated if the stakes are high enough. On the other hand, dialers are a good idea for residential use since

the security problem is on an entirely different level and modern criminals who are really electronically sophisticated would never waste time on most homes. For the wealthy home, with many valuables, the security problem should be approached as though it were a commercial job and again a dialer is not the answer. Instead I prefer, for these super-security problems, a direct leased telephone line to a central professional guard service. In this type of alarm system an intrusion triggers a coded message to a remote central station. At the station a receiver decodes the message, prints out the nature of the emergency along with the date and time, and a guard is dispatched to check into the situation. At the same time the guard service notifies the police. If the leased wire is tampered with, sophisticated electronic surveillance systems, which constantly monitor the integrity of this type of system, alert the guard service to this attempt at compromising the system or of any other reason, such as equipment failure, for the trouble signal. The leased-wire/guard-service combination is not cheap; count on laying out around eighty dollars a month or more, depending on how far you are from the central station and the degree of protection you need. A central station guard service is shown in Fig. 2-18.

Back to the taped message. Unless you have a dialer with a telephone dial or push-button programmer, you can't make up your own message. The programmer (Fig. 3-18) costs around $150 so it doesn't pay to own one unless you have many dialers or are a professional alarm-system contractor. The contractor who sold you the dialer can program the messages for you; his usual charge is $10. A typical message goes like this:

Fig. 2-18 / *A central guard service eliminates the use of dialers and is more reliable, therefore should be used in commercial applications where security needs are greater than in residential areas. Dialers are fine for home use, though, as an inexpensive link to police and fire departments.*

"This is an emergency taped message. There is break-in (or fire) at the residence of John Doe, 1345 Cliff Street. Please send help."

The sequence of messages for a three-minute tape is:

- Start dialer tape, wait 10 seconds
- Dial called number . . . 8 seconds
- Wait . . . . 3 seconds
- Put message on tape . . 18 seconds
- Wait . . . . 1 second

Total 40 seconds

Repeat sequence twice for a three-minute tape. This gives you three messages to three different telephone numbers, starting with the police (or fire) department.

Personally I prefer a six- or ten-minute tape with six or ten messages to as many different telephone numbers. That way somebody is bound to be in to take the message and call the police, if for some reason the police lines are tied up. Now let's look at the features that make a good, reliable dialer.

Multiple Channels

Unless you use a dialer for a special purpose, such as a medical emergency or some industrial process or temperature alert, or have a fire alarm (see Chapter Seventeen) as part of the intrusion system, you should have a two-channel dialer. This way one channel can call the cops if someone breaks in, and call the fire department if a fire breaks out.

◄

Fig. 3-18 / *Tape programmer puts dialtone blips on tape along with messages so the dialer will alert up to ten different phone numbers.*

Fire-Channel Override

The two-channel dialer should also have a fire-channel override so that even if the burglar emergency message is being transmitted by the dialer when a fire breaks out, the dialer will stop transmitting the intrusion tape, back up and switch to the fire tape. The fire tape message sequence should then be transmitted in its entirety.

Or, suppose a fire breaks out in the electrical wiring of the 110-volt AC circuits (not the alarm system, this is low voltage). This fire could conceivably burn through one of the alarm circuit wires and trip the intrusion alarm before the fire sensor detects the smoke or heat; or both sensors could trip at the same time. Now the dialer has to decide, since both fire and intrusion alarms are triggered, which tape message to send. The better alarms will always switch to and deliver the fire sequence first. In Chapter Seventeen I pointed out that arson is the nation's fastest-growing crime. A lot of arson is done after a burglary, either to cover up any clues or out of sheer viciousness. Either way, it's important the dialer react to the fire first as the greater emergency if for no other reason than to save the house from total destruction, even if no one is in the house.

Line Seizure

Back in the 1960's, dialers could be defeated by simply rushing to the nearest extension telephone the dialer is connected to and lifting it off the hook before the dialer could start. Today the better dialers have a line-seizure module that isolates all telephones connected to the dialer as soon as the dialer starts. Now the message will get through even

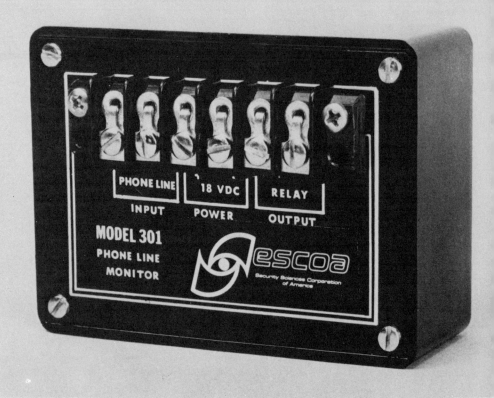

Fig. 4-18 / *Phone line monitor module, optional on most dialers, constantly checks your phone line and if it is cut (as by a crook from outside the house) turns on the burglar alarm.*

if all the telephones on that line are off the hook and the plaintive taped message from the telephone company is telling you, "The phone is off the hook, please hang up." Just make sure that any dialer with this feature resets itself and lets go of the phones so they will be back in normal service once the dialer has delivered all its messages.

Line Release

A few years ago your dialer could be jammed by placing a phone call to your house and thus keeping the line busy so the dialer could not get out. With the line-release or anti-jam feature, when the alarm is triggered incoming calls are intercepted and the line freed so the dialer can use it.

Line Monitor

The easiest way to defeat any dialer is simply to cut the telephone line from outside the premises. The line monitor device (Fig. 4-18) measures the voltage on the telephone line at all times, whether the alarm or dialer is activated or quiet. If the line voltage, as supplied by the telephone company, falls below a set level, the line monitor triggers the burglar alarm. The dialer won't send any messages, of course, because the telephone line is cut. But at least the alarm sounds and may scare off any potential burglar or home invader. If you're home and the alarm goes off, lock yourself in your bedroom (See Chapter Twenty-one "Fortress Room") and wait for police to arrive. Don't tempt fate by seeking a confrontation with anyone trying to break in.

Test Speaker

It's very important you be able to get a positive check-out on dialer condition every month or so, preferably without setting off the alarm. Good dialers have a test speaker built in, and a switch that isolates the dialer from the alarm so you can run the tape through both fire and burglar messages to check them.

Key Lock

The dialer cabinet should be key-locked, as should any remote switches. Otherwise a crook could turn off the dialer easily.

Dialer Abort

It's easy for the kids, or you, to trip the alarm accidentally. You could forget to turn it off (when you return) before the time delay expires, leave a door open when you go out so the alarm sounds after the exit-time delay period, or you could forget and leave the alarm on "instant" response and try to get out of the house with the time delay feature off.

In fact, up to 90 percent of all false alarms from alarm systems are due to owner carelessness, according to police studies and records in Seattle and Los Angeles. Understandably police are unhappy with dialers that call them out to false alarms. Each such call takes at least one squad car and officer out of duty for thirty to forty-five minutes, risks life and limb getting to the scene in a hurry, and costs all taxpayers money. Dialers are in many communities anathema to the police, who refuse to deal with them, and in many communities dialers are not allowed to call the police. Unfortunately it's not the dialer that is at fault, it's the alarm-system owner in almost every case. Police admit that there are many instances where a crook did trip the alarm and left in a hurry, leaving no trace, or tripped the alarm just to see how long it took the police to arrive, or to get the neighbors tired of answering the alarm. But these are in the minority of false alarms. Very few police departments these days permit dialers to call the 911 number, and if they do, refuse to respond to it.

In fact the false-alarm problem has risen to such heights that many communities are imposing fines on alarm-system owners if they are called out on one. In the New York City suburb of Scarsdale, police charge a sliding scale for false alarms. One false alarm is permitted, after which the fee is ten dollars for the next one, twenty-five dollars for the next falsie and fifty dollars for the fourth and additional alarms. The solution to false alarms lies, of course, in training all members of the family in the proper use of the alarm system.

Another solution is the subhead above, an abort switch on the dialer, or conveniently located remote from the dialer. This key-operated switch turns the dialer off if you accidentally trip the alarm. When the alarm system is reset, the dialer can be placed back in service at the abort switch.

Standby Battery Power

The dialer should have a battery standby in case the 110-volt AC main power goes out, or the line to your house is cut. The battery should be the rechargeable type and the dialer should have its own integral or at least optional charger so the battery is always at peak power.

High Voltage Protection

Lightning (or a crook) can cause the normal fifty-volt DC power on your telephone line to jump to six hundred volts or more and knock out the dialer. The better dialers defeat this problem by keeping the dialer circuits cut off and separate from the telephone line until the dialer is activated by an emergency.

Mechanical Features

A major problem plaguing cheap dialers is flat roller spots developing from long disuse. The tape is gripped between capstan and roller so the tape transport mechanism can move the tape along the tape head and thus deliver the emergency messages. If this pressure, over a period of time, causes flat spots to develop on the drive or pinch roller, the tape may move erratically or break. Erratic movement garbles the message. The higher quality dialers get around this problem either with specially compounded silicone or neoprene flat resistant rollers, or by a solenoid mechanism that keeps pressure off the tape until the dialer starts.

An industrial quality drive motor with automatic speed control is also important. Check these features by reading the dialer specifications, and Table 1-18.

A Word About Answering Services

By now it may have occurred to you that a good back-up number to have on your dialer message tape is an answering service. This is a good idea only if the answering service will pick up the phone no later than the third ring, and if the service operators are thoroughly trained in how to handle the emergency involved. Also, bear in mind that these services do not have armed guards or secure premises, so that a determined burglar could break in and keep the operators from answering the phones, or simply cut all the telephones coming into the service. This is another good reason why commercial establishments and wealthy, vulnerable residences should use only a well-established guard security service and not a dialer, as previously noted. The guard service headquarters, if it is a good one, has armed guards around the clock and is a veritable fortress to break into. Incoming telephone lines are buried and hard to get at to cut, and the guard facilities often even have their own emergency power, light, and air-conditioning facilities. Chapter Twenty-five gives all the details on these professional services. Let's go now to the next chapter, where I will tell you how to burglarproof and alarm your possessions.

19

HOW TO "ALARM" YOUR POSSESSIONS

Thousands of motorcycles, bikes, lawn equipment, cars, boats, trailers, and other portable goodies are ripped off every day. Here's how to attach an alarm to them that will let you know when anyone tries to walk, carry, or drive your possessions away from their happy home.

ONE OF THE SIMPLEST ways to tie your portable possessions directly into your burglar alarm system is with a "pull trap." This device is a simple, normally closed switch (Fig. 1-19) that in the armed mode is kept closed by a removable flat piece of metal wedged between two spring-loaded contacts. A piece of black nylon string is attached to the removable plate. The other end of the string is attached to whatever you want to protect. Should anyone move the alarmed goodie the plate in the pull trap will be pulled out and the alarm will sound. See Chapter Fifteen for instructions on wiring; the pull trap is wired into the circuit in series, just like the magnetic contact.

Fig. 1-19 / *Pull trap switch that attaches to your possessions and to your alarm system. Alarm sounds if string is pulled.*

Ordinary pull traps are easily defeated by shunting a piece of wire across the contacts or by cutting the nylon string. These traps depend on the element of surprise and invisibility of the black string at night. The standard pull trap costs around $3 (such as A.P.I.'s Model 177, which has a dust cover over the contacts to make it a bit more difficult to shunt them).

A better pull trap has been built, however, that is much more difficult to defeat. This is U.S.P.'s Model U-520, sold by A.P.I. (see Appendices) for around $8. The U-520 has a balanced magnetic action that detects minute increases or decreases of tension on the nylon pull string, and has a cover over the contacts. Any change of tension on the line, once it is armed, will set off the alarm.

Pull trap switches can protect other things besides possessions. For example they can guard a driveway (Fig. 2-19), a garden gate (Fig. 3-19), or a garage door (Fig. 4-19).

Automobile and Truck Alarms

There are three basic types of automobile and truck alarms. One type cuts off the ignition twenty to one hundred seconds after the car is started. This stalls the car out in the street and attracts attention. The car will start again after the alarm resets itself, in a brief period, but it will stall again, and again, and again. The second type cuts off the fuel supply, and the car stalls within a few feet or maybe a block or so, after the fuel in the carburetor bowl is used up. I prefer either the ignition or fuel cut-off type as a positive way to keep the car (or truck) from being stolen.

The third type of alarm system starts a siren, klaxon, or the auto's own horn shrieking as soon as a person breaks into

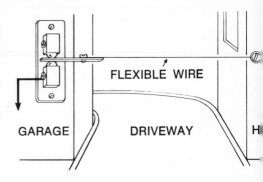

Fig. 2-19 / *Easy way to set up an alarm using a pull trap, to let you know if someone drives past a garage or other building.*

the car. The best models offer good protection, but do not stop the thief from hot-wiring the car and driving it off, siren howling and all. The cheaper of these alarms uses the car's own horn which is a poor approach for a number of reasons. First the horn relay could malfunction under steady use. Second, people are used to stuck horn relays and steadily sounding horns, and do not associate this noise with a car theft in progress, so the thief is pretty safe in reaching down with a pair of cutting pliers and simply snipping the horn wire to silence the alarm. Most of us, when this happens, usually on a hot day on a busy street, just reach in and bodily rip out the horn wire.

Table 1-19 gives a comparative analysis and some of the costs (not all manufacturers will state retail costs since installers often set their own prices and manufacturers do not care to second-guess the installer) of these three types of auto alarms. I have not included the auto horn type, the kind that uses the car's own horn, because it is too easily defeated.

The other systems are fairly easy to

TABLE 1-19

RECOMMENDED AUTO ALARMS

Make * Model	Alarm Supply Company			Draco	Aler- tronics	Wico	CAHS
	MR-I	*MR-II*	*MR-III*	*Screamer*	*53*	*TVS*	*Fuel- Loc*
Key Switch							
Inside	Yes	Yes	Yes	No	Yes	Yes	Yes
Outside	Optional	Optional	Optional	Yes	No	NN ‡	NN
Exit/Entry Delay	Yes	No	No	No	Yes	NN	NN
Siren Timer	Yes	No	No	NA	Yes	NN	NN
Auto Reset	Yes	No	No	Yes	Yes	NN	NN
Instant "On"	No	No	No	No		NN	NN
Klaxon Effect	Yes	Yes	Yes	Yes	Yes	NN	NN
Sensors							
Ignition Cut-off	No	No	No	No	No	Yes	NN
Fuel Cut-off	No	No	No	No	No	NN	Yes
Current	Yes	Yes	Yes	Yes	No	NN	NN
Voltage	No	No	No	No	Yes	NN	NN
Vibration	Optional	Optional	Optional	Optional	Optional	NN	NN
Mercury "tilt"	Optional	Optional	Optional	Optional	Optional	NN	NN
Inside Panic							
Switch	No	No	No	Optional	Optional	NN	NN
Gas Tank							
Protection	No	No	No	Optional	Optional	NN	NN
Jam-Resistant							
Siren	Yes	Yes	Yes	Yes	Yes	NN	NN
Separate Battery	No	No	No	Yes	No	NN	NN
False-Alarm							
Resistant	Yes	Yes	Yes	Yes	Yes	Yes	Yes
Cost †	$80	$50	$60	$70	$90	NA	NA

* See Appendices for manufacturers' addresses.
⋅† Suggested retail list prices, subject to change.
‡ NN means Not Needed.

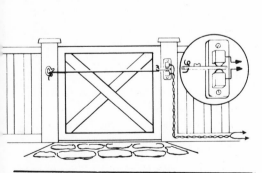

Fig. 3-19 / *Yard gates can be protected with a pull trap.*

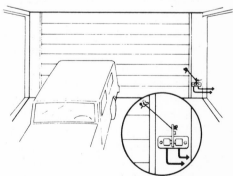

Fig. 4-19 / *An overhead garage door protected by a pull trap.*

defeat, too. For example, even with a hood switch that sounds the alarm when the hood is raised, the alarm can be silenced simply by removing a battery cable, thus cutting off electricity to the siren. Or even more simply, most car battery cables can be removed or cut from underneath the car to disable the siren before it can go off. A good solution to this problem is to provide the alarm with its own standby battery that will take over and power the siren and associated electronics if the car battery cable is cut.

Here are the other features of a siren-type alarm system I find desirable and that are in most of the alarms I have selected in Table 1-19:

- *Two-tone pulsating siren* that meets state noise-pollution regulations and puts out at least 112 decibels measured according to Underwriters' Laboratories specifications.
- *Exit-entry delay.* Lets you get out of the car and back in without triggering the alarm, and dispenses with outside shunt lock that can be compromised.
- *Inside alarm shut-off key lock*
- *Alarm timer* that turns off the alarm after four minutes or so. This complies with many state and municipal noise-pollution laws, and saves your battery.
- *Automatic reset,* so the alarm system is back in service after the alarm timer has turned off the siren.
- *Mercury switches* to arm hood and trunk doors.
- *Vibration switches* that trigger the alarm if an attempt is made to tow the car or steal the spare tire.
- *Inside-car panic button* that will trigger the alarm when pressed if the driver is threatened by anyone

outside (or inside) the car. The button can be on the dashboard.
- *The alarm must "latch"* or lock in the siren-sound mode even if the door or hood is closed in an attempt to stifle the alarm. ·
- *Siren should be jam resistant.* Steel enclosure over working parts should resist stabbing with a screwdriver or knife, for example.

There are two types of noise alarms, the current- or voltage-sensing, and the hard-wire system that uses contact switches on doors, trunk, and hood. The latter is wired to a control box just like the simple residential alarm system I discussed in Chapter Fifteen. This hard-wire system involves a lot of drilling, fitting, and wire pulling. And the wire must be carefully installed so that vibration does not fray insulation and so cause a false alarm or put the alarm system out of business. I see no reason to go to all this expense when the simpler current- or voltage-sensing system can be installed in one tenth the time for half as much money, simply by pulling a few wires in the motor compartment. Most of these systems do not even involve drilling or pulling wire through the fire wall between the passenger and motor compartments.

Any current- or voltage-sensing alarm you buy should have a warranty that states that it is designed to be highly resistant to false alarms due to temperature changes, radio transmissions, lightning, hot ignition systems such as the magneto system from a passing motorcycle or gasoline lawnmower, and miscellaneous electrical interference. For example, both the Draco Laboratories "Screamer" model and the Alertronics model (see Table 1-19) spell out this type of protection in their warranty.

Alertronics lists among its specifications a noise immunity to inductive currents under .3A at 100 mH and will not respond to RF1 of 100 W at six feet. The temperature range is from −30° F. to +245° F. and humidity is 90 percent at 85° F. for seventy-two hours. The Alertronics units have also passed a salt, shock, and vibration test that exceeds automotive requirements.

Of all the automotive alarms on the market, I like the Alertronics Model 53 second best, the Draco "Screamer" best only because it has its own battery standby, thus preventing defeat by cutting or disconnecting the car main battery.

For trucks and other commercial vehicles, I would use the Fuel-loc fuel cut-off system which positively disables the vehicle until the owner resets the system. I suppose one could get at the motor compartment, raise the hood, remove the air filter and drop gas by hand into the carburetor throat. In large trucks this would be all but impossible, given motor location. In smaller trucks, this would be a two-man job, one to drive and one to drip the fuel.

The ignition cut-off system made by Wico uses an eight-digit button combination code only the driver knows, and if this code is not punched in the proper sequence the alarm disables the vehicle by cutting off ignition.

The optional gas-cap alarm on some of the systems (Table 1-19) is a good idea now, and will be an even better one come the inevitable gas shortage. This alarm also keeps vandals from pouring sugar and other assorted nasties into the gas tank just for kicks.

How to Protect Your Boat

A sail or power boat is particularly vulnerable to being stolen intact or to vandalism. There's something about a good boat that seems irresistible to the violence-prone who don't have one. And the valuables inside are easily removed and sold. Thieves break into boats to steal marine radios, compasses, depth finders, navigation aids, and even galley equipment. Your sail or power yacht is usually moored or docked where it is not unusual to find people around the area. If the crook who rows out to your boat, or who is "working" topside at your boat at a dock, looks at all nautical, few will question his presence or even activity. Few marinas and harbors are so well guarded that a stranger will be automatically challenged.

For a boat or yacht alarm system you want something that will sound a very loud and distinctive noise should anyone try to break into the cabin via hatches or portholes. The alarm equipment should be thoroughly weatherproofed and the siren jam- and vandal-resistant. The system should also be easy to install and reasonably priced.

The marine alarm system I can recommend can be installed by you in a few hours or less. This is the Aqualarm No. 1916 that sells for around $75. The alarm contains a control box, two magnetic intrusion sensors, an alarm bell in a tamper-resistant steel box, and an exterior shunt lock-key switch. The system is easy to install, and comes with an unusual set of instructions: you can understand them. The system comes with a low-oil- or water-pressure detector with ⅛-inch pipe thread ($7.75), a remote 135° F. fire detector ($5); extra bilge detector ($12); and motor overheat de-

Fig. 5-19 / *Optional sensors for a boat alarm system. Top left, 135° F. heat sensor; top right, low oil or water pressure detector; bottom left and right, overheat detectors, both rated at 200° F. All for Aqualarm system.*

tector ($7.75) (Fig. 5-19). I wish I could tell you there is a reliable, false-alarm-free smoke and fume detector you could place in the motor compartment to warn you not to press the starter button until you have vented these explosive vapors. There is no such animal.

You could put an ionization fume detector (Chapter Seventeen) in the motor compartment, but you would have endless false alarms, both in the harbor and

underway. The heat sensor at 135° will at least give you a few minutes' warning so you can either get a fire extinguisher on the fire, or at least jump overboard with life jackets donned, or man the dinghy, before the yacht takes off skyward.

The Aqualarm has a distinctive bell that can't be mistaken for anything but a burglar alarm. Sirens in the harbor maybe; a bell, never, so this unusual sound is bound to attract attention and, one would hope, the harbor police or other authority.

An inexpensive way to alarm a dock and a boat moored at the dock, particularly an open power boat or sailboat, is to use a Tapeswitch CVP-1723 mat under seat and floor pads, and their 131 AMT switch under the dock plank mat, both wired into an existing burglar-alarm system.

Eaton has an "Auralarm" for boats that is essentially the same as the Aqualarm above, except that the alarm is a loudspeaker that puts out a voice announcement that "There is an intruder aboard the yacht WHATEVER at Berth 78, South Marina, please call police to investigate immediately" or any other programmed message you choose of that length. The system can use your existing loud hailer. The weakness of this system (besides its price of $250) is the vulnerability of the outside horn, which could be jammed by ramming a screwdriver down its throat, by cutting its wires, or by spraying shaving cream or anything else that foams up into its mouth. The Auralarm's electronics are absolutely first class, as they should be at the price. Magnetic contact sensors are used where needed, the control box has its own separate batteries, the programmed tape will run until you shut it off or the battery runs down. An outside key shunt-lock switch controls the unit.

Protecting Costly Artwork and Cabinets

Did you ever wonder what would happen if you tried to lift a Picasso or Van Gogh off the wall of an art museum? All hell would break loose, that's what

would happen. Most of these pictures have hidden magnets inside the frame, with a mating magnetic wide-gap sensor hidden behind the plaster or the paint of the wall. Move the picture a fraction of an inch and the alarm goes off. You too can protect your expensive and/or cherished paintings the same way, if you already have a burglar-alarm system installed. You can hide the switches or not, depending on how much money you want or need to spend (Fig. 6-19). Wire the switches in series, as described in Chapter Fifteen.

Locked drawers (no, I haven't covered *those* kinds of belts in this book, for some reason) even with good locks can easily be broken into. But if the drawers contain valuables, such as machine tools or costly parts or jewelry, you may want to have them trapped with magnetic sensors wired into the alarm system that will sound the alarm if the drawer is opened. Fig. 7-19 shows two ways of installing magnetic sensors in drawers. Whichever way you do it, the magnet must be on the drawer and the switch on the frame.

Freezers

If you have a lot of bread tied up in meat in a food freezer, you should have an alarm that tells you when the freezer dips to the danger point. You will still have three or four hours, at least, to have the freezer fixed; the alarm gives you instant warning as soon as the freezer goes on the fritz. Otherwise you may never know until you find soft meat. One self-contained freezer alarm is Dialalarm's "Freeze Guard" that sounds an alarm if the temperature inside the freezer goes above 25° F.

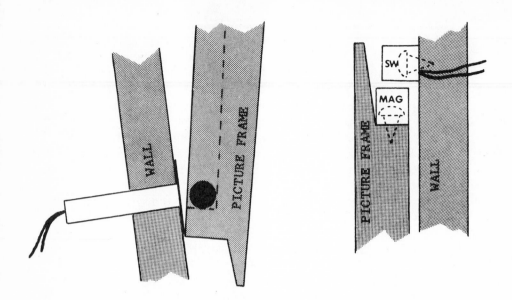

Fig. 6-19 / *Left, hidden sensors to protect wall-hung pictures.
Right, exposed sensors for pictures.*

Fig. 7-19 / *Two ways to install sensors to protect a drawer. Magnets go on the drawer, switches on door frame.*

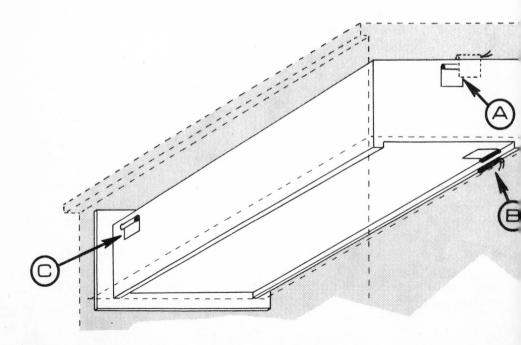

Water Level

Even if you don't have an alarm system, but need to be warned if the basement floods, a good self-contained alarm is made by Wessel. It has its own battery. Other water sensors from A.P.I. and other alarm equipment suppliers tie into the burglar-alarm system, or can be wired to their own control box.

Temperature

Thermostats for extremes of heat and cold are available for alerting you to dangerous conditions in greenhouses, industrial processes, boiler failure, barns, or of any other thermal condition you wish to measure. They can be tied into the basic alarm system or have an individual alarm.

Swimming Pools

If a neighbor's child falls into your swimming pool and drowns, you could be faced with a costly lawsuit for negligence in making such an "attractive nuisance" easy to get into. You may also want to keep unauthorized people (spelled K-I-D-S) out of the pool.

An excellent pool alarm, the "Pool Sitter" is made by Mark Engineering, Inc. (see Appendices) for around $250. This unit is UL-approved and has an underwater surveillance system on the sonar principle, using a hydrophone. Sensitivity is adjustable; the alarm is self-contained. It includes a surface-located poolside microphone so you can listen in remotely to monitor goings-on at the pool when the hydrophone is off and the kids are in the water. The surface mike can be moved to another spot in the yard at night.

Motorcycles

You can trap a motorcycle with a pull trap in your own yard or garage. But when you're away, you need another alarm for your expensive two-wheeler. You can use a sturdy lock and chain, but they can be cut. You can use the fork lock, but the bike can be lifted and put in a truck.

One good way to let you know when somebody is tampering with your motorcycle is to install a burglar alarm on it. The best alarm I have found is made by Alcotronics and sold in Harley-Davidson motorcycle stores. The alarm comes in two versions. The basic model has a sensitive reed switch that sets off a loud alarm on the motorcycle if the machine is disturbed. This model sells for around $35, has its own horn and battery supply, and is tamper-resistant. An add-on to the basic alarm is a wireless transmitter and receiver unit that in addition to the local alarm on the bike sends a signal to the receiver. If you have one of these units and someone tries to move the bike, the beeper in your pocket will let you know about it up to at least several blocks away, depending on local building conditions. This is great if you have to leave the bike in the street at night, or want protection when you stop for meals on a trip. The add-on wireless part costs another $85 or so. Both together cost $120, expensive insurance but worth it for the big bikes such as BMW's (like mine), Harley-Davidsons and Honda 1000's.

Remote Buildings

You may have an outbuilding with valuable equipment inside to protect, yet not wish to string wires for blocks or miles from your basic alarm system to do it. A simple solution is an inexpensive self-contained alarm unit, with its own control and siren in a key-locked steel box.

Such a unit is available from A.P.I. and is their model 449 for 110-volt AC operation only. You must have 110-volt wiring into the building for this model. It is easily removed for use in another building and is thus ideal for job-site tool sheds, foreman's shacks and the like, or for barns or watchman's shanties. The unit has a 118 decibel police-type siren that can be heard for a long distance. This model costs about $75 with a double-bitted flat key-lock switch. You will need to order A.P.I. No. 151 O.C. magnetic contacts and/or No. 178 O.C. pull traps separately. This unit takes only normally open sensors.

Trucks

Millions of dollars' worth of merchandise is stolen every year from trucks and truck trailers. Every day a truck and trailer are hijacked. All the locks in the world won't keep your truck trailer from being driven off and its contents delivered up at leisure. The fuel or ignition cut-off alarms noted above are one approach. If you haul a lot of valuable merchandise, I would also use a good alarm system designed especially for trucks.

An excellent truck alarm is made by Babaco. Their alarm has a truly painfully loud siren in a heavy steel tamper-resistant box, a motion detector that sounds the alarm if the truck is moved, its own battery separate from the truck battery with a built-in separate charger, UL-approved pick-resistant and attack-resistant lock switch, and a control box encased in an armored box. It also has an automatic alarm shut-off complying with noise-abatement laws that shuts off the siren after five minutes and resets the alarm, and specially made heavy-duty magnetic sensors for truck doors that resist false alarms due to vibration and damage from shifting freight and "hi-lo's."

When Babaco installs such a system all wiring is concealed and protected by armored cable, and the cables are securely strapped. This is not an inexpensive system, but your insurance-cost savings will help pay for it. One note: You can park a trailer for two or three months and the alarm's own battery will provide protection for that period.

20

ALL ABOUT MOTION SENSORS

For wide-area coverage to detect intruders in schools, factories, stores, warehouses, and homes, or for spot protection of safes, filing cabinets, and desks, there's a wide variety of motion sensors to fill your security needs. Here is a review of their uses, features, best applications and shortcomings, plus installation do's and don'ts and recommended equipment.

YOU COULD SEAL OFF a huge factory complex with a twelve-foot-high barbed-wire-topped fence, complete with gates guarded around the clock. Not only would the fence be very expensive, it still would not keep a determined person from climbing over it.

You could seal all doors and windows tight after working hours and still not be sure that someone has not hidden himself away during the day in the premises.

Motion sensors can erect an invisible barrier around a factory to alert your security guards to a trespass. The cost would be far less than a high barrier fence and certainly more aesthetically pleasing than such a physical barrier.

Inside a building, motion sensors can cover a large area at far less cost than hard-wire systems. Entire roof areas and walls of large warehouses, for example, can be blanketed so that anyone cutting his way through these parts of the building would set off the alarm once he dropped down into the invisibly protected zone.

Motion sensors can also cover long, narrow areas such as hallways and corridors and so can be used to protect schools and office building floors from intrusion. Ceiling- or wall-mounted units can fill a large or a small space with motion-sensing waves that trigger the alarm when a person breaches the barrier they create. By overlapping units, very large areas can be covered. Even huge outdoor areas such as airports, new-car storage depots, tank farms, and the like can be protected against intrusion with motion sensors.

For homes, self-contained motion sensors have their own control box, siren, and all circuitry for the alarm system. These units can also be used in small stores and for smaller office areas. For larger jobs, the sensors must be wired into a control box, or to a central station where their condition can be monitored by trained guards.

Basic Motion-Sensor Problems

Fundamental to all types of motion sensors is the fact that they can only be used in a situation where there is no motion. Or at the very least they can only be used where motion is the type that will not trigger the motion sensor. We will discuss this form of motion under specific types of motion sensors later on in this chapter.

Since by definition motion sensors cannot be used where most types of motion exist, it is obvious that they cannot be used in a space occupied by human beings (at least not when the humans are there).

For example, if you want the burglar alarm in an "ON" condition where you are home alone, a motion sensor would not work, because as soon as you move the sensor will trigger the alarm. For this application you need a hard-wire system (Chapters Fourteen, Fifteen and Sixteen). On the other hand, motion

sensors do make an ideal back-up for hard-wire systems in stores. Should the hard-wire system be defeated, the invisible motion sensor can still detect an intruder.

Thermal Detectors

One of the most efficient thermal detectors is my cat. She will find, and cover with her body, any thermal radiation from anywhere; the TV set, a sunspot on the rug, warm air from a heat register, anybody's lap. She would make a great intrusion detector if I could train her to react appropriately.

There is a better way to detect the presence of a warm moving body, however. This is with a so-called "passive" heat detector that measures the heat output, in the infrared range, from the room and its furnishings. This sensor "sees" the level of infrared radiation from walls, ceiling, floors and all furniture. Any sudden change in the total infrared heat in the protected area, as from a warm human body moving around, will cause the infrared detector to sound the alarm. "Passive" is used to describe a thermal infrared detector because it has only one unit, a receiver, unlike an ultrasonic system which emits high-pitched sound, or a microwave unit which emits ultra-high-frequency radio waves. The thermal system just sits there, measures what's going on heatwise, and blasts off if any sudden changes occur in what it's sensing all along. Fig. 1-20 shows the cover pattern.

Because thermal sensors are not self-contained they must be hard-wired into a control box, just as are magnetic switch contacts (Chapter Fifteen). However, because thermal sensors (Fig. 2-20) do cover a room of about twenty square feet, or a corridor 3 by 65 feet,

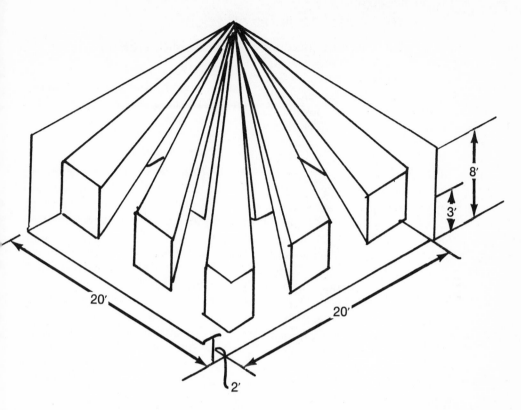

Fig. 1-20 / *Infrared motion detectors have a space coverage pattern as shown. As a person moves from band to band, his motion is sensed as a change in heat in the area.*

Fig. 2-20 / *Thermal sensors offer very stable coverage but in an area limited as shown.*

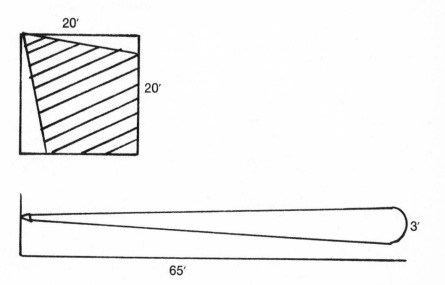

they are no more expensive than the same coverage via hard-wire, which will *not* pick up motion inside the space.

Motion sensors are an excellent back-up to hard-wire. It may be possible to defeat a hard-wire system by cutting a hole into the premises from an adjoining, unprotected building, and so defeat the hard-wire system that only protects doors and windows. This is a very common way of getting around otherwise excellent and costly burglar alarms of the hard-wire genre, and it's done every day somewhere in these United States—which is why a space-motion detector either as adjunct to another or as a primary alarm can offer excellent intrusion protection in many instances. Certainly it's going to be a lot less expensive to monitor a space than to install vibration sensors on all walls, ceilings, and windows (see Chapter Twenty-three).

Thermal sensors, once installed and adjusted, are very stable, reliable, and false-alarm free. You might ask what would happen if a smart crook could set the room thermostat up to body temperature of 98.6° F. Would the thermal sensor, which measures changes in heat output from that which is normal to the room at any given time, "see" a human body that's at the same temperature as the room? The answer is that it certainly would, because the sensor sees more than just the air temperature. It would take days to bring all the ceiling and floor and furnishing temperatures to 98.6° F., and you would *never* get outside walls that high because of heat loss to the outside. The sensor would still pick up an intruder, although it might react a bit more slowly under these conditions.

Recommended Thermal Sensors

There are a number of very high-quality passive infrared thermal sensors on the market, generally for about $175 retail per sensor (less installation and control box). Thermal sensors I can recommend include:

Rossin Corporation. The Rossin sensors have a differential sensing element that cancels out major room-temperature changes of an overall pattern, such as sudden heat gain from the sun or from warm air or air-conditioning registers. The sensing unit has a twenty-four-inch off-the-floor pattern that lets pets (and a crawling crook) pass without setting off the alarm. The sensor has a tamper switch that also sounds the alarm if its cover is removed.

Security General (see Appendices for addresses) has a Model 2000 unit that covers twenty square feet and with additional (overlapping) sensors can cover more space. Other excellent thermal sensors are made by MESL and by Mosler, for industrial and commercial use.

Pulsed Infrared Detectors

Pulsed infrared detectors work on an entirely different principle than the passive thermal units. The pulsed IF motion sensors transmit a beam of infrared light from between a transmitter and a receiver. Pulsed IF then is essentially an optical system. The beam of light is invisible, or all but so, and is aimed across a "trap zone" over which an intruder must pass to get to the goodies he wants to rip off. The light beam is "pulsed" or modulated to make the system more difficult to defeat.

Think of modulation as something like the sixty cycles per second your household electricity varies from plus to minus. That's why it's called alternating current. It could also be called pulsed. If you wave your fingers rapidly in front of a fluorescent light, you can actually see the pulsing. Without this modulation, a criminal could just aim a source of infrared light (such as a flashlight with an IF filter over the lens) at the IF receiver; then a confederate could walk right by it. To fool a receiver tuned to a specific pulsed frequency, an artificial source of IF light at that frequency would have to be used. Manufacturers do use various frequencies, one typical pulse rate being Hz50 (fifty cycles per second).

You can shoot these narrow IF pulsed light beams across a door or window, down a long corridor, or, with mirrors and strategically placed openings, around a home or office (Fig. 3-20). Or by cutting holes in the partitions and using multiple receivers, one transmitter can cover quite a large area, as shown in Fig. 4-20.

Transmitters and receivers can be arranged in a crisscross pattern to set up a trap zone at a gate or factory door (Fig. 5-20) or beamed five hundred feet or so from transmitter to receiver in a pattern around a building to set up a perimeter trap zone (Fig. 6-20).

The crisscross pattern in Fig. 5-20 can also be effective up to five hundred feet from sensor to transmitter, which would effectively monitor long areas up to six feet high. The beams, remember, are only about an inch in diameter, so what you have is a network of fine, invisible wires that would detect motion.

Note also that the network in Fig. 5-20 has sensors that react at different times to minimize or eliminate false alarms from animals and other non-human objects. The IF "fence" can be any height, so long as the overall range

of the sensors and transmitters is not exceeded.

For residential or office and commercial use, pulsed IF transmitters and receivers can be disguised as electrical outlets or, for longer ranges, can be attractively styled (Fig. 7-20). Remember, though, the one stricture on any motion sensor; it's no good if you want protection during the day when you're moving around the house, especially if you have pets.

IF Installation Tips

For outdoor use, any pulsed IF sensor must be heated to eliminate fogging of optical elements during bad weather. This ends a common source of false alarms or system malfunction. In fog, effective range can be cut as much as 50 percent.

Alignment of the transmitted beam with the optical receiving elements of the receiver(s) is very critical and must be done very accurately. This is why, since the beam is only an inch or so in diameter, you can't use pulsed IF where vibration occurs. Vibration could affect optical alignment and cause a false alarm. An earthquake, to use an extreme example, would set off every pulsed IF alarm in the quake zone.

Among the better makes of pulsed IF units, I can recommend those made by Colorado Electro Optics, MESL, and Mosler (see Appendices).

The transmitter generates its light energy from a gallium arsenide light-emitting diode that should last around twenty-four years; the IF source is at 9,400 Angstroms.

Photoelectric Sensors

As a security device, plain old photo-

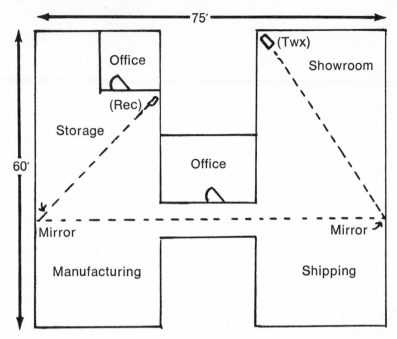

Fig. 3-20 / *You can do it with mirrors. Infrared light can be bounced around a building to protect a number of areas. Think of the light as a thin but invisible trip wire. IF units thus erect a motion-sensing "trap zone" to detect the presence of any intruder who "breaks" the beam.*

electric cells are just about useless. All you need do is shine a flashlight beam into the receiver to defeat the system. But if you want something expensive to ring a door chime, as in a store, when a customer crosses the threshold, photo-electric sensors are fine. The light beam, of course, is very visible.

Ultrasonic Motion Sensors

Ultrasonic motion detectors, like pulsed IF detectors, have both a transmitter and a receiver. The ultrasonic transmitter fills the protected space with sound waves well above the upper threshold of human hearing. Frequency of the ultrasonic sound is between 25,000 and 45,000 cycles per second. The receiver is tuned to the same sound frequency as the transmitter. Any person entering the protected space would disturb the pattern of sound waves within this area. The change in pattern will cause the receiver to go into the alarm mode.

Residential ultrasonic units are compact and come as a self-contained unit, sometimes disguised as a book. The 3M unit, for example (Fig. 8-20), plugs into the 110-volt outlet. It should be aimed at a trap zone near an entrance door and across as many windows as possible. Upon intrusion, an alarm within the unit sounds. You can also plug a lamp or a hi-fi that can blast a taped message that you're being robbed through an outside speaker (you furnish the speaker, the hi-fi and the tape). This unit is easy to defeat; all you do is pull the plug out of the socket and the noise stops. This type of unit might scare off an amateur, but it would be a minor impediment to a pro.

For the money, ultrasonic systems offer reliable motion detection, within the limits of their design. They can cover, with overlapping units, a large area, or the sound waves can be beamed along a long, narrow hallway. You can buy a more sophisticated self-contained system with built-in standby battery that defeats the plug-pulling attack noted above. Further, the circuitry has relays

that lock the alarm on until you turn it off with a key switch. Such a unit is made by Bourns, Inc. (see Appendices).

Ultrasonic Commercial Applications

The small transmitter and receivers of ultrasonic systems can be recessed and hidden in walls or ceilings. They are good back-up sensors to hard-wire systems in stores and offices, and can be wired into the hard-wire protective circuit along with magnetic switch contacts and fire sensors.

Fig. 4-20 / *Another way to obtain multiple area coverage with IF light is to use one transmitter and multiple receivers, with holes cut in the wall. Here trap zones are at ceiling, across an exterior wall over windows, and across a room.*

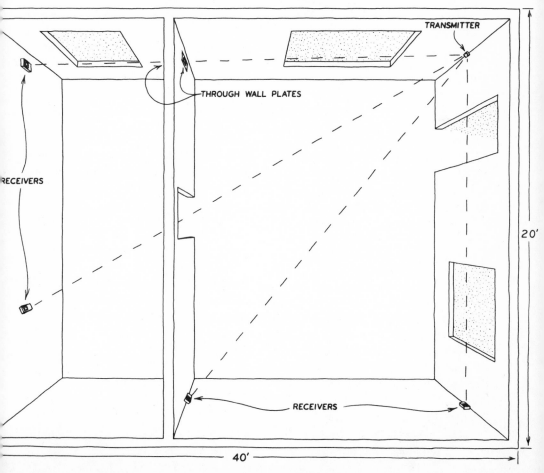

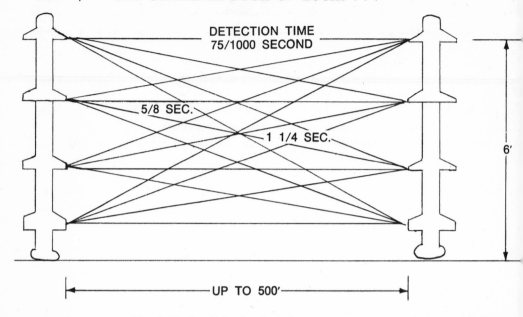

DETECTION TIME
75/1000 SECOND

5/8 SEC.

1 1/4 SEC.

6'

UP TO 500'

Fig. 5-20 / *Pulsed infrared motion sensors can be set up, using multiple transmitters and receivers, in a crisscross pattern over a long distance, outside or inside.*

Ultrasonic Detector Problems

Good as they are, ultrasonic detection systems must be used with great care. They are not suitable, for example, for a room with walls hung with rugs, because the rugs will, along with draperies, floor rugs, and furnishings, absorb the acoustic sound from the transmitter. By the time the sound reaches the receiver it may be weak, and the receiver may not be able to pick up any change in sound frequency when an intruder enters the room. In walk-testing one system I donned an oversize, heavy man's coat and walked slowly through the protected space, with the receiver sensitivity at maximum, in a "dead" room such as the one with the rugs on the walls (and the floor). Nothing happened. Had I been a burglar, I could have passed through the trap zone, although I doubt I could have made it back through carrying anything very large.

Ultrasonic Problems and Solutions

Problem: False alarms when heating or air conditioning blower turns on.

Solution: Install ultrasonic transmitter in direction of air flow from air outlets or fans (Fig. 9-20).

Problem: False alarms from waving curtains.

Solution: Tie them down.

Problem: False alarms every time the telephone rings, a car backfires in the street, and thunder occurs.

Solution: Glass vibrates to air waves from noise. If you have large glass areas, direct transmitter (or transceiver if combination unit) along windows, toward door trap zone (Fig. 10-20).

Problem: False alarms every time the system is turned on.

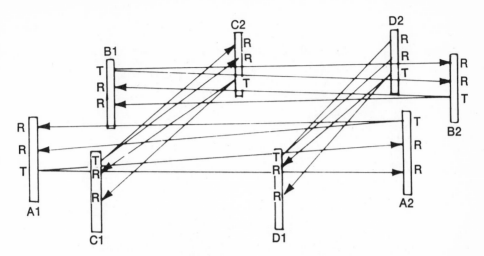

Fig. 6-20 / *Here infrared motion sensors are providing outside-perimeter protection around a building. Note overlapping coverage.*

Fig. 7-20 / *IF motion sensors can be decorator-styled for wall mounting, left, or disguised as electrical outlets for concealment, right.*

Fig. 8-20 / *Ultrasonic self-contained motion-sensor alarms for residential or private office use can be disguised as books. These units are made by 3M.*

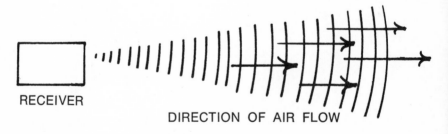

RECEIVER

DIRECTION OF AIR FLOW

Fig. 9-20 / *Ultrasonic motion sensors should be installed in the direction of air flow to avoid false alarms from air turbulence.*

Solution: The receiver and transmitter may be aimed at each other. These units must be installed side by side, about three feet apart. *Never* install different makes in the same area.

Problem: There are dead spots shown up by a walk test in the lobby of a building, where a person could bypass the trap zone.

Solution: Aim the transmitter diagonally across the lobby to eliminate dead spots by this trap zone (Fig. 11-20).

Problem: A burglar defeated the ultrasonic unit by spraying styrofoam into it.

Solution: Hide the transmitters and receivers in the wall and paint over them carefully with spray lacquer or fast dry-ing enamel; or put wallpaper over units. But if you do so, remember you cut their sensitivity about 25 percent.

Problem: When a machine starts up the unit false-alarms. Ditto when a heavy truck rumbles down the street.

Solution: Vibration will cause these units to false-alarm, for sure. Place them on a wall that is free from vibration, preferably an inner wall. If trucks still cause vibration that results in a false alarm, there may be no solution other than to go to microwave (see below).

Problem: A walk test a year after installation reveals the system is not responding to motion.

Solution: You probably installed heavier drapes, moved the furniture, added thicker rugs or did something else that absorbed more of the ultrasonic sound. Readjust the sensitivity and walk-test again. In a school, adjust sensitivity low enough to pick up smaller, juvenile-size bodies.

Problem: When the ultrasonic unit is on you get headaches.

Solution: Frequency of your ultrasonic unit is down below 20,000 cycles per second, too close to your threshold of hearing. You will have to install new units with a higher frequency, around 35,000 cps. *Check this before you buy!* Incidentally, the higher-frequency units can drive mice and rats out of the place.

Recommended Ultrasonic Detector Manufacturers

After reviewing the products made by hundreds of manufacturers and going over their specifications, I can recommend the ones made by these manufacturers (see Appendices for addresses): Sontrix, Ademco, Massa, Scan, A.P.I., Delta, Alarmtronics, 3M, Heathkit, Morse, Systron-Donner, Conrac, and Unisec. Residential models are made by Ademco, A.P.I., Delta, 3M, Scan, and Heathkit.

Microwave Intrusion Detectors

The most versatile of all the motion sensors are microwave motion detectors. They work on the same basic principle as ultrasonic sensors, except that instead of filling a space with high-frequency sound waves, they fill the space with ultra-high-frequency radio waves. The transmitter and receiver are mounted

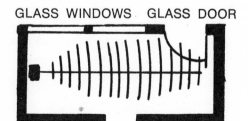

Fig. 10-20 / *To avoid false alarms from air currents due to movement of large glass areas, shoot the ultrasonic sound alongside windows, not at them, and set up trap zone at the doors, as shown.*

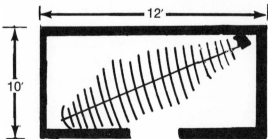

Fig. 11-20 / *In lobbies, aim ultrasonic unit diagonally across the space for best trap-zone coverage.*

side by side, about three feet apart. In some instances they are combined into one self-contained console box with control-box functions, built-in siren, and related equipment.

I said MW systems are versatile, and they are. By merely changing antennas, one basic model can cover an area 30 by 50 feet; 50 by 250 feet; 60 by 150 feet or 80 by 80 feet.

You can send a flat beam two feet thick, eight feet high and 250 feet long to erect an invisible wall of microwave radiation along the outside perimeter of a building. Anyone penetrating this barrier would sound the alarm. I suppose you could pole-vault over the unseen fence, if you know it is there and how high it is.

With overlapping units and varying antennas, you can very accurately direct microwave motion-sensor coverage to set up trap zones for almost any building configuration you have, be it wide and long, narrow and short, or whatever.

Microwave sensors can be very effectively used outdoors to do more than set up perimeter protection. They can project a flat, broad beam to set up trap zones around parked aircraft, over storage depot yards, in tank farms, and in electrical utility areas. When you think of all the crazies running around these days, and how vulnerable a highly technological society such as ours is to their attempts at sabotage, it's just plain common sense to protect these vulnerable areas. Guards can't be everyplace at once, nor can guard dogs (see Chapter Twenty-six). I would think any executive would want also to provide some measure of protection against intruders with arson on their minds, and against those who would sneak in and plant a time bomb.

The average microwave sensor can pick up man-sized objects moving three inches per second and up, or down, depending on sensitivity settings. Outdoor detectors made by recommended manufacturers (below) have built-in circuitry that compensates for smaller objects such as birds, bees, wind-driven debris, hail, rain, and snow. Unlike ultrasonic units, microwave detectors do not lose range or sensitivity under adverse weather conditions, nor are they bothered by dust and dirt coverage or dew and mist on the equipment as are ultrasonic units. Microwave sensors are also not bothered by air turbulence; or loud sounds or vibration to the extent ultrasonic units are.

Because MW radiation passes through thin plasterboard or wood walls, these sensors can effectively protect an office through these partitions. The radiation will not penetrate concrete, thick brick, or metal walls or floors. They are not affected by how "hard" or "soft" a room is, in terms of rugs, draperies or lumpen furniture that would absorb sound waves, as are ultrasonic sensors.

Not Radar or Dangerous

First of all, microwave motion sensors are *not* radar or anything like radar. MW sensors operate at 10.525 Giga-Hertz, radar at 450 to 900 MHz. MW motion-sensing systems put out an extremely low level of radiation, less than five milliwatts or five million times *less* than the 500 watts of the average microwave radiation in a microwave oven. MW sensor radiation will not affect radios, TV, calculators, hearing aids, or cardiac pacemakers. Nor will the radiation trouble animals or humans as do some ultrasonic units where the ultrasonic sound is too close to the threshold of human hearing.

My own feeling is that any alarm

manufacturer who calls his MW equipment "Radar" is not the type of supplier I would buy equipment from.

MW sensors are also unaffected by changes in temperature and humidity indoors, unlike other types of motion sensors.

How Microwave Works

As I said earlier, MW sensors work very much like ultrasonic sensors but use microwave radiation instead of sound radiation. The transmitter fills the space with high-frequency microwaves. The receiver monitors the "bounce" radiation off walls and other objects in the protected area. If an intruder moves into the area, the reflected or bounce radiation pattern changes, and causes the receiver to signal the alarm system and start the siren howling, a dialer to call for help, or a signal to go to a central station guard service which monitors the status of many MW sensors.

Microwave Problems

As you might expect, MW systems are not perfect. They do have their shortcomings, most of which can be worked around.

If you want to have a motion sensor in a warehouse or other building with large pillars or columns, or with shelving laden with thick boxed metal items, do not use microwave. The radiation will be blocked by any dense materials such as the above. Here is one application where ultrasonic detectors have a definite advantage over microwave.

Since MW radiation penetrates thin walls and glass, its effectiveness in areas with large amounts of glass is marginal. This would include automobile showrooms, where the radiation would penetrate to the street and passing people or cars would cause false alarms. You can use MW in these areas if you are careful to beam the radiation inward, away from the glass.

You might also have false alarms if MW radiation penetrates an occupied space adjacent, above, or below your own nonoccupied premises. For example, you may shut up the shop at 6:00 P.M. and arm the MW detector(s). But upstairs there is a tenant who moves around. The radiation could penetrate the ceiling and the moving tenant could cause a false alarm. You can work around this problem by beaming the radiation very carefully within the protected area. This, incidentally, is a good example of why MW systems should only be installed by experts. The walk test and subsequent adjustments can be fairly technical, and any false alarm problems you might have should be ironed out before you put the system into service.

Since MW receivers trigger the alarm when they sense motion, rotating fans, even water passing through plastic pipe, can cause false alarms. The sensors can be aimed away from fans, but the only solution to the plastic pipe problem is to wrap the pipe in aluminum foil, which is costly and is only practical at the time of construction. If the sensors are close to fluorescent lights, these could also cause false alarms; but it's only a question of moving sensors to another location.

Never aim MW transmitters and receivers at each other. The receiver should measure only bounce radiation and respond to any changes a moving body makes in this pattern.

Microwave for Stores

MW intrusion motion detectors are well suited to stores with large open

TABLE 1-20

MOTION DETECTOR COMPARATIVE ANALYSIS *

Sensor Type	Applications	Advantages	Disadvantages
Passive Infrared (Thermal). Senses heat from a moving body.	Small areas 20' x 20' or long corridors up to 65'.	Very stable, not prone to false alarms, easy to install, hard to defeat. Concealable.	Limited coverage.
Pulsed Infrared. Senses movement by disturbance of IF light beam.	Small or large areas up to 500' inside, to 1000' outside. Wider protection with overlapping sensors.	Hard to defeat. Can use mirrors to shoot protection around corners. Moderate cost for large or small areas. Good back-up to hard-wire. Ideal for warehouses. Concealable. Low cost.	False-alarm prone from vibration, dust on units. Requires very precise optical alignment between transmitter and receiver.
Photoelectric. Uses beam of visible light.	To ring a bell when a door opens, as in a store.		Almost useless as an alarm since the beam can be defeated with a flashlight, and is highly visible.
Ultrasonic. Senses intruder disturbance of ultrasonic sound pattern.	Small and large areas with multiple units. Ideal for large warehouses for aisle coverage where microwave won't work. Back-up to hard-wire alarm systems. Perimeter alarms outside a building.	Simple to align and install. Moderate cost. Hard to defeat. Can be tailored for wide variety of spaces.	False-alarm prone from air motion, turbulence, changes in humidity and temperature, sudden noise as when the phone rings, vibration of glass, or walls that cause air movement. These problems can be solved by correct application.

TABLE 1-20 (Continued)

Sensor Type	Applications	Advantages	Disadvantages
Microwave. Senses intruder disturbance of microwave pattern.	Stores, factories, offices, schools, marinas, airports, tank farms, utilities, indoor and outdoor applications.	Not affected by air turbulence, room furnishings, changes in temperature and humidity, air pollution. Versatile in applications, stable if properly and correctly installed.	Not for warehouses due to wave blockage by columns and shelves. Penetrates glass and thin nonmetallic partitions so must be carefully installed. Requires professional competence to install. False alarm-prone to moving fans, machinery, fluorescent lights.
Proximity. Sets up electrostatic field around a protected object. Sets off alarm if a person comes near or touches object.	For spot protection of up to a row of 20 desks, filing cabinets or safes.	Stable, moderate cost, wires into protective circuit or can have own control box. False-alarm free if properly used.	Protected items must be electrically insulated. Nearby metallic nonprotected objects must be grounded.

* All motion sensors except proximity units share the problem that protection cannot be made while a space is occupied. If you want protection while you're moving about the house, for example, you can't use motion sensors. A hard-wire system would be the answer.

areas. The MW energy should be beamed down toward the floor for best penetration into aisles and behind counters where a person could hide until the store closed. Locate sensors to minimize "shadows" from columns, beams, and larger display counters that cut sensitivity. Set up trap zones at stairs and escalators. In supermarkets, don't try to blanket the entire store; this is not practical since the radiation won't penetrate shelves. Instead use MW for trap zones near check-out counters and in the rear of the store.

In liquor stores, blanket penetration is impossible since MW radiation will not penetrate the goods on shelves. You can set up trap zones at front and rear doors and at the check-out counters or near cash registers. If the store has a walk-in refrigerator, a second unit can be installed inside it, if it does not "see" any moving machinery such as fans and refrigeration equipment, which can be shielded with wire screening.

Microwave for Warehouses

Use MW for trap zones at entrances in warehouses, along the perimeter corridors near outer walls and just below ceilings or roofs to trap intruders entering by cutting holes in these areas. Trap zones can also be established around areas in the warehouse where high-value merchandise such as TV sets, cameras, and the like are stored. Do not beam radiation where it can "see" rotating machinery such as unit heater fans.

Microwave for Factories

MW can provide stable trap-zone protection in factories, provided you allow for shadow effect of columns, heavy machinery, and parts. If manufacturing operations involving moving machinery

and people are involved, the MW radiation can be beamed away from these areas. A clear zone can be provided to permit guards to walk through the protected area without causing a false alarm. Be aware of false-alarm problems from mice and rats which can climb up into the protected area.

Offices and Schools

Best way to use MW in schools and offices is to beam radiation down long corridors and hallways to set up trap zones in front of rooms. MW units can squirt radiation down 300-foot-long corridors. You can also protect large auditoriums, gyms, cafeterias, and libraries with MW detectors, but watch out for beams penetrating glass or glass block walls.

Microwave for Banks

After-hours protection for vault and cashier areas in banks is a good application of MW. Microwave is also very effective protection for inside vaults.

For Residences

You can use MW in homes, but not if you want protection during the day when you're home and moving about inside, unless you're willing to stay upstairs. Self-contained MW transceivers have exit/entry delay that will let you get to the unit and shut it off on return before the alarm goes off, and time to get out of the house for the same purpose.

You have to be careful, though, to adjust range so radiation does not penetrate walls and go outside, where passing people or cars could trigger the alarm. Foil-backed insulation in exterior walls should pretty well contain the radiation inside. If not, even the waving branches of a tree (forgive me, Joyce Kilmer) could set off a false alarm.

Excellent residential self-contained MW systems are made by Advanced Devices, Pinkerton, and Racon. Pinkerton's Model Minuteman II covers a thirty-five-foot-diameter area; Racon's model 1000 covers 100 by 35 feet and costs $348. This is a lot less expensive than professionally installed magnetic switches on windows and doors, wired to a control box. Any residential unit should have tamper switches, outputs for an exterior siren or bell and telephone dialer, inputs for fire sensors, battery standby, and built-in or optional charger. A keylock switch is a must, as is a walk light so you can check the system without setting off the alarm.

Recommended Commercial MW

MW systems for commercial and industrial use I can recommend are made by these companies (see Appendices for addresses): Advanced Devices, Omni Spectra, Racon, Ademco, Shorrock, Security General, Peak Technologies, Alarmtronics, Pinkerton, MESL, and Johnson Controls.

About Proximity Detectors

Let's say you're a manufacturer of proprietary medicines, a producer of chemicals, or a manufacturer of automobiles. Somewhere in your plants are filing cabinets full of trade secrets a competitor would just love to have. You need to protect these filing cabinets from unauthorized entry twenty-four hours a day, yet cannot set up an alarm system in the general area because adjoining areas are occupied during the day. Or you want to keep snoopers away from key executives' desks when they are out of the office at any time. You may have a row of such desks, or even a row of safes or computer-tape safes you want guarded on the same basis.

The answer is a proximity sensor. One of these sensors can protect a row of nineteen or twenty filing cabinets, desks, or safes, without protecting anything more than four or five inches from them. These sensors are called proximity or "capacitance" sensors. They set up an electrostatic field around the objects to be protected. The capacitance effect of the human body changes the pattern of the electrostatic field around the protected item and sets off the alarm when a person gets to within ten inches or closer, or touches the protected item. To set up the electrostatic field around protected units, the units (desks, filing cabinets, safes, et cetera) must be electrically insulated from the floor and from each other. Any large metal body nearby, such as an unprotected safe, must be grounded. You can always tell when a safe or filing cabinet is proximity-detected by the insulating blocks underneath it.

The proximity sensor is hard-wired to a central control panel or box, to its own control box, or to a central guard station which can monitor this alarm.

Systron-Donner's Model CA-3 proximity alarm can protect up to twelve filing cabinets, is UL approved, has a sensitivity adjustment (so the field of protected approach can be as little as two inches or be the protected unit itself), has humidity and temperature compensation, and will sound the alarm if its wires are cut.

GTE Sylvania's Model CPS-1 can detect a human body up to two feet away, can protect up to twenty desks, meets military requirements, and goes off if wires are cut or power fails.

21

YOUR FORTRESS ROOM . . . A SAFE HAVEN!

For as little as $120 you can turn one room into a fortress haven against invasion of your home by psychopathic types. Here's how to create this bastion of safety.

HARDLY A DAY seems to pass without an account of a home invasion by brutal thugs, in which one or more members of a family are murdered or beaten without apparent reason. That home invasions by vicious criminals are on the rise is a fact that concerns police not only in our major cities; rural homes have become targets for these wanton attackers as well. The wealthy as well as the poor are equally likely to find a gang of hoodlums in their homes; the kidnapping of wealthy people and the beating or murder of the elderly seem almost to be a pastime among the criminally inclined.

Good locks and a working burglar-alarm system offer protection, indeed. But not against people who crash these barriers without regard for their own safety. One needs a place of safe haven, a fortress bastion within the home that will buy more time against a determined invader; time for police to come, time to live until they do. For as little as $120 you can turn your master bedroom into such a retreat; that is what this chapter is all about.

Which Room a Fortress

If you have a multistory home, select the second-floor master bedroom, or at least a second-floor room, as your fortress haven. That way you can get to it fast from the first or the third floor. If you have a single-story home, the master bedroom should be your barrier. Whichever room you choose, make sure it is not accessible from the outside via a nearby garage roof, for example. First-floor fortress-room windows should have bars on the *inside,* and one window's set of bars should be hinged so you can get out in case of fire; that set can be locked (see Chapter Eleven).

The Door

Unless you live in a very old home, chances are your interior doors are hollow-core or panel-construction. These types of doors a determined person could kick or hack his way past in a minute or two. To buy time against this attack install a solid wood-stave door and reinforce it as discussed in Chapter Nine. Also reinforce the door frame and pin the hinges as in Chapter Nine.

The Lock

On a strong fortress-room door I would install an interlocking deadbolt (Chapter 3) with a thumbturn on the inside and nothing showing on the outside to indicate a lock on the door. You can lock the door quickly with the thumbturn, there's no key to fumble around for, and if a child accidentally locks himself in, you should be able to tell him how to get out (if he can turn it one way he can turn it the other). Since the door is solid wood-stave design, and you have reinforced it with metal rods around the lock areas as described in Chapter Nine, the thumbturn is all you need to operate the lock. A key is not necessary. The thumbturn is quick to work.

A little slower to work, but adding a lot of locking strength to the door are two little Snib devices. These locking

devices I would install at about twelve inches from the top and bottom of the door. They're easy to install and use, and give you a wedge type lock that's very hard to force. The cost is about $4.50.

The Telephone

There are two approaches you can take to defeat attempts at cutting the telephone line into your home. First, if your home is under construction and you make arrangements with the phone company ahead of time, the incoming line off the telephone pole can be buried underground. There would be no charge for this service. In an existing home, the charge would be about thirty dollars or more if the line has to run under or around an obstruction such as a concrete roadbed.

Since the line can still be cut where it leaves the telephone pole, the other solution would be to install a CB transmitter/receiver in the fortress room. The antenna wire to the unit could of course also be cut and to defeat this attempt that part of the antenna lead-in wire outside the house should be inside an ordinary galvanized water pipe. The pipe of course can be cut too. The point of all these techniques is to slow up any attempt at isolating you before invading your home.

With a good antenna the maximum legal height above your home (see FCC regulations that come with your license) you should be able to reach out up to twenty-five miles to another base unit and ten to fifteen miles to a mobile unit (in a car or truck). That's in the country. In the city your range will be much less, but given the concentration of CB radio today, there will always be a clutch of CB'ers on the air who will be willing to help you. To call for help in a major city, use emergency channel nine, which is always monitored by a CB group and in some instances by police. In other places, use the trucker's channel nineteen, or switch to any channel in use and break in with your emergency call as soon as one of the parties stops talking. Use the word "Mayday" and say "Help" a lot to get listener attention.

Since the main power wires for house current can also be cut (or the power fail) your CB radio should be battery powered. I use the cheapest and smallest 12-volt auto battery in the Sears catalog, along with a small trickle charger to keep the battery topped up. The CB unit I like is United States-made and very reliable; it's E. F. Johnson Company's Messenger Model 123A with twenty-three channels.

Panic Button

If you already have a burglar-alarm system, you should have a remote panic button in the master bedroom that will trigger the alarm. If not, it's a simple matter to install one (see Chapter 15).

Costs

If you use a second-floor room, do not install a CB radio and do all the labor yourself, you can convert one room to a fortress bastion for about $120. Labor would be about $55. Adding a CB radio with antenna (less water pipe for lead-in wire) would be another $285. If you use a first-floor room, add about $50 per window for bars.

Here is a breakdown on estimated costs:

	Parts	Labor
• Replace hollow core door with solid core door	$85	$25
• Pin door hinges	1	10
• Snib locks (2)	9	5
• Install interlocking deadbolt with thumbturn only	25	15
• CB transceiver	150	0
• CB antenna and lead-in wire	100	35
• Bars for first-floor windows (per window)	45	5
	$415	$ 95
		415
		$510

Lights

You could also have a light switch inside the fortress room that would turn on lights in other rooms in the house and yard lights on and off to confuse invaders. You could also have a master light switch in the fortress room that would turn off all the lights in the house except in that room, to force invaders to use a flashlight or stumble around in the dark. Wiring costs vary so much depending on home construction I won't even try to estimate them. If your home is under construction then of course such wiring costs would be very nominal because wiring would be very easy to do before dry wall or plaster is applied.

The basic fortress room cost of around $120 is well worth the peace of mind it can bring, particularly if you feel vulnerable because of your location or personal situation.

22

PERIMETER INTRUSION DETECTION . . . WHERE CRIME BEGINS!

All about concealed sensors that detect an intruder the instant he walks on your property or climbs your fence.

OUT WHERE CRIME begins, at the very edges of your property, is the place to set up an early warning system of intrusion detection. Such a system will alert you to the presence of an unwelcome intruder anytime he trespasses on your land. You can ring the entire grounds with buried seismic detectors tuned only to human footfall or vehicular movement, or use both types for both kinds of intrusion detection. You can set up intrusion detectors of this type at specific sensitive areas on your grounds.

If you have a fence, you can turn it into one interconnected trespass sensor by attaching motion sensors to the fence. One thing is certain with these types of sensors, they give you around-the-clock early warning that could only be dupli-

cated by wall-to-wall human guards; and I'd bet on the sensors to do the job better.

The "tuned" sensors will only alert to what they are tuned to, the human body or a vehicle; nothing else will trigger them; not earthquakes, not rain, nor snow, nor sleet (forget gloom of night), nor animals of any size including bears. In Chapter Twenty I discussed perimeter protection with microwave and ultrasonic motion detectors. The seismic and fence (vibration) sensors in this chapter are much less prone to false alarms and can offer much more precise control of specific areas for specific types of intruders (people or vehicles, for example) than can the ultrasonic or microwave types in Chapter Twenty.

Seismic Sensors

As you walk over the ground your footfalls create a ripple of seismic energy that radiates outward, much like the ripple of waves created by a stone thrown into a pond. The seismic ripples of energy for each type of land disturbance are like a fingerprint; each type creates a specific and recognizable ripple pattern. For this reason it is possible to design seismic detectors that react only to a human footfall, or only to a vehicle. Combined, both human and vehicular seismic detectors can be buried underground to detect the passage of both. Seismic sensors can be buried in a path around a huge factory complex, or under a driveway or deep in the woods at sensitive areas to detect an intruder well before he can get to his goal.

Further, seismic sensors are "passive." They emit no sound, no radiation or light or heat and so, buried underground, are virtually immune to detection and therefore defeat.

BLID for Protection

One typical seismic-sensor system is Teledyne Geotech's Model IS-700 (Fig. 1-22). The zone of protection varies from around a foot to six feet wide, depending on how deep the sensors are buried; the deeper the burial, the wider the zone. Nothing outside the zone will trigger the sensors, so protection can be quite precisely located. The sensor itself, when triggered, signals a BLID processor that in turn sends a signal to a central guard station, either by direct wire or by radio. Typical cost for this system is $1,025 for a set of sensors to cover 150 feet, plus $381 for the BLID processor. Coverage can be as long as you need it, simply by adding more sensors and more processors. (BLID means "buried line intrusion detector").

Zone Protection

If instead of a long and narrow band of intrusion sensors as above, you want a broad-area coverage, Geotech's seis-

Fig. 1-22 / *Sensitive seismic-intrusion sensors can be buried underground for invisible and reliable perimeter protection around a large area of ground. Drawing shows Teledyne Geotech's BLID system.*

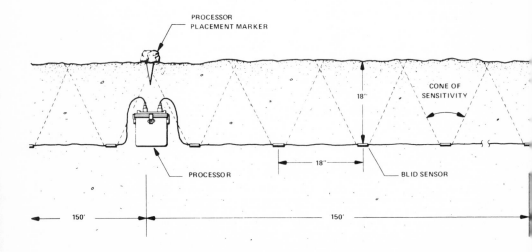

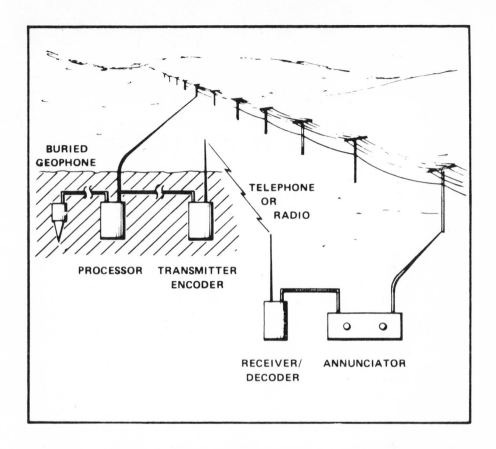

BURIED
GEOPHONE

PROCESSOR TRANSMITTER
ENCODER

TELEPHONE
OR
RADIO

RECEIVER/
DECODER

ANNUNCIATOR

GEOPHONE

AREA OF
SENSITIVITY

Fig. 2-22 /   *Top, buried seismic sensors can signal a central guard service by radio or telephone link from miles away. Bottom, a special seismic detector is designed for zone protection. Note circular trap area.*

COURTESY TELEDYNE GEOTECH

Fig. 3-22 / *One way to turn your fence into an intrusion detector is to install vibration sensors on every third fence post. Here a vibration sensor made by Norton Air-Space Devices is installed on a fence post.*

mic-detection system (Model IS-400, Fig. 2-22) will cover a twenty-five to two-hundred-foot radius for people, or a 1,500 foot radius for vehicles. For protection against both people and vehicles, use Geotech's Model IS-100.

Vehicle Seismic Sensors

Buried seismic vehicle detectors can be used alone or with the BLID system to detect vehicles as well as humans, as noted. Geotech's IS-300 vehicle detector can be buried under sidewalks, driveways, parking lots, or roads to detect snowmobiles, motorcycles, or bicycles, as well as the passage of cars and trucks.

This system can also be applied around entrances to detect the movement of magnets and so can pick up anyone entering a computer room or computer tape safe or vault with the intention of sabotaging these tapes and discs by erasing them with a magnet. More about computer security is given in Chapter Twenty-three.

Fence Sensors

You can turn your property fence into an intrusion perimeter detector in several ways. One way is to turn the entire fence into a sensitive microphone that picks up the noise of a person climbing the fence. The "microphone" in this instance is actually a very special coaxial cable that is tuned only to the vibration a person would cause by climbing the fence, or cutting the fence or the cable itself. This system, GTE Sylvania's Fence Protection System (FPS) can handle up to 984 feet of fence, and more by adding more cable. A signal processor in a central guard station can tell where the break-in attempt has occurred and actually can let the guard listen in to the noise at the break-in to determine what kind of attack is underway. This latter feature also reduces false alarms from large windblown objects, animals, and the like, and determines whether more than one person is climbing the fence.

Another less expensive but also less sensitive fence-alarm system is made by Air Space Devices Division of Norton Company. This system uses a vibration sensor mounted on every third fence post (Fig. 3-22). Each sensor is tamper-switched so the alarm will sound if the sensor cover is removed in an effort to defeat it. The alarm will also sound if the wire connecting each sensor is cut. Each sensor has a sensitivity adjustment, which is an advantage that reduces false alarms in area of high natural vibration, as for example from a nearby line of punch presses.

23

COMMERCIAL AND INDUSTRIAL SECURITY—AN OVERVIEW

In this chapter: Alarms to prevent shoplifting. Security for computers, schools, hospitals, apartment high-rise buildings. A review of modern security products for commercial/industrial application.

IF YOU OWN a store, live in a high-rise apartment building, or work in a high-rise office building, you don't need me to tell you that the risk of crime is great where you live and work. There are increasingly fewer apartment complexes these days of which it can be said no tenant (or condominium owner) has not come home to a burglarized apartment. In these troubled times schools are being vandalized to the tune of over $650 million annually, anything not nailed down in hospitals is being stolen, including drugs, and the loss of industrial secrets is a growing nightmare to business executives.

Despite all this crime, security is still a joke in many of these buildings. Given the competitive nature of high-rise apartment and condominium building today, you'd think builders would at least consider security as a sales feature, and in many cases they do. But I can defeat the security of most of the fancy new high-rise apartment buildings with no great effort, and so can crooks. High-rise office buildings are even more vulnerable. Formidable iron and steel and heavy plate glass doors do not a barrier make for even a moderately skilled burglar. A few determined men can sweep through an office complex and walk out with all sorts of expensive office equipment in minutes.

Burglar Alarms Catch Crooks

Yet it has been clearly demonstrated that burglar alarms in mercantile establishments, in hospitals, schools, and office buildings, do catch criminals and deter and prevent their crime. One classic study in Cedar Rapids, Iowa, involved installation of alarms in vulnerable downtown stores. The alarms were silent, did not ring on the premises, but were directly connected to police headquarters. As a result of these installations, Cedar Rapids police caught more burglars in the first eighteen months after the alarms were installed than in the four years before, and their conviction rate was 100 percent! The stores did not have a window or door sticker that let the burglar know he was facing an alarm system. Since professional burglars carry out ten to seventy jobs a year, taking just one out of circulation can be a major crime stopper.

Burglars Can Be Sophisticated

If the stakes are great enough, criminals can be as knowledgeable about electronics as the occasion demands. For example, in one multimillion-dollar heist of cash from the vaults of a Chicago security firm, one of the suspects was found to have in his home the printed circuit boards of the alarm company who made the alarm system installed in the security firm's vaults. It was clear that since the alarm did not sound during this burglary, electronic wizardry had been used to defeat it. There are ways to defeat even this insider attempt at compromising a security system, and these will be discussed later on in this chapter. First, let's review the alarm services now available to you.

Local Alarm Systems

Remember that we have already discussed the basic types of alarm systems, including hard-wire, wireless, dialers, infrared, microwave, and ultrasonic. To this collection I will add audio systems and some special window sensors in this discussion. But first I would like to review the various options you have as to how the alarm system calls for help and the relative merits of each option.

First, a local alarm system. This type of alarm does nothing more than cause a loud bell to start clanging away outside the premises should the alarm system be tripped. Someone outside has to hear the alarm and call the police. Normally it takes about thirty minutes between the time the alarm sounds, a Good Samaritan phones the police, and they arrive on the scene. Burglars know they can't depend on this much time, but barring the ill luck of a passing police car hearing the alarm, they do know they can break in, smash and grab and run with all the goodies they can carry out in a few minutes. The loss can be considerable.

This is why a local alarm will probably not be permitted by your insurance company if your premises are located where there are few people out at night and where police patrol is infrequent.

I should point out that any building requiring loss insurance can have their premiums cut up to 50 percent by installing approved burglar alarms. By approved I mean Class A-, B-, or in some cases C-rated Underwriters' Laboratories systems, installed by UL-certificated alarm system contractors. There's more about contractors and guard services in Chapter Twenty-five.

I would never install anything but a UL-approved alarm system of any kind.

The UL rating means the alarm equipment itself must pass rigorous tests, and that the equipment must be installed according to strict UL standards. The installing contractor must be certificated by UL, and his jobs are subject to unscheduled inspection by UL engineers (see Chapter Twenty-five).

Police Connect

Any type of alarm system, as I said above, can be connected to a local alarm bell. The same system can also be connected, via a leased telephone line, directly into the communications room of your local police station, if they will permit you to do so. There is a nominal police charge for this service, plus a moderate fee for periodic system check by the installing contractor, plus whatever the telephone company charges for the leased line (which does not have to be voice grade).

The disadvantage of a police-connect alarm is that the police are in no position to monitor or supervise your alarm equipment or telephone line connection for trouble. Police will not differentiate between trouble that causes a false alarm, and a real alarm. All alarms are treated as real and they respond to all of them. If you cause the false alarm due to carelessness, or if your system has a lot of false alarms due to malfunction, police may ask you to remove the police connect, or charge you for each false alarm that ties up their men and equipment.

Answering Service Connect

You could, instead of connecting to the police, connect to an answering service. Charges should be about the same for either type of connect. Therefore I can see no advantage in connecting to an answering service that has to handle a lot of other types of calls. Furthermore, answering service people are not trained security personnel and may not respond properly to an emergency signal. You could of course use a dialer to connect to an answering service or to the police or both (see Chapter Eighteen), but be warned that Underwriters' Laboratories will not approve this type of connection. The dialer would eliminate cost of a leased line, though, so if you don't need a UL-approved installation, a dialer is one way to connect to two or three or more parties. As to the answering service, it is also easy to defeat. An armed man can simply walk in, wait for an accomplice to set off the alarm, let the answering service take the call and make sure they do nothing about it. A professional central-station service, on the other hand, is (or should be) guarded like a fortress, and I'll get into this aspect in more detail in Chapter Twenty-five, and to some extent below.

Central Station Connect

By far the most reliable outside alarm connection is to a good central station guard service (Chapter Twenty-five). There are a number of ways this connection can be made. For example, you can have a private leased line, or you can have what amounts to a line-sharing or party-line connection known as a McCulloh loop. The older McCulloh loops use a mechanical scanning device that is slow and cumbersome and that can be compromised, by, among other methods, initiating a number of break-ins at once on the same loop.

Multiplexing

The modern way to connect a protected-premise alarm system to a central station is via a multiplexing method, basically an electronic McCulloh loop. A device called a "processor" scans each protected premise on the loop every few seconds and asks for a "handshake" signal. If the system is working properly it will emit a steady tone, and the processor, upon hearing this tone, will know that all is well. If, however, the tone changes to a pulsating and intermittent mode (with a distinct tone for fire and burglary) the processor initiates an audio and visual alarm at the central station. At the same time a printout is made of the alarm, its location, time, and type, for a permanent record.

A multiplex system can scan hundreds of premises in seconds and do it around the clock, with a scan of each every few seconds. This type of system is a supervised system because it monitors the health of each alarm system on the loop. Further, even should a malfunction occur, either in the alarm system itself or in the telephone line connection, sophisticated equipment at the central station can signal and print out the type of malfunction.

Multiplex systems are very hard to defeat. However, they are not impossible to get around if the criminal has a duplicate printed circuit board that can be plugged into the circuit between the protected premise and the loop connection to the central station. As in the case of the multimillion-dollar heist noted above, an employee had such a dupe board and was apparently able to put in on a line so as to duplicate the steady tone from the protected premise, even though the premise alarm had been tripped. Since the central station received the tone from the stolen board it assumed all was well.

There is one way to make a multiplex system just about impossible to defeat, and that is with a system offered by Currier Smith Corporation. Here two high-security minicomputers are used, one at the protected premise, one at the central station. A Primer Unit loads the two computers with identical but unknown data that is mathematical or algorithmic. This data follows no known pattern and processes a code in pseudorandom form that will not repeat itself for thirty years. The two computers must give each other the same code at any given instant or signal an error. To defeat this system would be virtually impossible. Furthermore, in case one phone line is compromised, the Currier Smith multiplex system uses back-up telephone lines.

A Word About Telephone Lines

In any large building there are large metal boxes or closet-like rooms to which all the building's telephone lines are run for one floor, or for all floors. This junction-box room is for the convenience of the phone company to facilitate changes in phone connections of subscribers in the building. Since telephone lines are also used for alarm systems, phone company installers often label lines used for alarms with a brown sleeve or even a tag that identifies the line with the name of the subscriber. Naturally, if the phone installer can identify lines used for alarm systems at the junction box, so can a smart crook. I would put this book down right now if you have an alarm system connected via the telephone line and check to make sure there are no tags on your alarm line in the phone company's junction box that identify your alarm system. The phone company's convenience is a lot less important than your security, and you can quote me.

Shoplifter Protection

One out of every forty to sixty people in a store at any given time is a shoplifter. Only one in every two hundred shoplifters is caught. Industry losses are way up in the millions from shoplifting losses and from merchandise stolen by store employees.

One way to guard against the casual shoplifter is to protect high-value merchandise with electronic alarms that go off if the item is lifted off the shelf or a rack, or taken out of the department.

There are special electronic labels that can be fastened to merchandise that, if not removed by a clerk after a sale, will trigger an alarm when the garment or whatever passes a special sensor at a check point (Fig. 1-23). The label requires a special tool to remove it. The sensors will not react to unprotected merchandise the customer already owns, even to metallic personal items. Two such label systems are made, one by KNOGO Corp. and one by Stoplifter International (see Appendices).

Another shoplift control is simply a wire you wind through whatever you want to protect. Should the wire be cut, the electrical contact is broken, just as the circuit is broken in a hard-wire system (see Chapter Fourteen). If the circuit is broken, the alarm sounds. This type of alarm can be defeated by shunting a wire across outside the protected merchandise, then cutting the line. The shunt will jump the cut line and the circuit will remain intact, so far as the alarm is concerned. This item is made by Se-Kure Controls, Inc.

A more secure device that is much harder to defeat uses a coaxial cable that would be very tough to shunt and if cut triggers the alarm. This cable can also be wound around or through the handles of TV sets, irons, radios, tennis rackets, bicycles and other merchandise on shelves. The audible alarm reaches an ear-hurting 100 decibels. This unit is made by Volumatic Ltd. (see Appendices) which also makes a snatch-resistant money case (Fig. 2-23) that stains the money inside with an orange dye, emits a thick pall of orange colored smoke and sounds a 100-decibel alarm should anyone snatch the case away from the rightful carrier. If the snatch is made in a car, the smoke would fill the car interior or pour out of windows. The smoke, dye, and alarm unit of the case can be purchased separately.

Another variation of the shoplifter prevention equipment is made by Delta Products. Their Clerk-Alert system also uses a cable threaded through whatever you want to protect. Any tampering, disconnecting, puncturing, or removal of the cable sounds the alarm. Protected items on the shelf can be moved normally without setting off the alarm.

While I will discuss strain sensors in the next section, I want to mention their shoplifting application here. Strain sensors and transducers produce a minute electrical current if bent. They are so sensitive that if mounted on a clothing store rack containing dozens of suits or fur coats and just one item is removed, the alarm will sound. The strain sensor should be mounted on the top pipe of the clothes rack. Should several suits be sold, the new position of the rack structural member on which the sensor is mounted will stabilize the sensor and the alarm will not sound until another sudden change is made as by lifting off one or more suits or coats from the rack.

Fig. 1-23 /   A coded label attached to merchandise will sound an alarm if it is not removed by a clerk when the sale is made.

Stress Sensors

Ultrasensitive stress sensors that can detect 10 to 50 millionths of an inch movement in building structural members and shelves or clothing racks is available from Systron-Donner (See Appendices). These sensors can sound the alarm when a person walks on stairs, fire escapes, roofs, floors, or any other area. Sensitivity is adjustable so the sensor can, for example, tell if a garment is lifted, and I do mean "lifted" from a rack, a TV is removed from a motel room floor or table, an item is stolen from a shelf. The stress sensors can or should be cemented to structural areas where they will receive the greatest strain or stress such as beneath staircases, on fire escapes, under shelves or in the middle of floor beams, under floors of homes and house trailers. Sensors must be placed on the beam supporting the floorboards where the intruder will step, such as doorways, halls, and near windows.

If your building is vulnerable to attack through the roof or through the walls, a strain sensor on one or more roof or wall structural member can be an effective way of triggering an alarm should such an attack take place. It takes just a microscopically small movement of the structural member to induce voltage in the strain sensor and trigger the alarm.

These little sensors, only 3 inches by ½ inch by ½ inch, can be used on any structural member such as floor or ceiling joists, stairways, beams, or porches. They can also be used on tables, desks, and in truck and van bodies, on picture frames, and on glass and brick partitions; in short, on anything that flexes a minute amount. The more flexible the object the sensor is mounted on, the greater the sensor range.

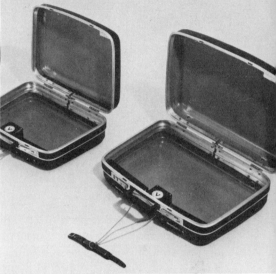

Fig. 2-23 / *A cash attaché case has a dye-and-smoke bomb inside. If an attempt is made to snatch the bag from the carrier, money inside will be dyed orange, and a dense orange smoke will issue from the case. At the same time a loud alarm will go off.*

An excellent strain sensor, made by Detectron Security Systems, Inc., must be used with a Processor which is wired into the protective alarm loop. Detectron's sensors have an LED walk-test light, and the Processor has circuitry that prevents false alarms from inevitable building settling, lightning, snow accumulation, or power line transients.

Store Windows

If you own a store, or even if you

Fig. 3-23 / *Window foil, to be effective, must be glued on about six inches apart. When this is done, appearance of the window display is spoiled.*

don't but want window glass protection, you probably have already seen one type of sensor on this glass. This is a narrow band of aluminum foil, taped in a special pattern and varnished to the glass. The theory is that if the glass is broken, the very thin foil will break, interrupt the protective alarm circuit, and trigger the alarm. My own experience has been that unless the foil is taped on four- to six-inch centers as in Fig. 3-23, the glass can be cut far enough away from the tape so as not to disturb it. Furthermore, the tape is thin and easily cut by children or vandals, or broken in the normal wear and tear of changing window displays. When the tape is broken the alarm will of course sound when the store is shut for the night. Some of these foil breaks are so minute as to be very difficult to find. And the application of the tape is fairly time-consuming and therefore costly.

A better way of protecting storefront glass against breakage is to use a tiny round sensor that fastens to the window with pressure sensitive tape (Fig. 4-23). These units are tuned to the frequency

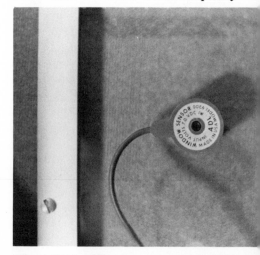

Fig. 4-23 / *This tiny sensor is glued on a window where it protects up to 10 square feet of glass area. Multiple sensors can be used for large areas, and are much less obtrusive than aluminum foil strips.*

of breaking glass, and will protect up to a ten-square-foot area. Multiple sensors can be used to protect any size window. Besides breaking-glass frequency (around 16 to 20 kc) these sensors are available for other types of attack, such as drilling (15 to 20 kc); crunching (to 10 kc), and other special vibrations. They can also be mounted on walls or ceilings.

However, for store windows these little sensors offer more than just good security. They are very inconspicuous, and so do not spoil the looks of an otherwise handsome window display designed to sell merchandise. Your display person will love you.

An excellent window sensor is made by Alarm Supply Company and costs around $6. Another good sensor is marketed by Signalarm (see Appendices).

The better window sensors will not go into false alarm if the window is tapped from the outside or flexes under heavy winds. They must, however, be wired into the alarm system control box.

Lacing an Opening

Take a thin wooden dowel rod, embed a very thin copper wire in a slit the length of the rod, seal the slit over, and you have the makings of the most positive and secure intrusion detector you can have over openings in the building such as ventilator fans, skylights or on walls of any kind. The dowel rods with the wire are placed behind the opening, on the inside of the building. The rods are on four-inch centers. Any attempt to get into the building through this type of protected opening will break the dowels and the wire inside, thus breaking the protective alarm circuit and sounding the alarm. Another way to do the same

thing is to place thin copper wire in an interlaced pattern behind the opening. I prefer the dowel-rod method because it's sturdier, less liable to breakage and corrosion, and so less likely to cause a false alarm due to a wire break.

Either the lacing or the dowel rod setup is a job for a professional alarm installer if the system is to be UL-certified (see Chapter Twenty-five).

Audio Security Alarms

At 9:00 P.M. a loud buzzer sounds in a security guard's central monitoring station. The guard flips a switch and listens. Over a loudspeaker comes a whispered conversation, then footfalls. He hears the sound of a ladder placed against a wall, then the sound of breaking glass. He knows that a building, miles away, is under attack and long before the glass breaks he has dispatched an armed guard and called the police. In another instance, the alarm sounds again, and the guard listens in. This time he hears normal conversation between two teachers and it is evident that the custodian of the school had not turned off the burglar alarm. Now guards are not dispatched, and the false-alarm condition is remedied by a call to the school.

These two episodes are typical of what happens when an audio alarm system is installed. If the building, such as a school, already has an intercom paging system with outside speakers, the speakers can be turned into sensitive microphones that pick up even the drop of a paper clip. Electronic circuitry in the alarm system prevents false alarms from normal yard noises, such as children playing, but will trigger the alarm if it hears breaking glass, footfalls inside the building or other abnormal sounds.

If the building does not have an existing paging system, tiny ultrasensitive microphones can be concealed in strategic areas to monitor areas as large as 2,500 square feet. As you may have gathered at the beginning of this section, the central station guard does not have to keep his ears glued to a battery of loudspeakers connected to a couple of hundred audio-equipped clients. If an alarm sounds in one of the buildings, as I said, a loud buzzer informs the guard that something is going on, that the audio system has picked up an unusual noise. A panel light or a printout tells him where the break-in or possible break-in has occurred. From his station the guard can listen in to the building to double check whether there is an actual intrusion, or whether the alarm is false, and take appropriate action.

Audio systems are expensive. They use leased, dedicated, voice-grade telephone lines, but they do eliminate a lot of false alarms and they do give some advance idea as to whether the police can expect to cope with one intruder, three or four, or a dozen.

The mikes in an audio system are frequency-sensitive, and a pulse counter keeps the alarm from sounding at the first sound. But if a second sound occurs, the alarm will sound; thus false alarms are reduced at the site. If a massive noise, such as breaking glass, occurred, the alarm would also sound. Better audio systems use a small computer programmed to distinguish between all noises normal to the protected environment and those which are peculiar to an intrusion or attempt at intrusion.

It's very tough to defeat an audio system. The phone wires could be cut, but then the alarm would sound and police would come for sure. In schools the kid vandals will punch holes through mikes if they can find and reach them, which is why they should be concealed and kept in baffled metal enclosures.

Audio systems are ideal for large warehouses, schools, large garages, and similar buildings. Since the central station can hear what's going on, it is possible for you as the owner or operator to talk to the central station direct, using the audio system. Normally you or your representative would be called by the guard service, along with police, in the event of an alarm.

Audio systems have other uses, too. For example, they have picked up the sound of running water from a broken pipe and so prevented a lot of damage to machinery and goods in process.

Acron Corporation and Alarmtronics Engineering make audio systems that can either use existing intercom speakers as microphones, or separate mikes. Like these systems, Multra-Guard, Inc., has a system (Fig. 5-23) that monitors various zones in a protected area and alerts the guard when an intrusion is detected.

I cannot recommend audio systems for residential use. There's always the possibility you will forget to turn the alarm off when you get up in the morning and anything you do or say will trigger the alarm system and be overheard at the remote central station. But more important, you cannot have protection during the day, if you're home alone, with an audio system, any more than you can with an ultrasonic, microwave, or infrared system.

Again, the only practical residential full-time alarm system is magnetic contact switches, hard-wired or wireless, connected to a control box. Delta Products does make a digital dialer (Fig. 6-23) that will call for help. The dialer has a sensitive microphone so that whoever answers the call can use it to listen in on the protected area. However, po-

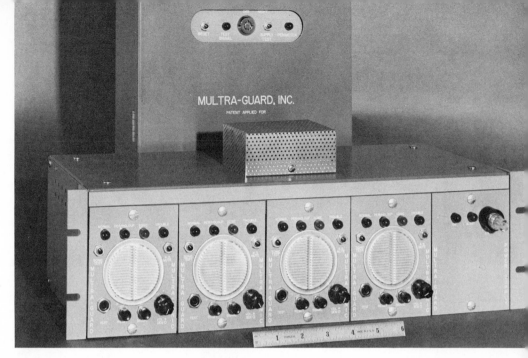

Fig. 5-23 /   *Acoustic or audio alarm systems can pick up even the drop of a pin inside a guarded area. Guard monitors can tell how many people are doing what by listening in.*

Fig. 6-23 /   *Variation of an audio detector is this Delta digital dialer with microphone pick-up. When the alarm is triggered, the dialer calls for help, then lets the called party listen in to the protected area.*

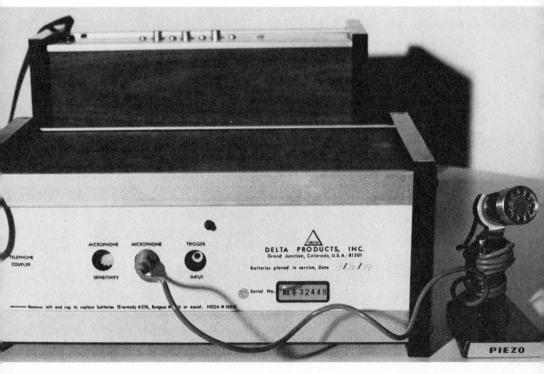

lice won't respond to a digital dialer because they won't know what the beeps are for or from whom they are coming. An answering service can tell, if they are trained well enough, but I still prefer the somewhat less reliable tape dialer which gives a straightforward voice message.

Access Control

How many people have a key to your place of business? Can you tell which of them has used his key at any time? No? Now hear this. Once there was a manager of an appliance store who came to work one morning to find he had been cleaned out during the night. Since there was no evidence of forcible entry, the insurance company would not pay off. But enter an access control lock, made by Silent Watchman. Inside this lock there is a telltale tape that prints out a special code that does tell which key held by which employee is used. The manager checked the tape, the tape told whose key had been used. Since that employee had an ironclad alibi, the finger was pointed at his son, who, dragged from his high-school history class, confessed.

There's more. Sophisticated electronic circuitry and a magnetically imprinted card (Fig. 7-23) can control access on up to one hundred entrances for more than twenty thousand employees, with central station printout (Fig. 8-23). Among other firms, this equipment is made by Rusco Electronic Corporation and by Cardkey (see Appendices).

CCTV

Closed circuit television has many obvious applications in monitoring hotel lobbies, corridors, loading docks, and bank areas where human discretion is needed to decide what type of action

Fig. 7-23 / *Access control with magnetically imprinted cardkey that actuates an electric door lock can keep unwanted people out of a restricted area.*

►
Fig. 8-23 / *This Rusco central station monitor is used with their magnetic cardkey. CCTV is optional. Note printout unit at right, which keeps track of cardkey usage.*

to take in a particular situation, and to deter crime by its very presence.

What is not a very good crime stopper is the phony TV camera you see in some stores. This inexpensive gadget would only fool an amateur; pros know it for what it is. And in any case, even if the camera was for real, a stick-up man could get his loot in a minute and be gone. It should be obvious to any thinking person that the fake, or even real, CCTV in a small store such as a liquor shop, is totally impractical. Who is back there watching the store through the

camera, to call the police? The owner's wife? His child? Why not use a one-way mirror instead? Who is going to spend his entire waking hours glued to a TV monitor anyway?

There are many practical uses for CCTV, of course, and for surveillance of occupied areas it does have some practicality, but not much so long as constant human vigil is required. Better applications for CCTV are monitoring sensitive areas at night, when no one is supposed to be around. Sophisticated circuitry will sound an audible alarm at a central station to alert the guard to watch a particular monitor, should the camera detect any movement. The guard can decide what action to take by watching the scene. The guard should be able to tilt, pan, control scanning speed, and even wash the lens remotely. CCTV will pick up and sound the alarm for such dangerous nonintruders as running water from a busted pipe, smoke, or any other moving object where quiet is supposed to reign.

Getting back to occupied-area CCTV surveillance, I do think supermarket parking areas and other private parking lots should be monitored, at least in areas where muggings and rapes have occurred. The guard can look at the monitor often enough, at least, to check for these crimes. However, if the camera is not concealed, a criminal can watch the scanning rate and do his stuff quickly when the camera is pointed elsewhere.

Protecting Apartment Complexes

The economics of size can drastically reduce the cost of a quite sophisticated and reliable alarm system in a large apartment building complex. For example, in one Washington, D.C., building with 1,020 apartments, per-apartment cost was only about $200. This system uses conventional magnetic switches on doors and first-floor windows, smoke and heat sensors. Each apartment has its own control panel, and the occupant decides when to turn the alarm on and off. Each panel has its own key-lock control switch, an emergency button that responds at a central guard station and a hidden emergency button in the apartment. A computer scans each apartment every few seconds to check the status of each apartment alarm, as well as sensors elsewhere in the building. The central station system of course can pinpoint which apartment has an active alarm condition, and tell whether the problem is an intrusion or a fire. A delay timer lets tenants in and out of the apartment without setting off the alarm. This system also guards key points in corridors, laundry rooms, game rooms, lobbies, and elevators.

I mention this installation in some detail just to point out that alarm systems need not be expensive if planned for early in the building design stages, and that they can be an effective merchandising tool.

One excellent integrated alarm system for high-rise apartment buildings is made by Westinghouse. The control panel (Fig.

9-23) has a talk capability with the guard station, an emergency or panic button, arm and acknowledge buttons, door control switch, and test button. The panel contains an audible alarm to alert the tenant to an intrusion or a fire. Fig. 10-23 shows how the system is connected to the central guard station.

Camera Surveillance

The Patty Hearst case has probably done more for the surveillance-camera industry than all the flacks they employ

Fig. 9-23 / *Westinghouse apartment alarm system connects apartment with guard station, has emergency call button, lobby intercom, inside audible alarm, test and other control switches.*

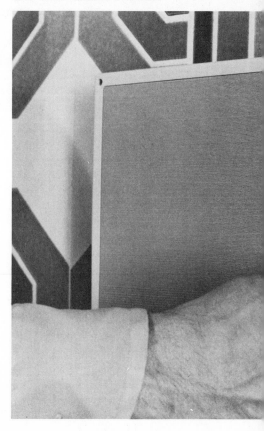

have done in the past twenty-five years. Certainly with a camera clicking off, slow frame by slow frame, what's going on during a robbery, it does not require your great-aunt to be watching a TV monitor over her knitting needles all the time. And unlike the human mind, the camera's film does imprint on its sensitized surface an objective portrait of the offender, and he knows it is a picture that will be highly incriminating.

These little cameras are not nearly as costly as CCTV and are a lot more practical for small stores (Fig. 11-23). The camera of course is not clicking away all the time, using up film. It starts only when a clerk presses a foot switch or other hidden switch. The better cameras, such as those made by Kodak, are Super 8mm, slow-frame motion, and have self-

adjusting shutter speed and lens opening to compensate for varying light levels during the day.

Computer Security

A disgruntled employee or an anti-establishment crazy can scramble your computer tapes so quickly and so thoroughly as virtually to put you out of business, if vital financial records and trade secrets are involved. The two aspects of computer security, alarm hardware and software aspects of computer use and the people who run them are what I want to cover briefly here. First, the hardware.

We have already discussed access-control systems and alarm equipment of every conceivable type. What remains is to apply this equipment to a computer facility. First, access control must be rigorous, and I would recommend one of the magnetic cardkey systems with recorded entrance/exit. The computer room itself should have vibration sensors on walls, ceilings and, if necessary, floors to detect any entry via these points, and magnetic contact switches on any exterior windows. I don't think a CCTV surveillance camera is advisable since computer people are pretty touchy about their privacy, and you may raise more problems with CCTV than it would solve. The only other solution to access control is a heavy steel door with magnetic lock and strike actuated by the magnetically coded card. Some firms use a clerk to check people in and out of the computer room. Being human, the clerk can err or be distracted, and so permit an unauthorized person to enter. Motion sensors, such as microwave, infrared, and ultrasonic units are useless because the room is occupied with moving people and machinery.

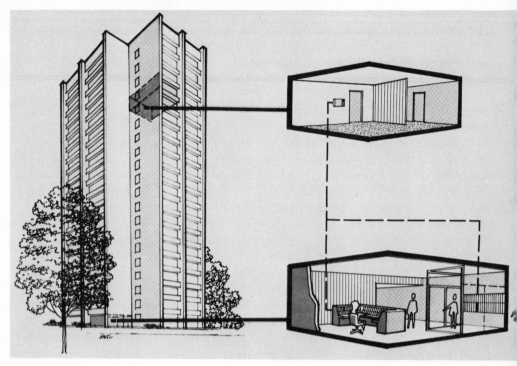

Fig. 10-23 /   *Apartment control panel is connected to a central Westinghouse guard station in a large apartment building.*

Any competent alarm installer can design a high-security intrusion-detection system and access control for you. Because computer tapes can be scrambled beyond hope with a powerful magnet that can be concealed on the person, all controlled access points should be equipped with sensors that will pick up a magnetic field. Teledyne Geotech, among others, makes such a sensor (see Appendices). You should also store tapes not only in a fire-resistant safe (Chapter Twelve) but in a magnetically shielded safe. Diebold's Data-Safe, for example, will protect tapes and discs inside against scramble attack by a 2,000-Gauss magnet, which if applied to the side of the safe will create less than a .01-Gauss electromagnetic field inside, far less than that required to erase your tapes.

Software aspects of computer security involve people and equipment use. Programmers in particular are or consider themselves to be creative people. They sometimes work long and odd hours. If a programmer shows up late for work one morning and your office manager or supervisor leans on him, you may have a very disgruntled employee on your hands. All computer people should be given scrupulously courteous treatment; not babied, but with the understanding that they have your whole computer world in their hands. Outside computer people, vendors and servicemen, should always be accompanied by one of your people because they could see your secrets, such as printouts, or even be after them.

Terminals should be turned off when not in use or the computer should print out this information so operators can be alerted. Program instructions or changes entered into the terminal should only be done by selected individuals using a key code, and such instructions recorded for later scrutiny. All computer activity should be logged, thus forcing personnel at least to go to greater lengths to hide any surreptitious activity.

I don't think you need worry, at this time at least, about tapping information that flows between terminals and a remote computer via telephone lines. The technology to do this is very sophisticated and hardly worth the effort. This is true, in spades, for telephone company microwave links (over rough terrain where coaxial cable is not strung). If you feel vulnerable, the transmissions can be scrambled, or cryptographed. Of course any computer-to-terminal communication can be compromised. What I'm saying is not to worry about non-sensitive data. And remember that the telephone company can help you filter any really sensitive data through a scrambler, which adds one level of security, or through a cryptographic code machine which adds a higher level of security.

Or you can buy your own scrambler from Technical Communications Corporation (see Appendices). Their Model DPD-72 which costs around $3,000 would require a properly programmed computer plus a person with cryptographic capability to defeat. For the highest security for a virtually undefeatable scrambler for computer data transmission, this firm offers their Model DPD-72A for $4,700.

Hospital Security

It was well after evening visiting hours when I entered a large hospital in Chicago. I was told I could not see my friend since the visiting hours were over. I nipped around the corner, took the elevator to the fifth floor and had no trouble getting to his room for an hour's visit. On the way out no one questioned me. In an even larger hospital complex I had no trouble at all in evading the guard and getting to patient floors. You won't be reading this section unless you work in, run, or are on the board of a hospital, so perhaps it comes as no surprise that only 23 percent of 196 hospitals in a survey had an alarm system and 33 percent admitted to inadequate guard services. Yet even rudimentary visitor control would require a three-shift guard service.

You also know, I am sure, that your hourly rated people have a high turnover, yet much of the disappearing foodstuffs, patient effects, and hospital bedding, clothing, and even drugs go out the door when these people leave, or before they do. A lot of high-grade meat and other food disappears in the garbage, wrapped in plastic bags for later retrieval.

Alarm systems for sure. Tamper-switched and high-security key-locked narcotics cabinets, yes. Patient-security deposit-type boxes under lock and key and a custodian would help. CCTV at key entry points and the parking lot where rapes and muggings occur could be a must in some hospitals. It may seem uneconomical to run a security check on hourly-rated people, but it's either that or face up to continued loss of anything in the place not nailed down.

Schools

As taxpayers we are forking out over $650 million a year just to repair the damage student vandals do to our

Fig. 11-23 / *Slow-frame Super 8mm Kodak surveillance camera can be a positive crime stopper. It works only when the clerk starts it with a floor switch.*

schools. Most of the vandalism is done to inner-city schools by inner-city students.

Lighting the school grounds and keeping random lights on inside the school does not help at all, according to a 1971 study that showed no correlation at all between the adequacy of lighting and the rate of vandalism. Will attacks on schools drop when they are open for night courses and recreational activities?

The more hours the schools were kept open, according to one survey, the more they were vandalized.

Positive steps that *have* reduced vandalism are good alarm systems properly maintained and monitored to detect break-ins, CCTV monitors in playgrounds, cafeterias, libraries, hallways, and parking lots, and, I regret to say, armed guards highly visible during the day.

24

HOW TO PROTECT YOUR PRIVACY

"The right of the people to be secure in their persons, houses, papers, and effects, against unreasonable searches and seizures, shall not be violated, and no Warrants shall issue, but upon probable cause, supported by Oath or affirmation, and particularly describing the place to be searched, and the persons or things to be seized."

AMENDMENT IV, U. S. CONSTITUTION

THE FOURTH AMENDMENT to the Constitution of the United States has been, in late years, more honored in theory than in actuality. Watergate was the tip of the iceberg of deep penetrations of personal and corporate privacy by electronic means. Corporate and private telephone lines have been and are still being tapped and bugged. Confidence in a government which illegally taps the private telephone lines of individuals cannot be said to be high, even today. As an individual in the public eye, or a corporate executive, your privacy may be invaded by anyone, anytime, with the fairly simple electronic knowledge and reasonably inexpensive electronic gadgetry easily available.

The bombing of prominent corporate executives by letter bombs, and of corporate headquarters and branch offices by larger, more lethal bombs, is a growing threat to the peace of our country. The kidnapping of company officials is currently even to be feared within the continental borders of America.

This chapter will cover the various methods of detecting and preventing the electronic invasion of personal and corporate privacy, and how to detect and protect against the growing threat of bombs of all types and kidnappings. Let's start with the electronic threat.

Electronic Surveillance

Your telephones can be bugged or tapped, or your office or home wired for sound with tiny but powerful radio transmitters. There may be a "bug" planted in your telephone, in your walls, your TV set, attached to the wires of your heating and cooling thermostat, behind a 110-volt AC wall socket outlet or in any of a thousand other hiding places.

Laser or microwave reflectors may be hidden behind walls against which powerful laser beams or microwave radiation can be aimed to pick up all conversation within a large area. The United States Embassy in Moscow, you may recall, was bombarded by microwave radiation so powerful it may have physically injured embassy personnel, and the answer to this problem is not yet certain.

Telephone Taps

A telephone tap is usually a clandestine device placed on your telephone line outside your premises, and so does not require penetration into the room. The telephone company has routinely tapped certain telephones in the past, for their own purposes, and cooperated with law enforcement agencies in this regard. Since Watergate and the focus of public opinion on tapping, this activity has, for now at least, abated somewhat, but don't count on this downtrend to continue.

You may hear clicks and noises on the telephone, and if you do it is faulty telephone equipment or an extremely amateur tapper who may have cut into your telephone line just outside the building or at the telephone pole. A sophisticated tap is entirely silent.

Your only protection against taps is to have a telephone scrambler (these I will discuss later on in this chapter) or not to discuss sensitive data on the phone at all.

Telephone Bugs

A telephone "bug" is a device placed in your telephone that transmits not only telephone conversations but all human conversation in the room to a clandestine listener. Some bugs are tone-actuated; that is, the bugger dials your phone direct, then sends a tone over the line that actuates the bug. Another method is a device that "lifts" your phone off the hook by defeating the cradle switch that shuts the phone off or disconnects it when the phone is put back on the hook or cradle. The phone remains down and seemingly disconnected, but actually the phone is now "live" and with a sensitive mike in the phone transmitter, everything in the room can now be overhead by the person who has dialed your number.

To defeat a telephone bug requires special equipment on the telephone that masks conversations so the bug mike can't pick them up.

Telephone line "sweeps" should be made either on an ongoing or periodic basis, with specially designed electronic surveillance equipment that will detect the presence of bugs and even tell you if your telephone line is tapped.

RF Invasion

There are myriads of tiny but powerful (up to a mile) FM transmitters that can be hidden in your room (not in a martini disguised as an olive). Their presence, and that of laser or microwave beams, can only be detected by sophisticated electronic "sniffers" on a room "sweep."

Private "Sweepers"

Equipment for a thorough job of detecting clandestine taps, bugs, and other audio privacy invaders is expensive, up to $3,500. If your company has a lot of phones and a lot of executive offices and homes to protect, this equipment may be a good investment for you, and I will give details and manufacturers' names below. If you are worried now, and don't want to invest in the equipment or the training to run it, there are many private firms who do such counter-surveillance work. If you can't find one in the yellow pages of your telephone book under security consultants and security control equipment and systems, there are three national firms I can recommend for this service; F. G. Mason Engineering, Inc.; Pinkerton; and Ashby & Associates (see Appendices).

Radio Transmission Security

I should also point out that any radio transmission can be tuned in and overheard, and if you need to protect the privacy of these conversations you should "scramble" them with the equipment I will note below.

Telephone Privacy Protectors

There are several grades of speech "scramblers" you can use with telephones and radio transmitters. The simplest and cheapest method is simply to invert speech frequency. The human voice in ordinary conversation goes from a low of around three hundred cycles per second to a high of around three thousand cycles per second. I am referring to speech only, not growling or singing or humming or whistling. The simple speech inverter turns the frequencies around so that the low frequencies and high frequencies of the conversation are switched in sequence. This type of frequency inversion is easy to defeat without electronic gadgetry. With a little training, anyone can learn to understand a frequency-inverted conversation; you don't have to be Donald Duck's girl friend.

A better way to scramble is with a pseudorandom generator that sends speech out in a random pattern. This also uses a matching decoder at the receiving end. But since the patterns are just that, they can be decoded with the proper equipment.

A still better way to speech security is to use a scrambler with spectrum shift that both inverts and shifts voice frequencies. The most secure scrambler of all is a bandsplitter which is a highly complex analog instrument that divides voice frequencies into bands of frequencies which are themselves shuffled around in a random fashion.

One of the best voice scramblers for telephones is Technical Communications Corporation's Model 207TW that uses a rolling code combination of bandsplitting and frequency hopping. There are also two radio models of this unit for use with AM, FM, and SSB transmitters. The 207's are wired to the units they protect and cost about $2,800.

But suppose you have men on the road who call in from time to time, and you want to scramble their conversations. For this you need a portable scrambler such as that made by Technical Communications. Their Model

Fig. 1-24 / *This portable device can "scramble" telephone calls to assure privacy. Made by Technical Communications, it requires a matching decoder.*

107P is carried in a portable carrying case (Fig. 1-24). A more compact version made by Mieco is their Privacom 25. Two are needed, at $285 each. This model has twenty-five codes that can be changed by pressing a button on each unit to the same code. This is a simple frequency inverter, the language of which is fairly easily compromised, so I would not use it for ultrasensitive data. Mieco's Model 38 uses four bands of frequency shifting, offers greater security, and costs $655 each. Their Model 35A costs $1,595, has five bands of frequency shift and Model 37 uses pseudorandom rolling codes and costs $3,700.

Other than scramblers, you can mask the telephone instrument so that taps and bugs are defeated by an envelope of random noise (you won't hear it). Ashby & Associates (see Appendices) Model 101 unit requires no connection to the phone, cannot be jammed, compromised, or bypassed, can be left on at all times (so you don't forget to turn it on), and can be used with United States and foreign telephones. It protects against compromise attempts from low or high voltages and implanted microphones in the telephone. It protects against transistor switches, high voltage swings, extra wires, bent hooks, shorting lines, capacitors and resistors, and radio or audio flooding signals. The 101 uses a complex shifting spectrum.

I should make one thing perfectly clear: I am talking about two methods of assuring telecommunications privacy. The first is scrambling the transmission. The second is setting up an electronic fence around the telephone instrument that defeats any taps or bugs in or on it. For maximum protection, use both methods. The first method uses electronic voice scramblers of varying degrees of security. The second uses electronic methods of shielding the telephone. The scrambler, for example, will not prevent a telephone "bug" from working so that conversations in the room can be heard even when the phone is on the hook and not being used. For this type of protection, use the Ashby device noted above, or the Dektor Cloak, a $3,500 single-line or $5,000 six-line device that detects and defeats all possible techniques for converting your hung-up phone, or its ringer, into a room bug. The Cloak detects radio frequency transmitters, telephone tap transmitters, power-line carrier transmitters, infinity transmitters (harmonica bugs), and listening on extension telephones (including nosy or spying telephone operators). The Cloak works on all foreign and domestic phones, either dial or pushbutton.

Radio Scramblers

If you use radio transmitters and want privacy, you can use a variation of phone scramblers, one of which I have already mentioned. Another model, made by Technical Communications for walkie-talkie use (Fig. 2-24) to be strapped to the transceiver case, costs $289.

"Sweeping" for Bugs

Yet a third way to protect your privacy is to sweep the room for any bugs, transmitters, or laser and microwave reflectors. I have already discussed private services for this purpose, since the equipment to make such a surveillance for these hidden electronic devices is very expensive.

For example, Counter Measure Security Systems' telephone bug detector costs $3,500. I won't go through the list of everything it detects, but there isn't a listening device in the world that has been used to date this unit won't pick up and sound the alarm about. Here are some of them:

- Series-type tape recorder starters
- Parallel-type tape recorder starters
- Series transmitters
- Parallel transmitters
- Audio frequency triggered switches (infinity transmitters or harmonica bugs)
- Hot wired microphones
- Resistance- or capacitance-defeated switch hooks (that "lift" the phone off the hook electronically)
- Resonant telephone ringers

The unit also detects all known methods of wiretapping from outside the premises and detects transmitter-type bugs.

Since bugs or miniature radio transmitters can easily be concealed on the person, you may want to check for this possibility when you are holding an interview or a conference. Counter Measure Security Systems has a Bug Alert that sounds a warning by meter and light, either of which can be on so as not to show. This portable device you can carry and use anywhere, and costs $1,000. It will also detect a bug hidden

Fig. 2-24 / *Voice "scrambler" provides privacy when using the public airwaves via a walkie-talkie. Requires a matching decoder.*

anywhere in the room, from a distance of twenty feet.

There are a great many other "sweeping" devices on the market, far too many to list here. The better models are made by firms already mentioned (see Appendices for addresses). I should add to this list products made by International Countermeasures, Ltd. (see Appendices).

Letter Bombs

Now we get into an entirely different subject, the area of terror, clandestine bombs, executive kidnapping, and industrial sabotage.

Letter bombs and other types of high-explosive attack were until recently pretty well reserved for political extremists of all shades, and aimed at those in political or other "sensitive" posts. Today the anarchists have begun mailing letter bombs to officers of major United States corporations, and I suppose it is only going to be a matter of time before this tool of anarchy becomes more widespread in this country.

Back in 1971, during one fifteen-month period, there were 4,310 reported bombings, more than thirty-five thousand bomb threats, forty-three people killed, 384 injured and $21.8 million worth of property damage.

Today the incidence of actual bombings, and related deaths, maimings, and property damage is growing as anarchists accept this form of terror as their instrument for ensuring social change, or as retaliation for some imagined harm. Whatever the reason, the fact is that every business executive of any corporation in the public eye, particularly those engaged in the manufacture of military products, however peripheral the involvement, must now concern himself with protection against bombs and kidnappings not only of himself but also of his family.

The latest and most pervasive and threatening bomb, not only because advance warning is never received but because of the ease of delivery, is the letter bomb. There are ways to protect against these deadly missives, but first, here is what to look for.

Letter bombs come in a variety of sizes and shapes, and the newer ones now use electrical firing systems instead of mechanical firing pins or systems. The number ten envelope size, an ordinary business-letter envelope, may contain one of these bombs. If so it will be stiffer and thicker than an ordinary letter and so bear extra stamps. Weight may be from two to five ounces. The letter will be thicker toward the middle, possibly $\frac{1}{8}$ inch at the sides and as much as $\frac{1}{4}$ inch at the center. When the letter is opened a pressure-release mechanism is triggered and the firing pin goes off. The $\frac{1}{4}$-inch area in the center is the firing pin and is a rigid area.

More powerful letter bombs come in larger manila envelopes, from $\frac{1}{4}$ to $\frac{1}{2}$ inch thick, disguised as a pamphlet. Envelope colors and sizes vary all over the map, from 3 by 6 inches up to 8 by 11 inches or larger.

Still more powerful bombs are being sent through the mails as a package, disguised as a book or a gift of some sort and they come in a wide variety of shapes, colors, and sizes.

All of these devices, even the smallest letter bomb, can kill or maim not only the person unfortunate enough to open the envelope or package, but those also in the immediate vicinity. If the spate of mailed bombs keeps up perhaps executives' secretaries and the mail room people should receive extra compensation for hazardous duty. Certainly they should all be briefed on what a letter bomb looks like, and be suspicious of any mailed (or delivered) package that looks out of the ordinary.

Letter Bomb Detectors

The bomb in a letter can be detected best by X-ray inspection. I don't trust visual manipulation or inspection, though certainly that is better than nothing, or taking a chance.

Several firms make special X-ray devices for package and letter inspection. One of them is Torr Laboratories' (see Appendices) MailScan (Fig. 3-24) that looks something like an office copier. It views contents of a parcel 18¼ inches by 12¾ inches by 6 inches thick or the equivalent of about 1,400 cubic inches. The parcel, or a batch of letters up to six inches thick, can be examined in less than ten seconds. Copper wires as small as .006 inches can be observed and low density plastics, typical of explosives used in letter bombs, are easily identified. When not examining letters and small packages, the MailScan can serve as a quality control tool or for radiographic studies or check of parts for internal defects. Fig. 4-24 shows an actual X-ray photo taken with the MailScan of the contents of a sealed package. Note the time-bomb mechanism in the lower center part of the photo and the loose staples on the heel of the shoe.

The Postix letter-bomb detector made by Balteau Electric Corporation (see Appendices) will accept letters up to 10½ inches by 15¾ inches by 1½

◄
Fig. 3-24 / *Letter-bomb X-ray scanner.
Fluoroscopes letters and packages to check
insides for any bomblike device.*

inches thick and packages up to 8 inches
by 8 inches by 4 inches. The Postix has
an internal conveyor belt that moves at
3½ feet per second.

Another approach to letter-bomb detection, used only with letters, is Astec's
Letar-Gard Model 3000. This unit scans
letters for any electrically conductive
material including both ferrous and non-
ferrous metals, in solid or liquid form.
A sensitivity adjustment allows for
staples and the like. If metallic materials are detected or sensed, the unit
sounds a shrill alarm. I would not say
this unit is as reliable as the two X-ray
machines described above, but it is quite
▼
Fig. 4-24 / *Actual fluoroscopic picture
of a package. Note bomb "works" at bottom center.*

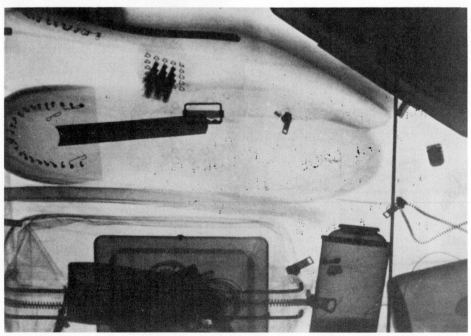

inexpensive compared to them and so a useful adjunct to a small office.

I should also point out that both the X-ray units mentioned meet all Federal standards and regulations as to safety in connection with radiation hazards.

Bomb Threats and What to Do About Them

Terrorists are sometimes not anxious to hurt a lot of people and so they will watch the building, determine when occupancy is minimal, and plant a bomb timed to go off at that time. But you can't count on their bomb expertise, and so must initiate a search for the bomb as soon as possible after a phoned bomb threat. All such threats must be taken seriously, not like the one some years ago which I experienced.

It happened one afternoon at about 1:30 P.M. at the Midwest Stock Exchange in Chicago. The telephone operator notified me that she had just received a call that said a bomb had been planted in the trading-floor area of the Exchange. The floor had about 150 people on it during the trading day, plus visitors in the gallery above the floor. I notified the president of the Exchange, Mike Tobin, who, being a pretty gutsy guy, immediately left his office and ran down to the trading floor. He grabbed the loudspeaker microphone and told the floor people the news about the bomb and suggested they could leave —perhaps, indeed, ought to leave. There was a moment's pause in trading, a dead silence above which only the ringing telephones and electronic trading mechanisms could be heard ticking and purring. The local and New York Stock Exchange tapes continued their mad pace across either side of the room.

Suddenly the raucous din of the Exchange's floor resumed, stock trading, buys and sells, went on as before and so far as I could tell not one floor trader, not one messenger, not one person left the place. I think now it would be different; that was back in 1971. Today we take bomb threats more seriously, I hope, and Mike Tobin, like other top executives, would *order,* would in fact have planned a quick evacuation on an orderly basis. People should not be given that type of choice. The police came with their bomb-disposal squad and could find no bomb.

If your company does receive bomb threats, remember that someday one of them could be for real. If you find a bomb, you may not have time to call any bomb-disposal squad, and may have to contain it yourself. For that reason I feel that the security department of any major company should have on hand one bomb-disposal blanket and know how to use it. One such blanket (Fig. 5-24) is made by Volumatic Ltd. and costs about $200. Another is made by Pinkerton's, and costs about $150.

There are a number of excellent pamphlets with sound information on how to handle a bomb. Two of them are *Bombs, Threats and Search Techniques* published by the Department of the Treasury, Bureau of Alcohol, Tobacco and Firearms, ATF P 75502, and *Industrial Defense Against Civil Disturbances—Bombings—Sabotage,* available from the Office of the Provost Marshal General, Department of the Army, Defense Supply Agency, Cameron Station, Alexandria, Virginia 22314. The booklets detail bomb search and evacuation procedures, how to handle a bomb if you find one, and give a lot more data about which I urge you to read for

yourself. Guardsmark, a professional security consulting firm, also has an excellent booklet, *Planning For The Bomb Threat*. Guardsmark is located at 22 South Second Street, Memphis, Tennessee 38103. The booklet also lists the locations of U. S. Army Explosive Ordnance Detachment Control Centers around the country you can call on if your local police do not have a bomb-disposal unit.

Meanwhile, here are a few tips about handling any container that looks, seems, feels, or ticks like a bomb:

Don't bring anything that seems to be or is a bomb into a police station. They will be just as helpless as you unless their bomb-disposal unit is on hand, assuming they have one.

Don't put a bomblike device into water; it may explode immediately.

Don't handle the package, try to untie its string or pull open a glued-down container; it may explode immediately.

Don't let anyone smoke near a possible bomb. Smokers will do anything.

Don't take for granted a package that says "Do Not Open Until Xmas" or some other innocuous phrase. Bombs are often disguised as a goody.

Don't attempt to twist or turn any part of a pipelike device. You may set off the bomb if it is one. Never shake, rattle, or roll any bomblike or suspected bomb package; you may set it off.

Don't move a package you think is a bomb to a location where great damage might be done if it went off, such as near a crowded area, under steam pipes, near an electrical generator, and above all do not place the package near a source of heat.

Executive Kidnappings

Enough executives have been kidnapped lately to give all the nation's top brass pause to think about preventing such an occurrence. One way is to use an armored limousine to get back and forth to work in. The limousine should be driven by a person trained in skillful evasive driving maneuvers.

One manufacturer of armored automobiles is Tetradyne, Inc., Richardson, Texas. Standard commercial autos are equipped with steel armored bodies and bullet-resistant windows.

Too bad, fellows, but that's one of the penalties of success. One becomes a target for terrorists and crazies at the top of the ladder. I wish I could offer another panacea, but until we find a quick way to change human nature and the human condition, it's going to have to be armored cars, locks, burglar alarms, letter-bomb detectors and a well-trained police department.

◀

Fig. 5-24 / *One way to contain a possible bomb until the police or military bomb disposal unit arrives is to cover it with a special "blanket" made for the purpose, such as the one shown here.*

25

HOW TO SELECT AN ALARM INSTALLER AND GUARD SERVICE

So many guards who work for private protective services are so poorly trained they can get you into costly lawsuits. So many guard-service central stations are inadequate they can be compromised. So many alarm installers know very little more about alarms than you do. Here's how to pick the right guard service and installer for your needs.

WOULD YOU HIRE a fifty-five or sixty-year-old man who has never fired a gun in his life, whose background you have not checked, give him a gun, and set him to work guarding your property? This man has absolutely no idea as to his legal arrest powers, when he is permitted to use his weapon and when, as your agent, he may kill someone illegally and cost you a fortune in legal fees and adverse judgments. Yet this is done every day by so-called professional guard services across the nation. Let me say right away that not *all* guard services

are this lax. The better-known ones, Pinkerton, Holmes, Burns, and other old established firms, do give their new guards pretty much the same training received by police rookies, and pay them a lot better than guard services that are looking for older, less physically able men who do not command the top dollar.

A sixteen-month study of private guard services conducted by the Rand Corporation for the Law Enforcement Assistance Adminstration, U.S. Department of Justice (*Private Police in the*

United States, Volume I: R-869/DOJ and Volume II: R-870/DOJ) revealed a chamber of horrors so far as this area of crime prevention is concerned.

The study found that guards received little or no training in the basics of law enforcement. Specifically:

- Of 275 security employees, 50 percent who answered carried guns and only 19 percent had received any firearms training on their present job.
- Over 97 percent of the security personnel made serious errors that could lead to criminal or civil charges in misuse of force and arrest authority.

The study also found that "substantial dishonesty and poor business practices exist" in the private-guard industry and that in most states governmental controls over these services and their employees either did not exist or were not enforced or exercised. Finally, the Rand study stated that: "The typical private guard is an aging white male, poorly educated, usually untrained and very poorly paid. He averages between forty and fifty-five years of age, has had little education beyond the ninth grade and has a few years experience in private security."

In selecting a private guard service with a central station facility, here are a few tips to guide you:

- The service should be UL-qualified to do Underwriters' Laboratories-certificated work and be able to issue you a certificate that your alarm system has met a specific UL Grade (check with your insurance company as to which grade they prefer you have).
- The company should have been in business for at least five years and have many customers you can check with as to the firm's capabilities and qualifications.
- Check your local police station as to their experience with the guard service's alarm installer. Ask about their runners (guards who check out alarms in your premises). Do they arrive ahead of the police or are they frequently tardy?
- Will the guard service spell out in writing its guard training program and policy?
- Does the guard service have liability insurance that protects you? Firms such as W. H. Brownard Corporation, One Merrick Ave., Westbury, New York 11590, offer third-party fidelity coverage as well as comprehensive across-the-board coverage. This includes coverage for assault and battery, errors and omissions, false arrest, invasion of privacy, libel and slander, contractual liability, canine, special broad-form property damage and other situations.
- All guards' backgrounds should be checked, guards should be bonded, and every guard should have passed a polygraph (lie detector) test.
- You can provide the guard service with a key to the premises so they can get in to investigate an alarm condition. But the contract should spell out that guards must not enter without police. Do not give the guard service the key to deactivate the alarm. This you should do yourself.

The Central Station, a Fortress

The central station itself, terminus of

your alarm, should be all but invulnerable to attack and compromise. Elsewhere in this book I cautioned against the use of ordinary telephone answering services and telephone dialers for commercial establishments; neither are reliable enough for this duty. A direct leased telephone-line connection between your premises' alarm system and a remote central station manned by trained guards offers by far the greatest security. Underwriters' Laboratories defines a central station as ". . . one in which the operations of electrical protection circuits and devices are signaled automatically to be recorded in, maintained and supervised from a central station having trained operators and guards in attendance at all times. Guards are dispatched to make immediate investigation of unauthorized entry or opening of protected properties from which signals are received."

Central stations, it goes almost without saying, are useless, no matter how elaborate their electronic equipment, if they can be immobilized by an armed attack. This is why the better central station is built like a fortress, and equipped to withstand a determined and forcible attack. Otherwise all the alarm systems connected to the central station would be useless if the station were to be overrun by a criminal gang, which could then pillage all the stores involved at their leisure.

One of the best central stations I have seen is that of the Foell-McGee Alarm Company, Louisville, Kentucky. A front view of this station is shown in Fig. 1-25, a rear view in Fig. 2-25. Note the almost total absence of windows, the squat but still handsome appearance, the radio transmitter tower. This is to me the ideal central station. Access control is strict, riot guns hang on the walls inside ready for instant use. You see no telephone or power lines coming

Fig. 1-25 /   *Front of an ideal central station. Note absence of windows, fortresslike appearance, ventilator intake at top of roof, radio antenna at right.*

to the building because they are buried underground where it would be difficult if not impossible to cut them, certainly not without being seen. The firm does not discuss external perimeter alarms, but it is very likely they are installed to detect stealthy nighttime attack.

Also buried are fuel tanks for a motor-driven electrical generator with output enough to drive all building utilities and the alarm circuits, plus battery standby. The transmitter mast says the firm has radio as well as telephone links to police and fire departments and to its own roving guard cars. Note, from either photo, that the ventilation air intake is at the very top of the building, where strain sensors could detect any attempt to climb the roof to pour any harmful or anesthetic gas into the building.

Inside the building, elaborate and reliable instruments print out a hard copy of any alarm condition, giving the customer's code, the time and date and the nature of the alarm. From the central station the condition of every customer's alarm system can be checked, any attempts at defeat noted and any malfunctions registered.

A typical central-station control bank is shown in Fig. 3-25. An annunciator alerts the guard to an alarm condition and at the control bank he can check as to the nature of the alarm (burglary, fire, false alarm). The central station can also monitor nonsecurity situations such as the temperature of freezers, operation of boilers and air conditioners, water levels and anything else that can be measured.

Central Station Grades

Underwriters' Laboratories grades central stations in three categories according to response time required. Grades AA and A response time must

Fig. 2-25 / *Rear of the Foell-McGee Alarm Company central station, with windows of heavy bullet-resistant glass. Inside are alarm panels. Note absence of power and alarm wires, which are buried to make them difficult to get at to cut.*

Fig. 3-25 / *Typical central-station control panel.*

not exceed fifteen minutes. Grade B response time must not be over twenty minutes and Grade C response time must not be over thirty minutes. That is, the time difference between when the alarm sounds at the central station until the guard or runner arrives at the protected premises must not exceed the specified time for the grade involved. Grade AA differs from the other grades in that it has special protection for the connecting lines, such as multiple paths to the central station. Grade AA also has electronic circuitry to detect any attempt at compromising the system, such as random time and frequency signals, computer-generated that must match with like signals at the receiving end. Otherwise it is possible for criminals to duplicate alarm OK signals at the protected premises and then disarm the alarm system while maintaining this signal to the central station.

Alarm System Grades

The various grades of alarm systems, AA, A, B, and C should be certified as such by the issuance by the installer of a serial-numbered UL central-station alarm certificate, on a UL certificate form. This document certifies that:

". . . the installing company whose name appears hereon is listed by Underwriters' Laboratories, Inc., as furnishing Grade (grade inserted) central station burglar alarm systems and is authorized to issue this certificate to the equipment described hereon as its representation that such equipment and all connected wiring and devices is in compliance with requirements established by Underwriters' Laboratories, Inc. for the class."

UL conducts field investigations of representative alarm installations of the installing company to make sure it continues to install alarm systems in accordance with the terms of the certificate.

In addition to alarm grades, UL classifies the extent of alarm protection in three categories.

- *Installation 1:* "Completely protects all windows, doors, transoms, skylights and other openings leading from the premises, all ceilings, floors, halls, party partitions, and building walls enclosing the premises, except building walls which are exposed to street or public highways, and except that part of any building wall which is at least two stories above the roof of an adjoining building."

- *Installation 2:* "Protects with traps all inaccessible windows; and with screens (or foils and traps) all accessible windows (except stationary show windows), doors, transoms, skylights and other openings leading from the premises; and protecting all ceilings and floors not constructed of concrete, and all halls, partitions and party walls enclosing the premises." Under this classification UL also permits this option instead of the above: "Protecting with supervisory circuits only all movable openings leading from the premises, and providing a system of invisible radiation to all sections of the enclosed area, so as to detect four-step movement." Another permissible option is: "Protecting with traps all inaccessible windows; with screens (or foils and traps), all accessible windows (except stationary show windows), doors, transoms, skylights, and other openings leading from the premises; and providing a network of invisible beams to subdivide the floor space of each floor or separate section of the protected area into three approximately equal areas, and more where necessary, to provide at least one subdivision per 1000 sq. ft. of floor space."

- *Installation 3:* "Protecting with screens (or foils and traps) all accessible windows (except stationary show windows), doors, transoms, skylights and other openings leading from the premises." An optional method is to: "Protect with contacts only all movable accessible openings leading from the premises and providing one or more invisible rays or channels of radiation with the minimum overall length of the rays or radiation equivalent to the longest dimensions of the area or areas so as to detect movement through the channel." A third option is to: "Protect with contacts all doors leading from the protected area or areas and providing a system of invisible radiation to all sections of the enclosed area so as to detect four-step movement."

Even if you are not having a central-station system installed, but a local alarm on a store, I would still urge you to at least have a UL Grade C system, installed by a UL-certified contractor.

Buy or Lease?

If you buy the alarm equipment outright, you are stuck with maintaining it, unless you have a maintenance contract with the alarm company. If you lease the equipment, you are first going to be dealing with a contractor who is in business to stay, and he will be liable, on a continuing basis, for its performance. I would opt for leasing.

Remember, the burglar-alarm field is growing like mad. There is little or no governmental regulation at any level of alarm-company salesmen or installers. Many installers are very poorly qualified and could never pass a licensed electrician's test. And many of them have questionable backgrounds, to say the least. There are a few schools that teach burglar-alarm installation, but they do not screen their students. As I said earlier, Omega State Institute, Chicago, requires all students to take and pass a polygraph (lie detector) examination. A substantial percentage of aspiring students flunk the examination, because of some criminal record or inclination.

Since so much crime is committed by so-called professional security guards, I would extend the same caution to alarm-system installers. I would definitely not want any alarm-system installer to be totally familiar with my alarm system and know how to defeat it. For this reason I urge you to insist that the alarm company change installing crews halfway through the job. Barring such change, I would at least insist that the alarm company give evidence that they have made a background check on installers. Otherwise you all but give installers a key to your premises.

Remember, too, that of the thousands of alarm companies offering their services to the public, only about 350 central-station firms are UL-approved to install UL-certificated central-station systems.

As for alarm-company salesmen, they are far more sales- than technically oriented, and for most of them you won't have to scratch very deeply to penetrate to the core of their engineering knowledge of the systems and equipment they are trying to sell you. I would stay away from any alarm company whose salesman exhibits little knowledge of the basics of systems and equipment.

Finally, it is absolutely vital that the alarm company be able to service what it sells, which is why I recommended a service-and-maintenance contract that very clearly defines periodic inspection and maintenance calls.

So far as the four thousand alarm installers of this country are concerned, few have been in business longer than ten years, most around five, to judge from a comparison of those listed in a ten-year span in the Manhattan (New York) yellow pages. One of the major shortages in blue-collar workers these days, in fact, is of trained alarm installers. So check out any alarm company carefully, before you sign that contract!

26

THE PROS AND CONS OF GUARD DOGS

Should you have a guard dog for the house? If so, what kind? Will a guard dog provide more security for less money in commercial premises? What are the legal problems associated with guard dogs? These are among the questions you will find answered in this chapter.

ANY COMPETENT dog trainer can turn your kindly, child-loving canine house pet into a ravening, snarling beast who will chew up an intruder into tiny pieces. Your ex-pet will also chew you and the kids up as well. What you don't need is a man-killer attack dog. Before I go any further, let me quickly list the four basic types of guard dogs, and where and how they should be used.

The Alarm Dog

For home use, an alarm dog is all you really need. This type of animal merely puts up a good front. He barks loudly when a stranger enters his "terri-

tory," snarls at them, stands up to intruders. Such an animal basically is a "front." He is trained never, under any circumstances, to bite anyone. This type of dog is also useful to announce the presence of a customer in a store where the proprietor cannot watch the premises all the time. The dog will bark and let the owner know that a customer has arrived. The dog may also scare the customer off, but that's a chance you take when you use a dog in a store to replace a simple photoelectric alarm bell. The dog, of course, does more than the announcing-type alarm; it will often deter a robber from attacking the owner.

Almost any type of dog will serve as

an alarm dog to detect, announce, and scare an intruder or stranger. Even a tiny fox terrier, with sharp teeth and a loud sharp bark, can be a deterrent to crime.

I should point out that dogs have fantastic sensory powers. They can smell an intruder up to a quarter of a mile away and hear sounds no human ear could detect.

If your pet dog is already a good alarm dog, no further training is needed. If your animal is too docile, he may need training, or even may be unsuitable for training. My advice is to consult your veterinarian. He can tell you whether or not your dog is temperamentally suitable or trainable to be an alarm dog, and is healthy enough and has good enough eyesight to serve this purpose. He can also recommend a competent dog trainer if the animal is otherwise usable as an alarm dog. Dogs that make good alarm dogs are boxers, terriers, and dachshunds. If you do not have a dog or want one trained, consult your veterinarian as to a reliable kennel operator. The rise in crime has spurred the establishment of many kennels that are simply not qualified to offer reliable, healthy animals or properly train them.

Dogs for Personal Protection

The next category is a dog a little nastier or who has the potential for being a little meaner and scarier than a simple alarm dog. Such an animal will bite if ordered to do so, will bite in self-defense or if he thinks you are being attacked. This is the type of animal that has reasonably good judgment about who is a threat and who is not, and that will respond to orders, especially an order to let go. This animal is taught to growl and snarl, to bare his teeth, to be extremely threatening. It is high in courage

and alertness and is the type I would want along with me if I were a delivery truck driver, a woman on a stroll along a city street, or if I lived alone. Doberman pinschers, German shepherds, and boxers make good personal protection animals.

Attack Dogs

Next in order of lethality are attack dogs. These are the dogs used by police and the military. The dog has a handler who gives the dog orders and supervises the dog's function. This type of dog is trained to be extremely vicious, to the point where he actually enjoys biting and lives for the day he can sink his teeth into warm human flesh. This type of dog is also trained to let go on command, a vital role if human life is not to be taken. The attack dog is also used by a security guard who is trained as a handler, to patrol a building. The dog can easily sniff out anyone who has hidden in the hopes of burglarizing the place after hours, as in a large store. The only problem with an attack dog is that he may show poor judgment and bite anyone, if the handler's attention is diverted.

Patrol Dogs

The absolute living end (I use the word advisedly) in an animal as a lethal weapon is a patrol dog (Fig. 1-26). This type of dog is trained to patrol premises empty of all human life. The dog is typically not sold but leased in order to make sure it is used properly. The animal will do its very best to kill anything it can reach that moves, no holds barred. There is no trainer-handler around when it goes on its appointed rounds, so any intruder will either have to run or shoot to kill if he's going to live much longer.

Fig. 1-26 / *This is a guard dog. He patrols behind locked doors. He lives for the day he can sink his teeth into warm human flesh. He prowls fenced-in car lots, inside factory buildings and wherever he can be used where the only people would be intruders.*

Shooting a ferocious patrol dog that's coming at you full speed, snarling and with its teeth bared, is not the easiest feat in the world, especially since you know you'd better not miss. Most intruders simply take off when they hear the deep bass bark and snarl of a hundred-pound trained patrol dog. Furthermore, such an animal will detect the presence of an intruder long before he has penetrated the premises by breaking through a locked door or climbing a fence. The intruder has every opportunity to go away, and most of them take that option, gladly. Anytime you doubt this statement I urge you to visit a kennel specializing in patrol dogs. You won't even be out of your car a block away, in the parking lot, before the entire kennel is in an uproar. You will see the many (and repaired) gashes torn by the teeth of these dogs in the heavy wire of their kennels. The trainer can demon-

strate how the 1,500-pound pressure of their jaws can snap a broom handle as easily as you would a toothpick.

Patrol dogs are unleashed in fenced used- and new-car lots, automobile dealer shops, factories, junkyards, and in buildings under construction to prevent theft and vandalism (where the premises are fenced).

For example, National K-9 Security, 3375 North Milwaukee Avenue, Northbrook, Illinois 60062, will only lease patrol dogs. The company has a fleet of flatbed trucks covered with kennels of heavy lumber. The dogs are delivered at the close of business hours and picked up again the next morning. To prevent any employee of the firm the dogs are leased to from getting into the dog-guarded premises, National K-9 put their own padlocks on all doors. No one gets in until a National handler comes, opens up the place and puts the dogs in the kennel on the truck. The only person the patrol dog won't try to kill is, in fact, National's handler.

The cost of leasing such an animal is around one dollar per hour per dog. That's a lot cheaper than a human guard. Furthermore, the dog won't steal, sleep, or goof off on the job, can detect an intruder a lot sooner than a human, and is a lot scarier and so a more potent crime stopper. A patrol dog only works alone, so its training is more extensive than one that works with a handler. If you bought such an animal, you would also need a handler just to get the dog in and out of the premises and you would still have to pay about $1,000 for a good one, and be responsible for its care and feeding.

National K-9 does train security guards as dog handlers when the guard is going to have the animal with him on patrol duty.

Legal Aspects . . . When Fido Bites

Up until a few years ago the courts usually held that "Every dog deserves one free bite," on the basis that until the dog did so it could not be concluded that it would, but that the next time would no longer be free. Now, however, that one free bite could be anything but free and could, in fact, be quite costly to the owner or lessee.

For example, a New Jersey court has stated: ". . . all dogs, even those ordinarily harmless, have a potential for biting, and . . . owners should, as the social price for keeping them, compensate those innocently sustaining injury. . . ." The key word here is "innocently." A deliberate break-in by a burglar could hardly be considered innocent, although here again one is reminded of the legal strictures against the use of force in de-

fense of property only, sans any threat to human life. However, this could be true provided the invader did not know that there was a patrol dog inside. National K-9 and other professional patrol dog lessors make sure the invader knows that there is a patrol dog on the premises by plastering the gates, fences and all doors with a sign that says "WARNING, GUARD DOG INSIDE. TRAINED ATTACK DOG" or words to that effect. Now the criminal knows what he faces, and if he still elects to try to break in and is killed, one can hardly say he was either innocent or unaware of the risk he took.

But if you have a trained personal guard dog you keep in the yard at night or during the day and it bites a child that climbs the fence to retrieve a ball, you could be sued and lose. One case I might point out is the Indiana junkyard dealer who kept a patrol dog in the yard at night. A child scaled the fence and was mauled by the dog. The junkyard dealer, despite the fact that he claimed the child was an illegal trespasser, was forced to pay substantial damages. The point here is that if there is any possibility an innocent person could be harmed by your attack or patrol dog you lease from a kennel, you should have insurance against such a contingency, and the kennel should, ideally, have third-party insurance.

If your homeowner's policy does not cover your dog, you can buy a comprehensive personal liability policy which will cover bodily injuries caused by the pet. A business concern or company that uses patrol or attack animals can be covered under a special multiperil policy or under a comprehensive general liability policy. All dogs used for alarm, personal protection, attack and patrol should be vaccinated against rabies.

27

TIPS THAT COULD SAVE YOUR LIFE

Here are practical tips that could save your life should you face a rapist, burglar, or mugger. This chapter gives you the facts on legal self-defense, the use of weapons and other forms of lethal and nonlethal defense. What to do when going on vacation, driving, camping, babysitting, to prevent crime. Special hints for apartment house security. Community crime efforts. Ways to reduce shoplifting, theft of computer data, truck theft. Tips for doctors.

THIS CHAPTER is the "software" part of this book. The only security equipment we will mention is good, plain commonsense tips on how to survive in this crime-ridden world of ours.

Before You Go In

As you return to the house, get into the habit of checking all exterior doors and the windows for any sign of forcible entry. Note how the key turns in the lock. If it turns easily, or does not fit into the keyway, the lock may have been forced or damaged by an attempt to pick it open. If you see any sign of forcible entry, such as tool marks on the door frame or door, or on the window frame, STOP! Do not enter the house! There may be an armed criminal inside who, if cornered, could take your life. Instead, go to a neighbor's house and call the police.

- Don't leave a key or a note outside the house or key inside the mailbox in an apartment building.

• Scratch your driver's license or social security number on all belongings with an electric engraving tool. Many police departments will lend you the tool. Take a color photo inventory of all valuable possessions and send a copy to your insurance company together with a statement as to when and how much you paid for each item. Many cities report a dramatic reduction in burglary when homeowners identify all possessions, and put a decal to this effect in the window. Wen Products, Inc., makes a very fine electrical vibrating tool with a tungsten carbide engraving tip that sells for about $8. The firm also furnishes a window decal with the tool that says: "WARNING, these premises are protected. Valuables have been permanently engraved with code marks to assist law enforcement agencies in their positive identification. They can be traced by POLICE."

If you have valuable paintings, you might register them with International Art Registry, Ltd., an affiliate of Guardian Industries, Inc. This organization can help you deter art theft, speed return of stolen art and ensure placement of insurance on fine art. You can reach them at 26 Columbia Turnpike, Floral Park, New Jersey 07932.

• When you're out shopping, or on vacation, leave the air conditioner on. If on vacation, and you have a window air conditioner and it's summer, you can switch it to "fan only."

• When on vacation, disconnect the phone. Burglars have been known to phone a home from a nearby phone booth, rush to the house and listen for a ring. If the phone keeps ringing they know no one is home.

• Cancel newspaper and milk delivery. Have the post office hold your mail. Ask a neighbor to pick up hand-delivered flyers and if a trusted neighbor, leave a key with him so police or firemen can get in in an emergency. Have grass cut or snow shoveled regularly. Park a second car close to garage door and lock both. Put trashcans in garage or basement.

• Use timers to turn lights on and off at night, and a photoelectric switch to turn yard lights on and off automatically when sun sets and rises.

• Inform police when you leave and when you will return. Do not leave ladders outside the house.

• Never leave a combustible pile of trash, such as dry leaves or wood, piled up outside the house. These accumulations are a temptation to arsonists, whose number seems to be increasing.

If You Meet a Burglar

• If you should confront a burglar in the house, keep calm, speak softly, give him ample opportunity to escape, be sure he knows you are unarmed and do not intend to hurt him. He's probably as frightened as you are and wants to get away from you as badly as you want him to. If it's night and you hear creaking noises, DO NOT INVESTIGATE THEM. Instead call police, if you can without leaving the room. (See Chapter Twenty-one on a fortress room for just such an emergency.)

• Do not booby trap the house! You might hurt someone while you are out and no one is at home. If you do, you could be sued and lose plenty. Remember the farmer in the Midwest who injured a burglar with a booby-trapped building. The burglar was convicted and went to jail, but he sued for the injury, won, and the farmer lost his farm.

About Self-Defense

The law is very clear about when you may and may not kill. If you see an invader in your home, and he threatens to kill you and you kill him first, that's legal killing in self-defense. If you shoot the burglar in the back as he's fleeing down an alley, that's murder. You are supposed to give the criminal every opportunity to live, short of letting him harm you or a loved one. Only the police can shoot a fleeing criminal and even then the shooter had better be sure the man is in fact a criminal.

I hate to say this, but if you do have to shoot to defend yourself, or use deadly force to do so, be sure to kill and not to wound. Otherwise the burglar if still conscious can shoot or knife you, and in any case may bear a grudge and get you later, when he's out of prison or the hospital. But be sure you act only out of a clear and present danger to your life.

Unless you're an expert in hand-to-hand combat, do not engage a criminal physically. Above all do not depend on a quickie one-week course in self-defense; the criminal could be stronger and more skilled than you, especially if he's survived the rigors of street fighting in the inner city.

About Guns in the Home

I am definitely opposed to a handgun in the home. If a burglar breaks in at night, you're going to be groggy and he's not. Chances are he's a lot more expert with a handgun than you, and if he sees you with one he will certainly try to kill you. If you hide the gun in one place and bullets in another because of the children, you may not have time to use the gun even if you are an expert shot.

If you feel vulnerable and want some sort of weapon, the only one I can recommend is a double-barreled 12 gauge shotgun loaded with 00 buckshot. This load spreads out only thirty inches at sixty feet and will cut a man in half. As for knives, unless you have had commando training or the like, do not try to outfight a knife wielder with your own knife unless you know he's trying to kill you. Then stick to underhand, upward thrusts and do not try to jab from above. The mark of the experienced knife fighter is the thrust upward, preferably into the rib cage or Adam's apple part of the throat.

You can buy police-size or pen-size military tear gas weapons in some sporting goods stores in some states (Figs. 1-27 and 2-27). However, many states now outlaw them, since they are used to commit crimes. They can, however, be used inside the home. The tear gas is a very potent deterrent. I know because I accidentally got some in the face, just a few droplets, and every one felt like a red hot poker until I washed my face for ten minutes in warm water and soap. Don't use tear gas if the criminal is armed, though.

Foiling the Rapist

When confronted by a rapist, the best defense is to run to the middle of the street, if you can, and scream as loudly as you can. If you're caught where you can't run and there's no one to hear your

Fig. 1-27 / *Pocket-type tear gas weapon. Operates by pulling down on nozzle lip. Good protection if you can get within a few feet of an attacker.*

screams, try to reason with the rapist. Tell him you have a venereal disease, preferably syphilis. Or tell him you're pregnant, or just recovering from an operation. Try to distract him while you reach in your handbag for a weapon such as a nail file. If you find a weapon, and the rapist is unarmed, try to jab him in the jugular vein in the throat, just under the Adam's apple. Or kick him in the groin. While he's out of it, run away. Kicks in the stomach, stomping on his instep, and jabbing in the eye are good tactics. But use force only as a last resource; he will probably be stronger than you are and if aroused could kill you. If you do scream, yell "FIRE" because that will bring people out a lot faster than yelling "RAPE." It could be their house on fire, but it certainly would not be their rape. Don't let the rapist think you are memorizing his description, but try to do so.

Safety Tips for Women

- List your telephone number only by first initials.
- If you are walking and a car follows you, turn and run in the other direction. The car will have to turn to follow you. Scream as you run.
- Never admit anyone to your house unless you know who they are. Check everyone who comes to the door. If a stranger wants to use your phone for an emergency, offer to call his party for him, but leave him outside.
- Don't enter a self-service elevator with a stranger. If a threatening-looking individual enters after you, get off at the next floor. As a courtesy to the next passenger, return the elevator to the lobby floor in case it's needed in an emergency.
- When entering the lobby, do not let a stranger enter an apartment building with you. If necessary, leave for the protection of the street.
- Carry a clutch purse only. If you use a purse with a shoulder strap, a good tug can knock you to the ground and you could be hurt. While on a bicycle, keep your purse hidden or in a closed carrier. Do not carry any more cash than you need, or credit cards you will not use that day.
- Stay out of laundromats late at

Fig. 2-27 /   *Police-type tear gas weapon. Sends stream of liquid tear gas about 15 feet. Very effective against attackers, but do not use if opponent has a gun.*

night; they are known hangouts for criminals and perverts. Always use apartment-building laundry facilities with a companion.
- List your name on an apartment building mailbox by first initial only.
- Memorize police, fire department, and rape hot-line telephone numbers, and the numbers of trusted neighbors.
- While driving, stay on well-lighted, well-traveled streets. Keep windows closed and doors locked. Avoid being blocked by another car by always keeping at least one car length behind, especially at stop lights and stop signs. Give yourself room to drive away from any attempt to break into your car. Keep the car in gear ready for a quick getaway. And don't leave your purse or other valuables on the seat while you drive.
- On coming home, ask the driver to wait until you are inside.
- On mass-transit units (bus, subway, streetcar) make sure you are not followed as you leave. If a threatening person or group gets on, you should get off at the next stop and take the next transport.
- If your car becomes disabled in a darkened street or isolated area, lock doors and keep windows rolled up until police come. Ask strangers to phone police for you, but do not open your window to talk to them. If your car stalls on an interstate highway, do not open your window to any person you cannot, from appearance, trust. A state trooper will come by eventually. Tie a handkerchief to the radio antenna to signal distress.
- Do not stop to aid disabled motorists, even another woman. If you have a CB radio in the car, you can be a Good Samaritan and call for help.
- Park as close to a street light as possible, if at night, or to the stores if in a shopping-center parking lot. Before reentering the car, make sure no one is hiding in it.

For the Babysitter

- Never let a stranger in the house.
- Do not admit that you are alone in

the house with the children if anyone phones. Tell them "your parents" can't come to the phone right now but will call them back.

• As the parent, you should phone the sitter every few hours while away to check up on things.

• If you have a burglar- or fire-alarm system, make sure the sitter knows how to operate it and how to respond to the alarm.

• For the sitter and all the family, put police, fire, and medical emergency numbers in large type on the wall near or on the telephone instrument itself.

• The sitter should always know where to reach you, with telephone number(s). The sitter should always keep the phone open and avoid lengthy phone calls.

• Teach the sitter about hazards in the house; she may have an electric stove and not know about turning off your gas range securely, for example.

• Include your regular sitter in at least one evacuation fire drill.

Fire Escape Plan

Obviously you should leave the house as quickly as possible if it is on fire. What is not so obvious is the anguish that can prevail if a loved one cannot be found, and the distinct possibility of disaster if a distraught parent rushes back into the burning house to look for a missing child. Avoid this heartache by prearranging a meeting place outside the house where you can take a quick head count.

Bedroom doors should be kept shut at night to give you and the children extra time to escape and to keep deadly fumes in the room to a minimum. Children should be taught never to open the bedroom door in a fire but to feel it. If the door is hot, the children should stand by an open window until help comes.

Do not pass from room to room in a fire situation without making sure you are not entering a lethal trap full of superheated, poisonous air that can kill you very quickly. Avoid using main hallways or the main stairway, which may be fume-filled. Use the escape ladder noted in Chapter Seventeen.

The kids should know how to use sheets, blankets or towels to stuff around door cracks to keep fumes and smoke out of the room.

Above all, do not waste time trying to use the telephone, save valuables, or dress. Get out as fast as you can! As you leave, close doors behind you to slow down the fire, perhaps bottle up the blaze, giving firefighters a chance to confine it. Otherwise the entire house can become a chimney and the building can go up quickly in a roar of flames.

Finally, if you are downstairs and the kids sleep upstairs, never call them down in a fire, you could be calling them to their death! Evacuation should not be through main fire, smoke, and fume routes, but out windows to the fresh air. If necessary and if you are downstairs, you can use your ladder to reach upper-story windows.

Use Your Locks

This should go without saying, but since so many people do not lock their doors when at home, for convenience of children or themselves, let me say, loudly and clearly, KEEP ALL DOORS AND WINDOWS LOCKED even when at home! A prudent burglar will not chance a noisy confrontation with you, but there are enough crazies running around these days who would love the chance to get at you face to face. In hot, humid weather wood swells and the door may stick. Be sure it is shut all the way and that the lock is engaged.

How to Use the Telephone

The 911 emergency number in many cities will call police and fire departments directly. Now there's a new twist to the number, an electronic addition that should save additional lives. Many times people will dial 911 and then hang up, either because they have to, or out of sheer panic. In this case it has been either impossible or time consuming to find out who called and where they live. Now, though, a computer automatically prints out, at the fire and police department, the name and address of anyone who dials 911, even if you dial and hang up immediately. Don't count on this computer printout, though, always hold on and talk to police yourself.

If you receive nuisance or obscene calls, the computer can also find the caller for you, if you make arrangements beforehand. The telephone operator can also intercept all incoming calls for one week and ask for the name and number of the calling party. This is a nuisance for callers but a scare to obscene callers.

If your community has an electronic telephone-switching system, the telephone company can automatically switch all your calls to an answering service, to a friend or to another number you can answer, when you are away. Ask for the Call Forwarding service.

Never engage in conversation with a stranger who calls you. Hang up on all nuisance calls. As a last resort you can change phone numbers. I can't encourage an unlisted phone number because you may need to be reached in an emergency. You could, instead, simply ask that your number not be in the phone book, but be reachable via Information.

Project Whistlestop

One community crime-fighting effort that has proved effective and that is spreading across the country is called Project Whistlestop. The project consists of providing an entire neighborhood with a shrill whistle with a distinctive note, and with stickers to post on home and car windows. People in the neighborhood cooperate in calling police when they hear the whistle. The window sticker notes that the home is a member of and supports the Project, and so helps unify this neighborhood cooperative effort to combat crime. In one South Side neighborhood in Chicago, the Project has led, according to Project organizers, to a 41 percent reduction in purse snatching, 37 percent cut in auto theft, and an overall reduction in five categories of crime by 16 percent within the first nine months of the Project.

For information on Project Whistlestop, write Whistlestop Community Services, Edgewater Community Council, 5609 North Broadway, Chicago, Illinois 60660.

Other citizens' projects include one in Stamford, Connecticut, in which the police department has issued a card with a special police emergency number to citizens who use the number to report anything suspicious in their neighborhood. I've done that myself. Once I saw a man sitting in a car a few houses down the block, looking at homes and jotting something down in a notebook. He moved the car down a few houses and jotted something else down. I called the police and gave them his license number, but by the time they arrived a few moments later, the man had left. The police did give me this person's name and address. The next day this same man turned up at my front door and identified himself as the Fuller Brush man. I greeted him by name, much to his amazement. To this day he thinks I am clairvoyant. To save this man any embarrassment, I called the police back and told them who he was. Nevertheless, he could have been a burglar "casing" homes, although he would have had to be singularly inept to be that obvious about it.

Other cooperative citizens' programs are basically the same, and are heartily approved by police, who need all the eyes and ears and suspicious minds the neighborhood can provide. Don't be concerned that police will think you are a pest. Police appreciate concerned citizens who have their own safety and that of their neighbors in mind. New York City has a Block Security Program that involves a square block or larger area of residents. Members of the Program meet regularly to discuss security problems in the neighborhood such as lighting, fences, gates, and areas within their own buildings. Funds are raised to provide for equipment for voluntary, unpaid patrol and escort programs in outdoor public areas and common areas of multiple dwellings.

Shoplifting

Aside from the electronic antishoplifting gadgets described in Chapter Twenty-three, your employees should be taught to be alert for attempts at stealing merchandise. But are they? One Texas city police department decided to find out. Beaumont, Texas, police, with the help of eleven persons from their own department, including secretaries, all in civilian clothes, staged a shoplifting crime spree in twenty-two stores in Beaumont. Only store managers knew about the effort. The police wanted to see how much they could steal during one normal shopping day. A large van, centrally located to the stores involved, was used as a "depository" for stolen merchandise. In just two hours these amateur "crooks" lifted over $1,250 worth of merchandise. A few hours later, when so much had been accumulated officers had trouble counting it, one woman went out and stole a calculator.

It was found that store people were easily diverted while another person stole merchandise, they were not alert or too trusting, and in some cases there were not enough employees to handle the shoppers. This "operation" was an eye-opener to store owners. I only hope it does not serve as an inspiration to would-be shoplifters but rather to store owners to tighten security via employee education, if nothing else. Employees should be instructed to look for:

- Booster boxes; empty boxes that look like packages but which can be set down over merchandise. A spring device inside snaps down and retains the stolen goods.
- Shoppers with empty shopping bags, baggy clothing, large purses, or raincoats when it's dry outside.
- Till tappers. Teams of two or more. One person engages the clerk in conversation while the till is open, the other takes paper money from the till, or even the entire till if it's small enough.

Theft ℞ for Doctors

Physicians and other professional people need to be especially alert for burglars and robbers. In addition to the alarms and locks discussed in previous chapters, office personnel must be educated to be aware that the emergency "patient" or "client" may be a robber waiting to get the boss alone, or the professional products salesperson may be a professional criminal. Office personnel should have an emergency procedure, with a call button for such a situation, that can alert others in the office to call police.

Truck Thieves

Delivery-truck drivers need to be especially alert, particularly if money is collected. A safe in the truck and a sign on the truck that says the driver has no cash are two precautions. The truck should be locked when not in use. The driver should watch for suspicious vehicles that may follow him, and jot down their license numbers. Cab drivers should not deliver people into alleys or permit the passenger to get out and walk around to the driver's side for payment.

APPENDICES

Bibliography

California, State of, Office of Criminal Justice Planning. *Burglary Prevention Handbook*. Sacramento, Calif., 1973.

Clark, Ramsey, *Crime in America*. New York, Simon & Schuster, 1970.

Federal Bureau of Investigation. *Crime in the United States*. Uniform Crime Reports for 1970, 1971, 1972, 1973, 1974, and 1975. Washington, D.C.

Graham, Hugh D., and Gurr, Ted R. *Violence in America*. Washington, D.C., National Commission on the Causes and Prevention of Violence, 1969.

Kakalik, James S., and Wildhorn, Sorrel. *Private Police in the United States: Findings and Recommendations*. Vols. I and II. Santa Monica, Calif., The Rand Corporation, 1972.

Klotter, John C., and Cusick, Robert I. *Burglary Prevention, Investigation and Prosecution*. Louisville, Ky., The Southern Police Institute, University of Louisville, 1968.

Morris, Norval, and Hawkins, Gordon. *The Honest Politician's Guide to Crime Control*. Chicago, The University of Chicago Press, 1970.

National Advisory Commission on Criminal Justice Standards and Goals. *Community Crime Prevention*. Washington, D.C., 1973.

————. *A National Strategy to Reduce Crime*. Washington, D.C., 1973.

Newman, Oscar. *Defensible Space*. New York, The Macmillan Company, 1972.

Pollock, David A. *Methods of Electronic Audio Surveillance*. Springfield, Ill., Charles C. Thomas, 1973.

President's Commission on Law Enforcement and Administration of Justice. *The Challenge of Crime in a Free Society*. Washington, D.C., 1967.

————. *Crime and Its Impact*. Task Force Report on Assessment. Washington, D.C., 1967.

————. *Juvenile Delinquency and Youth Crime.* Washington, D.C., 1967.

————. *Organized Crime.* Washington, D.C., 1967.

U.S. Department of Justice. Law Enforcement Assistance Administration. *Crime in the Nation's Five Largest Cities.* Washington, D.C., 1974.

————. *Patterns of Burglary.* Washington, D.C., National Institute of Law Enforcement and Criminal Justice, 1973.

————. *Private Police in the United States.* Vols. I and II. Washington, D.C., National Institute of Law Enforcement and Criminal Justice, 1971.

————. *Sourcebook of Criminal Justice in the United States.* Washington, D.C., National Criminal Justice Information and Statistics Service, 1973.

Winslow, Robert W. *Crime in a Free Society.* Belmont, Calif., Dickenson Publishing Company, 1969.

Retail Sources of Burglar Alarms

Alarm Products International, Inc., 24-02 40th Ave., Long Island City, N.Y. 11101. (212) 937-4900.

Alarm Supply Co., Inc., 12551 Globe Road, Livonia, Michigan 48150. (313) 425-2500.

Emergency Products Corp., 25 Eastmans Road, Parsippany, N.J. 07054. (800) 631-8054.

Informer Alarm Supplies Co., 200 S. Eden St., Baltimore, Md. 21231. (301) 732-4288.

Mountain West Alarm Supply Company, 4215 N. 16th St., Phoenix, Ariz. 85016. (602) 263-8831.

Newbrite Alarms, Inc., 166 Laurel Road, East Northport, N.Y. 11731. (516) 757-8600.

Protecto Alarm Sales,* Box 357, Birch Run, Mich. 48415. (517) 624-9521.

Universal Security Instruments, Inc., 2829 Potee St., Baltimore, Md. 21225. (301) 355-9000.

Vancor Security Systems,* 84 Thurston St., Winter Hill, Boston, Mass. 02145. (617) 623-6415.

* Specializes in sales direct to consumer. Ask for catalog.

Burglar and Fire Alarm Equipment Manufacturers

Acron Corporation, 1095 Towbin Ave., Corporate Pk., Lakewood, N.J. 07801

Ademco, 165 Eileen Way, Syosset, N.Y. 11791

Advanced Devices Laboratory, Inc., 316 Mathew St., Santa Clara, Calif. 95050

Air Space Devices, P.O. Box 197, 15323 Garfield Ave., Paramount, Calif. 90723

Alarm Device Mfg. Co., 165 Eileen Way, Syossett, N.Y. 11791

Alarm Products International, Inc. (A.P.I.), 24-02 40th Ave., Long Island City, N.Y. 11101

Alarmtronics Engineering, Inc., 154 California St., Newton, Mass. 02195

Alertronics, Inc., 20 Boright Ave., Kenilworth, N.J. 07033

AMF Monitalert Security Systems, 125 North Royal St., Alexandria, Va. 22314

Applied Metro Technology, Inc., 51 Main St., Orange, N.J. 07050

Aqualarm, Inc., 544 West 182nd St., Gardena, Calif. 90248

Arrowhead Enterprises, Inc., Anderson Ave., New Milford, Conn. 06776

Ashby & Associates, Suite 511, 1730 M St., N.W., Washington, D.C. 20036

Babaco Alarm Systems, Inc., 1775 Broadway, New York, N.Y. 10019

Balteau Electric Corp., 63 Jefferson St., Stamford, Conn. 06902

BRK Electronics, P.O. Box 471, 780 McClure Ave., Aurora, Ill. 60538

Bourns, Inc., 6135 Magnolia Ave., Riverside, Calif. 92506

CAHS, Inc., 540 Columbus Ave., Mount Vernon, N.Y. 10550

Cardkey Systems, Div. Greer Hydraulics Inc., 20339 Nordhoff St., Chatsworth, Calif. 91311

R. B. Clifton, Inc., 11500 North West Seventh Ave., Miami, Fla. 33168

Colorado Electro Optics, 1840 Commerce St., Boulder, Colo. 80301

Conrac Security Detection, 223 Boston Post Road, Old Saybrook, Conn. 06475

Counter Measure Security Systems, 300 South Thayer, Suite 8, Ann Arbor, Mich. 48104

Dektor Counterintelligence and Security Inc., 5508 Port Royal Road, Springfield, Va. 22151

Delta Products, Inc., P.O. Box 1147, 630 South Seventh, Grand Junction, Colo. 81501

Detectron Security Systems, Inc., Bay St., Sag Harbor, N.Y. 11963

Dialalarm, Inc., 7315 Lankershim Blvd., Hollywood, Calif. 91609

Draco Laboratories, Inc., P.O. Box 09313, Glendale, Wis. 53209

Eaton Corporation, P.O. Box 25288, Charlotte, N.C. 28212

Elan Industries, Inc., 2429 University Ave., St. Paul, Minn. 55110

Electric Wastebasket Corp., 145 W. 45th St., New York, N.Y. 10036

Fire-Lite Alarms, Inc., P.O. Box 823, 40 Albert St., New Haven, Conn. 06504

Heathkit, Benton Harbor, Mich 49022

Imperial Screen Co., Inc., 5336 W. 145th St., Lawndale, Calif. 90260

International Countermeasures, Ltd. (ICM), 1107 South Mannheim Road, Suite 206, Westchester, Ill. 60153

Johnson Controls, Inc., Protective Systems Div., 507 E. Michigan St., P.O. Box 432, Milwaukee, Wis. 53201

Walter Kidde and Co., Inc., 675 Main St., Belleville, N.J. 07109

KNOGO Corp., 112 State St., Westbury, N.Y. 11590

Kolin Industries, Inc., Box 357 D. Bronxville, N.Y. 10708

Kwikset, 516 E. Santa Ana St., Anaheim, Calif. 92803

Linear Corporation, 347 S. Glasgow Ave., Inglewood, Calif. 90301

Mark Engineering, Inc., P.O. Box 450, 63 Great Rd., Maynard, Mass. 01754

F. G. Mason Engineering, Inc., Box 309-1700 Post Road, Fairfield, Conn. 06430

Massa Corp., 280 Lincoln St., Hingham, Mass. 02043

Micro Technology, Inc., 703 Plantation St., Worcester, Mass. 01605

Microwave Electronics Systems, Ltd. (MESL), Lochend Industrial Estate, Newbridge, Midlothian, Sco F3200, England

Mieco, 109 Beaver Court, Cockeysville, Md. 21030

Morse Products Manufacturing, 12960 Bradley Ave., Sylmar, Calif. 91342

Multi-Emac Co., 21470 Coolidge Hwy., Oak Park, Mich. 48237

Multra-Guard, Inc., 1930 E. Pembroke Ave., Hampton, Va. 23363

NAPCO Security Systems, Inc., 6 Ditomas Ct., Copiague, N.Y. 11726

O-Lite Co., Box 1421, Greenwich, Conn. 06830

Omni Spectra, Inc., 1040 W. Alameda Drive, Tempe, Ariz. 85282

Peak Technologies, Inc., 5430 Old County Road, San Carlos, Calif. 94070

Pinkerton's, Inc., 100 Church St., New York, N.Y. 10007

Pinkerton Electro-Security Co. (Division of Pinkerton's), 61 Sutton Rd., Webster, Mass. 01570

Plectron Corp., Overton, Neb. 68863

Pyrotector, Inc., 333 Lincoln St., Hingham, Mass. 02043

Pyrotronics, 8 Ridgedale Ave., Cedar Knolls, N.J. 07927

Racon, Inc., Boeing Fd Int., 8490 Perimeter, Seattle, Wash. 98108

Rittenhouse Div., Artolier Lighting and Sound, Emerson Electric Co., Honeoye Falls, N.Y. 14472

Rossin Corp., 1411 Norman Firestone Blvd., Goleta, Calif. 93017

Rusco Electronic Corp., 1840 Victory Blvd., P.O. Box 5005, Glendale, Calif. 91201

Scan Security Systems, 310 Willis Ave., Mineola, N.Y. 11501

Security General, 848 A Stewart Ave., Sunnyvale, Calif. 94086

Security Sciences Corp., 3621 Wells Fargo, Scottsdale, Ariz. 85251

Se-Kure Controls, Inc. 5685 N. Lincoln Ave., Chicago, Ill. 60659

Sentrol, Inc. 14335 N. W. Science Park Dr., Portland, Ore. 97229

Shorrock, Shadsworth Rd., Blackburn BB1, 2 PR Lincolnshire, England

Signalarm, Inc., 357 Cottage St., P.O. Box 3728, Springfield, Mass. 01101

Silent Knight Security Systems, 2930 Emerson Ave., So. Minneapolis, Minn. 55408

Silent Watchman Corporation, 4861 McGaw Rd., P.O. Box 7893, Columbus, Ohio 43207

Sontrix, 4593 N. Broadway, Boulder, Colo. 80302

Statitrol Corp., 140 S. Union Blvd., Lakewood, Colo. 80228

Stoplifter International, 6116 North Central Expressway, Dallas, Tex. 75206

Systron-Donner Corp., 6767 Dublin Ave., Dublin, Calif. 94566

Tapeswitch Corp. of America, 320 Broad Hollow Rd., Farmingdale, N.Y. 11735

Technical Communications Corp., 442 Marrett Road, Lexington, Mass. 02173

Teledyne Geotech, 3401 Shiloh Rd., Garland, Tex. 75041

Thomas Industries, Inc., 207 E. Broadway, Louisville, Ky. 40202

3M Company Photographic Products-Surveillance Products, 3M Center Bldg., 220-3E, St. Paul, Minn. 55101

Torr Laboratories, Inc., 2228 Cotner Ave., Los Angeles, Calif. 90064

Transcience, 17 Irving Ave., Stamford, Conn. 06902

Unisec, 2251 Bancroft Ave., San Leandro, Calif. 94577

United Security Products, 11 Glenn Crescent, Centerport, N.Y. 11721

Volumatic, Ltd., Taurus House, Kingfield Rd., Coventry, CV6 5AS England

Wessel Hardware Corp., Erie Ave. and D St., Philadelphia, Pa. 19134

Westinghouse Electric Corp., Electronic Protection Systems, 1111 Schilling Rd., Hunt Valley, Md. 21030

Wico Corp., 6400 W. Grosse Point Rd., Niles, Ill. 60648

INDEX

Page numbers in italics refer to illustrations.